SOUND THE GREAT TRUMPET

THE STORY OF ISRAEL THROUGH THE EYES
OF THOSE WHO BUILT IT. HERE IS THE
DAY-TO-DAY LIFE IN ISRAEL AS EVOLVED
THROUGH THREE GENERATIONS OF MOD-
ERN JEWISH COLONIZATION.

Sound
The Great Trumpet

Edited by M. Z. FRANK

◆

"Sound the great trumpet for our freedom;
Raise the banner for the ingathering
of our exiles."

Jewish Daily Prayers

WHITTIER BOOKS, INC., NEW YORK

Designed by Sidney Solomon

CONTENTS

◆

SOURCES

◆

THE GREATER PART of this book consists of translations, abridgements and condensations especially prepared for it. The originals are nearly all in Hebrew.

The three selections in Chapter 2, under the general heading of *The Portal of Hope* (pages 32 to 40), are composites of several pen-sketches by Moshe Smilansky, which appear in the first volume of his series *Mishpahat Ha-adamah* (Family of the Soil), published by Am Oved, Tel-Aviv, 1940.

Smilansky's pen-sketch of *Aaron David Gordon* (79 to 83) is an abridged translation from the third volume of the same series.

Smilansky's *Story of a Love* (186 to 194) is a condensation from the original novel, which appeared in two pamphlets published by Sifruth, Warsaw, 1911.

Much in the editor's introduction to Chapter 2 is based on Smilansky.

The editor's introduction to Chapter 3, like all his introductions, is based on many sources, but two specifically need be mentioned here: Shlomo Zemach's autobiographical book *Shanah Rishonah* (First Year), published by Am Oved, Tel-Aviv, 1952, and Bracha Habass's biography of Ben-Gurion (*Ben-Gurion ve-Doro*—Ben-Gurion and His Age) published by Massada, Tel-Aviv, 1952.

From Homel to Petah-Tikvah by Eliahu Eventov (50 to 60), *Pangs of Integration* by Aliza Shidlovsky (93 to 95) and Yavnieli's account of his mission to Yemen in the editor's introduction to Chapter 9 are abridged versions of articles which appear in the large compendium on the Second Aliyah (*Sefer Ha-aliyah Ha-Shniyah*), edited by Bracha Habass, published by Am Oved, Tel-Aviv, 1947. That large volume (788 pages) has served the editor as the main source to draw upon in his introductions to Chapters 3, 4 and 5. Ben-Zvi's account of the founding of Hashomer in the editor's introduction to Chapter 5 are taken from the compendium *Hashomer*, published in 1937 by the Labor Archives Division of the Histadrut.

On the Threshold and *Wild Growth* by Ephraim Auerbach (96 to 113) have been condensed from the Yiddish manuscript supplied by the

author. The two books appeared in Hebrew in Tel-Aviv, published by
N. Twersky.

The Watchman and the Wall by A. Reubeni (117 to 136) is a
condensation of a novella published in Hebrew by Achiever, Jerusalem,
1911, and in Yiddish by Dos Land, Jerusalem, 1914. The editor used
both versions.

Genesis by Shlomo Reichenstein (159 to 182) has been condensed
from a novel *(Reshith)* jointly published by Am Oved, Tel-Aviv, and
Kibbutz Ein Harod, 1943.

Street Symphony by Yitzhak Shenhar (202 to 217) is an abridged
translation from a story which appeared in the collection *Yamin Yedab-
beru* (The Days Speak), published by Schocken, Jerusalem and Tel-Aviv,
1945. (The author's name then was Shenberg.)

Moroccans at the Wailing Wall by Ari Ibn-Zahav (233 to 236) is
made up of fragments from the volume entitled *Besod Aniye Hakkotel*
(With the Beggars at the Wailing Wall), Yavenh, Tel-Aviv, 1947.

Nineteen Seventeen (1917) by Mordecai Tabib (237 to 244) is an
abridged translation from a chapter in the autobiographical novel *Ke-
essev Ha-sadeh* (As the Grass in the Field) published by Sifriat Poalim
(Workers' Book Guild), Tel-Aviv, 1948.

Scrolls of Fire (345 to 353) consists of abstracts made from the
biographical and personal correspondence sections in the large volume by
that title *(Gvile Esh)* edited by Reuven Avinoam, published by the
Israel Ministry of Defense, 1952.

The Other Israel by Amos Eilon (365 to 373) is an abridged translation from a newspaper article in Ha-aretz, republished in pamphlet form
by that newspaper in 1951.

The following selections are taken from English translations published
in various collections and periodicals issued by the Jewish Agency office
in Jerusalem and reprinted abroad and from the files of *Israel, Life and
Letters,* the periodical published in New York by the American Fund for
Israel Institutions:

Israel Zvi by Yitzhak Shenhar (195 to 201) tr. by Israel Schen.
In a Jerusalem Cafe by S. J. Agnon (218 to 220) tr. by I. M. Lask.
The Minyan by S. J. Agnon (221 to 224) tr. by I. M. Lask.
At a Glance by Yehuda Bourla (229 to 232) tr. by M. Z. Frank.

The Threefold Covenant by Yehuda Yaari (245 to 250) tr. by I. M. Lask.

He Walked Through the Fields by Moshe Shamir (265 to 270).

Hai's Well by Asher Barash (273 to 283) tr. by I. M. Lask.

Bracha by Yonat and Alexander Sened (284 to 290).

The Citadel by Moshe Carmel (312 to 313) tr. by I. Halevy-Levin.

Ashes by Yigal Mossinson (303 to 311) tr. by Dov Vardi.

Armed Civilians by Shlomo Nitzan (322 to 323).

The Battle of Mishmar Haemek by A Haganah Correspondent (324 to 329).

The Burma Road by Menachem Talmi (330 to 344).

My Way in Israel by Zachariah Nissim (374 to 388) tr. by I. Halevy-Levin.

Some of the above selections were abridged and edited for this volume.

The original English translations were also made by I. Halevy-Levin and others, including some edited by Yehuda Haezrachi and Herbert Howarth.

In some cases the name of the translator is not given in the original English source.

Of the above list, two are parts of larger works:

He Walked Through the Fields is part of a novel by the same title *(Hu Halakh Ba-sadot)* by Moshe Shamir, published by Sifriat Poalim, Tel-Aviv, 1947.

Bracha is from a book entitled *Adamah le-lo Tzel* (Land Without Shadow) by Yonat and Alexander Sened, published by Hakkibbutz Hameuchad Publishing House, Tel-Aviv, 1951.

The first selection in the book, *The Fettered Messiah* by Joshua Bar-Joseph (22 to 26) has been condensed from the original and from the English translation made by I. M. Lask for the American Fund for Israel Institutions. It is part of a trilogy entitled *Ir Kesuma* (Enchanted City), published by N. Twersky, Tel-Aviv, 1950.

In Judea and Galilee by David Ben-Gurion (61 to 73) has been similarly edited and abridged from the collection of Ben-Gurion's speeches and articles edited by Mordecai Nurock and published by The Philosophical Library, New York, 1954.

Daganiah by Joseph Baratz (84 to 92) is an edited abridgement from a pamphlet which appeared in the American edition published by the Jewish National Fund Library, 1937.

Letters from the Desert by Moshe Mossinson (296 to 302) are taken from a book which appeared in an English translation by Hilda Auerbach, under the editorship of Shlomo Grodzensky, published by Sharon Books, New York, 1945.

Passages from Grodzensky's introduction are also quoted.

The Story of the Jewish Legion by Vladimir Jabotinsky (140 to 153) is taken from a book under that title which was first written by the author in Russian. The English translation by Samuel Katz was published in New York by Bernard Ackerman in 1945.

That's How It Is With Us by Shim'on Sam Smaragd (257 to 264) is taken from a book originally written in English and published posthumously, edited by Molly Lyons Bar-David.

The Cactus Pear (originally The Sabra) by Dorothy Bar-Adon (354 to 357) was originally written in English.

The major part of the introduction to Chapter 10 consists of selections from *Henrietta Szold, Life and Letters,* edited by Marvin Lowenthal, published by Viking Press, New York, 1942.

The introduction to Chapter 12 is taken from Chaim Weizmann's autobiography entitled *Trial and Error,* published by Harper and Brothers, New York, 1949.

Cafe Kadimah by M. Z. Frank first appeared in the issue of November 1953 of The American Zionist, New York.

Introduction

THE TRUMPET HAS MANY SOUNDS

I

THERE WAS tension in the air that Friday afternoon in Tel-Aviv. There was an air of expectancy. People sat glued to their radios or stood outdoors in front of loudspeakers. On Rothschild Boulevard, in front of the Municipal Museum, the pavement was lined, along the roped-off sidewalk, with men and women who stood quiet, almost immobile. Their faces were grim, but their eyes shone.

In the hall of the museum the paintings had been removed for the occasion. Only on the main wall hung a large portrait of Theodor Herzl, founder and first president of the World Zionist Organization. Herzl's intense black eyes seemed to look down with benign encouragement upon the short stocky man who sat in front of his portrait at the head table. This was David Ben-Gurion, for the past thirteen years Chairman of the Zionist Executive and for the past few weeks Chairman of the temporary National Administration.

At three o'clock Ben-Gurion arose. With his back to Herzl and facing the audience, he began to speak. He first mentioned the unfortunate absence of two men who belonged at the head table but who were unable to leave Jerusalem, which had been under siege for months. Then he read from the document in his hand.

The audience consisted of Zionist leaders and of local dignitaries. Also present were members of the press. Never before had Tel-Aviv seen so many newsmen and cameramen from all over the world.

"The land of Israel was the birthplace of the Jewish people," was the first sentence in Hebrew.

"Exiled from the Land of Israel, the Jewish people remained faithful to it in all the countries of their dispersion, never ceasing to pray and hope for their return. . . .

"We hereby declare that the National Council shall act as the Provisional State Council and the National Administration shall constitute the Provisional Government of the Jewish State, which shall be known as Israel."

From the ceremony Ben-Gurion drove off to secret military headquarters to direct the defense of the new born Republic.

This was Friday afternoon, May 14, 1948.

At five o'clock the next morning Egyptian airmen dropped their first bombs on Tel-Aviv.

II

A hundred years before, ancient and holy Jerusalem was a small primitive town in one of the most retarded provinces of the backward Turkish Empire. A wheeled carriage was never seen on its streets or on the roads leading to the Holy City. People traveled to and from Hebron or Jaffa astride a donkey or a camel. The privileged few went on horseback.

There was nothing in Palestine to indicate even the seeds of the careful and laborious planning for a modern Jewish state. Nothing except a dream here and there in the hearts of a few nonconformist individuals —and a lone orange grove on the outskirts of the primitive port town of Jaffa. The orange grove was planted for the Jews by Sir Moses Montefiore.

The next half-century saw the beginnings of vast changes.

Fifty years before the State of Israel was formed horse-drawn vehicles made regular trips carrying passengers between Jaffa and Jerusalem. Early in the 20th century the Turkish Government built a railway between the two cities. Trains were among the slowest in the world and often stopped in the middle of a field when an important passenger decided to alight in order to see what his workers were doing.

Palestine in 1900 had several modern agricultural colonies established some twenty or twenty-five years earlier by European settlers. Most colonies had been founded by Jews from the Russian Empire and Rumania. Once, a vagabond scholar-poet from Galicia stopped over in one of these young settlements. He was on a mission for an erratic adventurous Scotsman named Sir Laurence Oliphant, who planned to direct Jewish immigration from Eastern Europe to Palestine rather than to America. During his stay at the Jewish colony, the poet-scholar, Naphthali Herz Imber, composed a poem, whose first two stanzas are today the best known Hebrew stanzas in the world:

> As long as within his innermost heart
> Life does throb in a Jew,
> And, turned eastward, straining,
> His eye looks to Zion
>
> Still unfaded is our hope,
> Our age-old hope,
> To return to the land of our fathers,
> To the city in which David dwelt.

For those who already lived in Palestine, Imber changed the last two lines of the refrain:

> To live as a free nation in our land,
> The land of Zion and Jerusalem.

Long after the author of these verses died a poor man in America, soldiers of Israel's Army of Defense stood at attention when the words were sung or its music played, and Jews in Madison Square Garden in New York rose to sing them. The hymn, now the Israel national anthem, is known as *Hatikvah*—The Hope.

In 1890, when Jewish pioneers from Russia founded the new settlement of Rehovot, they sang a marching song in Hebrew, whose refrain runs:

> Together let us go forward to return
> To the land of our fathers,
> To our beloved land,
> The cradle of our childhood.

These songs were also sung by Jewish children in some of the schools in Palestine. There were a few modern schools in the agricultural settlements and in Jaffa and Jerusalem, none of them higher than the elementary level. The teachers used the Hebrew language as the medium of instruction and the pupils, under their influence, conversed in Hebrew. Some adults also used Hebrew for every day conversation.

In 1900, the World Zionist Organization was three years old.

*   *   *

But all these were mere specks on the horizon of a bleak landscape.

In the Galilee, in the north, wheeled carriages were not to be seen until 1915. Arab serfs still ploughed the meager soil of the Holy Land with a crooked stick.

The majority of the twenty or thirty thousand Jews in the country were extremely pious and conservative. They lived on charity from abroad, spending most of their time in prayer and study.

The center of activity was outside the country. The Zionist Congresses met in Basle; the Zionist headquarters was in Vienna while most Zionists lived under the rule of the Czar of Russia.

More Jewish children spoke Hebrew and sang the "Songs of Zion" in Russia than in Palestine. The leading Hebrew books and periodicals were published in Warsaw, Vilno and Odessa. Tel-Aviv, which a generation later was to become the center of Hebrew literature, was just the wind-swept sand-dunes to the north of Jaffa.

In 1900, Palestine was still one of the most primitive and desolate sections of the already decaying Turkish Empire. Full of malaria-infested swamps, its forests had been denuded, its water-beds run dry, and its soil eroded.

It was a beautiful country, but neglected by centuries of misuse.

It was a lawless desert.

* * *

For the next two decades there was steady progress, but it was slow and painful.

The British, who took over the administration of Palestine following World War I, added new impetus. They held a mandate from the League of Nations, under whose terms they were to "facilitate the attainment" of Zionist aims. This they did—to an increasingly limited degree.

The immigration from Germany in the middle 1930's, after Hitler's accession to power, greatly accelerated the process of modernization and brought a substantial increase in the Jewish population.

World War II and its aftermath welded the Jewish community of Palestine into a nation.

Since the decision by the United Nations on November 29, 1947, to establish a Jewish State, the country has undergone changes at a rapid pace.

III

The transformation of Palestine within a few decades came with the planned return of an ancient people to its historic homeland.

Jewish immigrants settled the wastelands of Palestine in much the same way British immigrants colonized the wilderness of New England, Canada or Australia. But the unique aspect of Jewish colonization in Palestine has been that every settler saw in his migration part of the

Return and Restoration, for which the Jewish people never ceased to hope and pray.

*   *   *

A glance at the Jewish prayer book will give an inkling of how the Jews hoped and prayed.

Three times daily, in the so-called Eighteen Benedictions, or Silent Prayer, observant Jews say:

"Sound the great trumpet for our freedom, raise the banner for gathering our exiles, and gather us together from the four corners of the earth into our own land. Blessed be Thou, o Lord, who will surely gather in the scattered ones of His people of Israel.

"Restore our lawmakers as in olden times and our state counsellors as of yore."

In grace after meals similar prayers are recited just as frequently.

At a traditional wedding ceremony, the following is chanted with a festive tune:

"Soon, Oh Lord, our God, may there be heard on the roads of Judea and the streets of Jerusalem the sounds of joy and merriment, the voices of brides and grooms, the happy laughter of newlyweds and of young men at their banquets."

Every Bar-mitzvah boy and every man called up to cantillate the weekly portion of the Prophets says among the benedictions after the reading:

"Have compassion, Oh Lord, on Zion, for she is the home of our life. And do Thou redeem the suffering one speedily, within our lifetime. Blessed be Thou, Oh Lord, Who will surely cause Zion to rejoice in her children."

And so, for many centuries, in supplications and lamentations, in joy and in sorrow, in innumerable customs and ceremonies, the Jews kept alive the memory of Zion and the hope for the Return and the Restoration.

*   *   *

The State of Israel evolved out of the call of the trumpet for which the Jews have prayed and hoped. But the trumpet and its sounds have not been the same at all times to all Jews.

For centuries most Jews literally believed that some day the Messiah would appear riding on a white donkey and issue the blast from the ram's horn which shall gather all the Jews, living and dead, from all over the world into the Holy Land. Those buried in the countries of Dispersion would have to roll underground until they reached the sacred soil before being resurrected. Jews buried in the Land of Israel would be more fortunate.

To many, perhaps most, orthodox Jews in the ghetto the Messiah's call was little more than a devotional exercise expressed in words. To a few dedicated individuals in every generation it was a call to leave all behind and make the dangerous pilgrimage to the Holy Land.

Yehuda Halevi, the famous 12th century poet and philosopher, left his native Spain for Palestine, in order to "roll in the dust of its relics" and to "wander broken-hearted among Zion's ruins." He believed the spirit of prophecy would descend upon him when he trod the sacred soil.

Moses Maimonides, who lived shortly after Halevi, made an effort to settle in Palestine, after persecutions by the Moslems forced him to flee Spain. When he found conditions in the Holy Land unbearable, Maimonides went to nearby Egypt. But he was buried in Israel near Tiberias in the Galilee.

There were many others like Yehuda Halevi and Moses Maimonides.

Modern Zionism put a new interpretation on the Sound of the Trumpet when, late in the last century, its adherents began organizing to restore the Jews to Palestine and Palestine to the Jews. The Zionist interpretation always had and still has different versions.

Nor has the call been equally audible to all men at all times. It could sound like a small voice coming from the heart which only the sensitive could recognize. Or it could blare forth for the whole world to hear. Nothing could be less spectacular and less glamorous than the migration of the few straggling young men and women from Russia in the years 1904 to 1914. They had to sneak past Turkish officials and went almost unnoticed by the Zionist movement, whose leaders frowned upon this foolhardy adventure. And yet, forty years later, the leaders produced by those daring youngsters became world figures who changed the course of history. One of them became the first Prime Minister, another the second President of Israel.

IV

Because Jews for many centuries fasted, lamented and prayed for the Trumpet of the Messiah, Jewish engineers today are laying irrigation pipes in the Negev and Jewish scientists in Jerusalem, Haifa and Rehovot are engaged on projects for utilizing atomic energy for industry and for desalting the water of the Mediterranean.

Yet the undertaking of a concerted effort to bring about the Return and the Restoration by ordinary human endeavor constituted a break with the traditional past. In this organized effort many strictly religious Jews have also participated. But it is a new approach, which dates from the latter part of the nineteenth century. Says the second part of the third paragraph of the Declaration of Independence:

"In recent decades they . . . reclaimed the wilderness, revived their language, built cities and villages and established a vigorous and ever-growing community with its own economic and cultural life."

This book deals briefly with the age-long traditional approach. Most of the volume is devoted to depicting how "in recent decades" Jews in Palestine, and later, in Israel, "reclaimed the wilderness."

This is not a history book. It is neither a history of Zionism nor a history of Jewish colonization in Palestine, though it covers the latter.

The purpose of this book is to give the reader a series of pictures of life in Israel during the decades it evolved from a wilderness into a modern state, and the years following the establishment of the state.

The selections are taken from the records of men and women who participated in the effort. Most of the authors are writers. Some were leaders or humble pioneers.

This is an anthology. But, although literature figures in the book quite prominently, it is not a literary anthology. The chief aim is not to illustrate how Israelis write, but to show how Jews in Palestine and Israel lived in various periods.

Some selections are direct translations. Others are abridgements or condensations. In many instances the editor thought it best to tell the story in his own words and to offer introductory and explanatory notes.

This is not a source book for theoretical or abstract discussion. It is not a collection of essays on Zionist or any other ideology. The emphasis is on life, events and people.

To be sure, one book of some 400 pages cannot give a complete picture of life during several decades in such an unusual and fascinating country. But it is to be hoped that it gives a reasonably accurate bird's-eye view. It is also hoped that many readers will go on from this volume to a more detailed study of whatever specialized field of Israeli life may interest them.

THE FETTERED MESSIAH

THE TALE of Sarah, Hayim and their people forms part of the saga of three generations of Safed, as told in the trilogy "Enchanted City" by Joshua Bar-Joseph, himself a native of Safed.

In Safed, among ancient graves of legendary saints, ten thousand exiles from Spain and Portugal, in the sixteenth century, established the Sephardi community of mystics. They studied the Cabbala and sought to penetrate the hidden meaning of God's words, and to find the key to the redemption of the world and of Israel.

In the early nineteenth century *hassidim* from Eastern Europe formed their own Ashkenazi community in Safed. It is the Ashkenazi community which Bar-Joseph describes in his trilogy.

world in which Satan, the Prince of Darkness, is impersonated by a huge

Towards the end of the saga, by 1917, the Jews of Safed come into contact with the Jewish colonists of the Galilee—the modern Zionists. But most of the novel deals with Jews from another world—the world in which the Messiah could be brought to earth by prayer and fasting; the world in which Satan, the Prince of Darkness is impersonated by a huge black monster of a dog, who keeps the Messiah in chains.

From the Sephardi mystics the Ashkenazim learned the legend of Rabbi Joseph de la Reina, who attempted to release the Messiah from his shackles and to bring redemption to the world.

The story which Widow Sarah tells little Hayim embodies the traditional Jewish approach to the Return and Restoration before the advent of modern Zionism.

Joshua Bar-Joseph

◆

THE FETTERED MESSIAH

TOWARDS EVENING, after Hayim had finished his day at the *heder,* he would run to Aunt Sarah's.

He liked to be in her somber-looking room, when it was filled with shadows in the twilight.

And Sarah, in her slow old voice, would begin telling the story:
. . . The face of the scholar quivered as he sat over his folios, alone amid the large shadows in the prayer-house—because he heard the Messiah quiver in pain. The Messiah strained at his shackles . . .

And so, the man rose from his studies. He covered his shoulders with a white mantle, placed the Holy Book under his armpit and walked out through the open window. . . .

Filled with wrath and indignation, the man strode across the darkness of the clouds. He was now ready to reach the verge of heaven with his white mantle and from there to swoop down to the dark dungeon of the Messiah and undo his shackles. . . .

But suddenly the skies darkened and terrifying lightning flashed, illuminating everything with a dazzling white glare, and the loud thunder reverberated. . . . The black-bearded man who wore the white mantle began to tremble, and his face became very pale . . . for he saw a huge black dog rise from the couch where the Messiah lay in chains. As the black dog advanced from the fettered Messiah towards the scholar in the white mantle, he loomed as large as the Jermak Mountain.* The eyes of the dog were like two green suns. His teeth were like sharp rocks of red and violet fire, and

---

* The town of Safed is built on the slope of the Jermak Mountain.

when he gritted them there was lightning and thunder and a loud creaking noise, and white smoke came out of his nostrils. The monster shook his head violently, and a great golden candlestick leaped up to rest on his head. That was the sacred candlestick of the Temple in Jerusalem which Satan had stolen when the Temple was destroyed. The candlestick had turned pale with fury and humiliation and it now shone with a golden fire. . . . The candlestick on the dog's brow danced a mourner's dance. Eight black flames leaped from it and swallowed the surrounding sparks of fire. Making long strides, the hound drew near, stride by stride; the heavens were set quaking by each step and at each motion of his heavy yet sinuous body, a tremulous roar was heard from afar.

The scholar in the white mantle shrank back in fear and raised his face to Heaven.

He who sits in Glory surrounded by a bright blue light and golden angels heard the supplication. The azure sky smiled gently and little by little grew brighter. Terror was now gone from the eyes of Rabbi Joseph de la Reina and they became tranquil in the reflected radiance. From on high came the singing of Psalms and gold-white angels hovered around the scholar's head whispering into his ears.

Thereupon Rabbi Joseph took courage and firmly strode towards the huge dog. And as he strode, this great scholar murmured the names of holy angels and the Exalted and Awesome Name of the One Who is Omnipresent and Everlasting.

And lo and behold—a miracle! The dreadful monster which had been advancing with the sureness of a devouring beast towards its prey, now began to retreat in fear before the lean man murmuring prayers. Nor was that all. With every step he took in withdrawing, the dog shrank in size while the horrendous colors of his mouth and eyes became fainter and fainter. The fiery candlestick detached itself from the head of the beast and flew away. Now in place of a terrifying monster was a miserable little cur wagging its tail and rolling its eyes and fawning at the feet of the man.

Now, the white-mantled scholar thought to himself as he smiled into his black beard, the time has come to cast this monster out of this world and out of the other world too! And so he caught the

cur by the scruff of his neck and began carrying him towards the
Dark Mountain. For only the Dark Mountain would swallow up
the monster and not throw him back to the sinister forces who
would restore its carcass to life. For seven days and seven nights
the scholar was to travel, just as the angels had whispered to him,
across seas and land and hills and dales, over high mountains and
through deep precipices. He was to give the dog no bread to eat
nor water to drink, until he perished of hunger and thirst. When
the man saw that the dog had no more life in it, he was to fling
the carcass into the black abyss, return to Safed, immerse himself in
the pool of the Saintly Scholar Rabbi Isaac Lurie and purify his
soul of every stain or blemish. Only then was he to return to this
place and proceed without interruption or interference to the dungeon
where the Messiah was imprisoned in chains. Then with his pure
hands would he rid the Redeemer of his shackles and bring Redemption to the Jews and to mankind. . . .

For forty-nine days and forty-nine nights, seven times seven days
and nights, as the angels enjoined him, the white-mantled scholar
dragged the cur toward the Dark Mountain. The beast grew weaker
and weaker.

At first, the wretch tried to win the man's heart by wagging
its tail. It had a pitiable-looking tail like a worn-out old broom,
every shake of which evoked much compassion in the Rabbi's heart;
it was as if he were witnessing infants in death agony, or women
expiring in childbirth, or old men pleading for another day of life.
But Rabbi Joseph de la Reina was firm.

Then the dog made his green eyes look sad and sick. Though
the hues of the Satan still skulked in them, he filled them with the
tears of innocent suffering; he dropped his eyes and raised them
a trifle, in plea and supplication. But Rabbi Joseph de la Reina
remained firm and gave the dog neither food nor drink.

Finally the dog tried with his voice. He whimpered and he
wailed like an injured dove, like a sick child, like a hungry orphan,
like a bridegroom pleading against the murder of his bride under
the wedding canopy, like a sinner in his penitence, like an old
beggar woman thrown out into the street. The wretch wept and
howled and his echoes resounded far and wide. But Rabbi Joseph

knew these were the wiles of Satan, so he stopped his ears and, gritting his teeth, he dragged the dog along to his appointed grave in the Dark Mountain.

Three days before they reached the black abyss the dog feigned death and made his own carcass feel as heavy as a mountain. The man in the white mantle did not flinch. Sweating and panting, he dragged the carcass to the brink.

Then Rabbi Joseph stood still for a moment to take a pinch of snuff. He had had neither food nor drink for forty-nine days and nights and he wished to refresh himself just a trifle with the scent of the snuff before the final effort. To make sure that the monster did not escape, he placed his foot on the neck of the dog when he opened the snuff-box and raised the fragrant powder to his nostrils.

He sniffed one pinch and then another and thanked God in his heart for the success of his undertaking thus far. He felt a sense of satisfaction that it was he, Rabbi Joseph de la Reina, who had been elected by Him Who dwells on High,—he, of all men, to bring about the Redemption of Israel and the world.

But here the wily beast caught the familiar scent of man's self-satisfaction. Greatly encouraged by it, he summoned his remaining strength for a new effort. With a smile of dissembled meekness in his green eyes, he sighed a deep sigh of resignation and spoke like a human being. Humbly, he said:

"You are much to be envied, you, who are but mortal flesh and blood, that you have achieved what has been denied to greater men in bringing me to these nethermost depths. My end has come and I have but one request. Do, I beseech you, after you have flung me down, pray to All-Highest for my lost soul. May He of the Blessed Glory take compassion on me and join the holy sparks that are in my soul to those of the Righteous of the Universe. . . . "*

With these words the wretch succeeded in stirring up pride in the man's heart. Rabbi Joseph de la Reina smiled to himself and thrust another pinch of snuff into his nostrils, saying: "Perhaps I

---

* Jewish mystics believe that there is a divine spark in everything, even in the most evil.

will pray to His Blessed Name, not for your sake, but for the sake of the holy sparks in your unclean soul . . . "

The dog closed his eyes in abject humility and then opened them with a smile of despair, as if begging for pity. In a voice which sounded like a prayer he entreated: "Before you fling me down, will you please let me sniff some of your snuff so that I may overcome somewhat the pangs of my inescapable death."

The man in the white mantle who had withstood the dog's tears and whimperings could not withstand this plea. The angels had warned him against giving the beast anything to eat or drink—but this was snuff and was permissible, he thought to himself. He bent toward the black dog and opened the snuffbox. . . . Fire burst forth from the monster's nostrils and consumed the snuff. The smoke incense curled up from the box and rose to the arch-father of all abomination. Unwittingly Rabbi Joseph de la Reina had offered incense to the Prince of Pollution.

The powers of the monster returned. He leaped to his feet, rising as tall as a mountain. His eyes again filled with life and shone like two green suns. His teeth grew hard as flinty rock; lightning flashed and thunder roared as he gnashed them in fury. The fiery candlestick leaped once more upon his head. His claws grew sharper. . . .

The man clad in the white mantle, in his bewilderment, forgot the combination of holy names and holy letters which would protect him from the power of Satan.

The black dog sprang upon him and, thrusting his sharp teeth into the Rabbi's heart, began to eat his flesh and to drink his blood.

Nothing was left but the white mantle of Rabbi Joseph de la Reina. Then it fell into the black abyss. . . .

And so the Messiah remains shackled to this day. . . .

2 VALLEY OF DESOLATION BECOMES THE PORTAL OF HOPE

I

THOUSANDS OF devout Jews in every generation have fasted Mondays and Thursdays and risen at midnight to lament for the Destruction and to pray for the Restoration. From time to time a movement arose to take concrete steps in the direction of the Return.

Early in the nineteenth century pious scholars in Eastern Europe began settling in the Holy Land.

They had no political plan. They had no thought of founding colonies or building a Jewish economy. This was a movement of pilgrims and worshipers who believed that a prayer offered in the Holy Land had more effect than one recited in the Exile and that a commandment fulfilled in Jerusalem or in Safed was more pleasing to the Lord than a good deed performed in Vilno, Warsaw, Kovno or Pressburg. Also, they were convinced that by their very sojourn in the Holy Land they were hastening the advent of the Messiah and the Kingdom of Heaven.

Nevertheless, these other-wordly Jews were, in their own way, pioneers and heroes. They had to brave the rigors of the climate and the fury of fanatical Arabs to establish themselves in the country.

Jewish communities were established in the Four Holy Cities: Jerusalem, Hebron, Safed and Tiberias.

Religious leaders in the Diaspora organized collections of funds to maintain synagogues and academies and various charitable institutions in these cities, and to support deserving scholars so that they might devote their time to study. In time the Jews in the Holy Land came to depend almost entirely on assistance from abroad. They were organized according to country or region of origin and each group received funds from their "own" communities in Europe or in Asia and Africa. Funds were distributed by local administrators, or *gabbaim,* appointed by leaders abroad. The distribution of funds—*halukah* in Hebrew—became the mark of the Old Yishuv, or Old Community.

The Old Yishuv in Jerusalem also benefited from the munificence of two great philanthropists—Sir Moses Montefiore in England and Judah Touro in the United States. The money provided by these two men— especially by Montefiore—made it possible for the Jews of Jerusalem to build new quarters for themselves outside the city walls which were the beginnings of modern Jewish Jerusalem.

While the austere Talmudic legalists and scholars were drawn to Jerusalem, the *hassidim,* who stressed emotion and mysticism, were attracted to Safed, the capital of the Galilee in the north. In Safed a community of Jewish mystics had already been founded in the sixteenth century by cabbalists from Spain and Portugal.

The landscape of Safed and its environment—its high mountains and valleys, the howling winds and torrential rains in the winter and profuse vegetation in the mild summer—is conducive to the contemplation and dreaming of the mystic. In modern times it became the favorite spot of Israeli artists.

In the vicinity of Safed are to be found the graves of ancient saints, including that of Rabbi Shimeon bar-Yohai, the father of the Cabbala. To this day colorful celebrations are held each Spring at his grave at Meron, near the cave where, according to tradition, he hid from the Romans for seven years while writing the Book of the Zohar, the classical work of the Cabbala.

II

In 1825 the Jewish leader from England, Sir Moses Montefiore, paid a visit to the Holy Land. A leading Jerusalemite by the name of Shlomo Zalman waited on him and urged upon him to buy land for Jewish colonization in Palestine. Sir Moses favored the idea, but the Jewish leaders of the Holy City objected very strenuously. To seek to bring about the return of the Jews to the Holy Land by mundane efforts was sinful, as it meant tampering with the prerogatives of the Almighty. More so, the leaders of the community, who administered the distribution of the funds among the pious scholars, had a vested interest in the status quo and saw in any change a threat to their power.

In 1845, Sir Moses Montefiore again visited the Holy Land. Shlomo Zalman was no longer among the living. But his son, Mordecai Solomon, waited on the British philanthropist and pleaded for the same cause his father had in 1825. Again the communal leaders objected. Sir Moses then planted an orange grove for Jews in Jaffa, by the sea, somewhat removed from the tight control of the Jerusalemite leaders. Mordecai Solomon himself took up farming on his own in the vicinity of Gaza.

In 1878, the son of Mordecai Solomon, Moshe Yoel Solomon, together with Joshua Stampfer and David Gutmann, founded what is the oldest Jewish agricultural settlement in Palestine. This was Petah-Tikvah, now a flourishing town of over twenty thousand people.

But some important developments took place before the founding of Petah-Tikvah.

In 1868, Charles Netter, an Alsatian Jew, established the first Jewish agricultural school in Palestine, near Jaffa. It is still being operated by the Alliance Israélite Universelle, with headquarters in Paris, of which Netter was an official.

About the same time, German Protestants began establishing colonies in the Holy Land—near Jerusalem, Jaffa, Haifa and in a few places inland.

Moshe Yoel Solomon, who subsequently became one of the three founders of Petah-Tikvah, saw the German colony near his native Jerusalem. He then wrote in the Hebrew magazine he published:

Our hearts rejoice to see our Homeland turn into a garden when cultivated by industrious hands. But our faces are covered with shame at the thought that the first to rehabilitate our soil are strangers while our own people stand aloof . . .

*   *   *

A Jerusalemite scholar by the name of Rabbi Joshua Yellin, the father of David Yellin, led in an abortive attempt to found a colony near Jerusalem. Another such attempt was made in the Galilee. Both colonies—Motza near Jerusalem and Rosh Pina in the Galilee—were resettled by colonists from Eastern Europe shortly after being abandoned by their original founders.

*   *   *

In 1882 pioneers from Russia and Rumania founded a group of settlements, of which Rishon le-Zion in the south and Zichron-Yaakov in the north were the most important.

This early colonization grew out of a movement known as Hibat Zion or Love of Zion. It developed gradually during the second half of the nineteenth century.

In 1897, when Herzl founded the World Zionist Organization, the Lovers of Zion (in Hebrew, Hoveve-Zion) joined it.

Of the three founders, only Stampfer died in Petah-Tikvah. He was one of the most remarkable men in modern Jewish history.

When Petah-Tikvah was evacuated, all three—Solomon, Gutmann and Stampfer—took up residence in Yehudiyeh. Gutmann had become progressively poorer and had no money left when the time came to return to the original settlement. He sustained himself by growing dates in Yehudiyeh, until his early death. Solomon tried to create in Yehudiyeh a cultural center and succeeded for a while in attracting some of the leading writers of Palestine to that Arab village. But in time they left it and he, too, had to move out. He went back to his native Jerusalem, where he spent the remainder of his life as a writer. Stampfer, however, true to his sterling character, went back to Petah-Tikvah and became the leader. He died as mayor of Petah-Tikvah in 1908.

* * *

About one year after the group of Jerusalemites founded Petah-Tikvah in Judea, another group of pious Jews in Safed, in the Galilee, made a similar attempt to establish themselves as farmers. They bought a plot of land in the northernmost part of the Holy Land called Geoni. Like the settlers of Petah-Tikvah, they too, had to abandon the place. A few of them later joined the settlers who had come from Rumania and formed, on the same site, the colony of Rosh-Pinah, in 1882. There was another similar attempt made at Motza, near Jerusalem, which had to be abandoned.

The year 1882 marks the beginning of the relatively large migration of pioneers from Eastern Europe to Palestine. This was the beginning of the First Aliyah. Petah-Tikvah, Geoni and Motza had been mere preludes.

The First Aliyah was a mere trickle compared to the mighty stream of Jewish migration from Eastern Europe to America, the Argentine and other countries of the New World and, to a lesser extent, to Western Europe. But Palestine was not a natural country of immigration: it was not a place where the immigrant would naturally expect an improvement in his lot as an individual. Palestine was economically far less developed than Russia or Rumania, and the political regime which ruled it was hardly any better. To Palestine went people who were primarily motivated by the desire to effect a revolution in Jewish history and to lay the foundation of the Third Jewish Commonwealth.

According to Moshe Smilansky, who was perhaps the most articulate representative of the First Aliyah, his contemporaries were of three types: traditional scholars who imbibed the love of the Holy Land from daily religious practice and customs and who differed from other pious scholars only in refusing to wait for miracles; plain folk who were driven by an instinctive urge which they were unable to explain; Western-educated men and women who arrived at the Zionist idea by a process of rational thinking and proceeded to put their idea into practice by going out to pioneer in the wilderness. A handful of the latter type became famous in history as the BILU.

The name BILU is made up of the initial letters of the first four words of a verse in Isaiah (Chapter 3, verse 5) : "Oh, House of Jacob, come and let us walk (in the light of the Lord)." The slogan was adopted by a group of Jewish university students in Southern Russia, when they formed an association to colonize Palestine.

Who were those men and women who ventured into the unsown wastes of their ancestral land to blaze a path in the wilderness and to clear a way for others? Who were those stout-hearted Jews whose daring and fortitude made it possible for those who were to follow them to achieve the miracle of creating a Homeland?

Who were they who first settled the trackless and waterless sands in a disease-ridden country, in a difficult climate, among a half-savage population, under the oppressive and corrupt rule of the Turkish Sultan?

MOSHE SMILANSKY

Moshe Smilansky

◆

PORTAL OF HOPE

1. THE FOUNDERS

IN THE WINTER of 1869 a boy of seventeen stole out of his father's house in the dead of night and started walking from Hungary to Palestine. All he had was a map of Europe and Asia and the equivalent of one dollar in cash. More than four months later he arrived in Jerusalem.

He was Joshua Stampfer, the son of a small town religious functionary.

The boy had received a good traditional Jewish education and had matriculated in the German-Magyar secondary school. After his matriculation he had spent some time at the Rabbinical Seminary in Berlin, where he came under the influence of the Director, Dr. Azriel Hildesheimer, one of the early Lovers of Zion in Europe. The boy's father strongly disapproved of any new-fangled ideas about the founding of Jewish agricultural colonies in Palestine. The rabbinical student was recalled home. He quarreled with his father and went off to tutor his cousins on a farm. Their father happened to be a Lover of Zion, too. When Joshua Stampfer returned home, he again quarreled with his father. Then, when all Hungary was gripped by a wave of national enthusiasm in the wake of its first national elections, young Stampfer, who felt a strong sympathy for the Magyar national movement, decided to go to Palestine and emulate the Hungarians.

About one year after Stampfer's arrival in Jerusalem, the communal leaders who administered the dole from the funds collected in Hungary arranged for his marriage to the daughter of a man

who was the recipient of a relatively good allowance. The groom
was expected to study at the yeshiva (Talmudic academy) maintained by the Hungarian Jews. This was bitter defeat, for in his
native land Stampfer had dreamed of dotting Palestine with institutions of learning whose students would divide their time between
the study of the law and farming. But he had to bide his time.
Later he found kindred spirits in Moshe Yoel Solomon, the editor,
who was a native Jerusalemite, and David Gutmann, a Hungarian
Jew like himself.

Gutmann arrived in Jerusalem later than Stampfer and brought
a considerable sum of money with him. He became the financier
of the project. Solomon was the theoretician. Stampfer was the real
leader.

The three men formed as association in which they enlisted
about one hundred Jerusalemites and newcomers, to establish an
agricultural settlement.

At first they planned to settle in the Valley of Jericho, which
was far inland, to the south of Jerusalem. . . . When they set out
to survey a site proposed for sale, they were attacked by ruffians
hired by the administrators of the dole. The three friends beat off
the attack, but after the incident, they took care to maintain strict
secrecy about their plans.

The land in the Valley of Jericho was bought, but the Turkish
authorities refused to register the sale. Other plans met with similar
frustration. Word then reached them of a sizable plot of land for
sale in the plain of the Yarkon River, not far from Jaffa.

The place was Mlebes, where there had been a succession of
sturdy Arab tribes gradually being debilitated by the climate and
then falling prey to still more vigorous predatory tribes who later
underwent the same fate.

On a summer morning in 1878 the three friends, joined by a
fourth man named Barnett, set out from Jerusalem to Mlebes. The
land looked good, but the Arab inhabitants had a sickly appearance
and many of them were blind.

Barnett, a well-to-do businessman from London, exclaimed that
this was the "Valley of Achor," or the "Valley of Desolation,"
mentioned in Hosea. Solomon then recited the rest of the verse:

"And I will give her her vineyards from thence, and the Valley of Desolation as a Portal of Hope" (Hosea, Chapter 11, verse 17).

A Greek physician brought in from Jaffa pointed out that the birds did not descend for worms and flies because of the polluted air and strongly advised against settling in Mlebes.

But the three friends were determined and they called the new settlement Petah-Tikvah—Portal of Hope.

Solomon, Gutmann and Stampfer were the first to put up their tents in Petah-Tikvah. Gutmann would go out each day to the gates to welcome any new settler who might come. When there were finally ten men in the place and it was possible to worship in a congregation, he raised his hands to Heaven and thanked the Almighty for having let him live to see that day.

When the Passover came, the settlers celebrated the Seder together. At the ceremony Stampfer delivered an oration in which he said:

"Say no longer, Oh thou sacred land, 'I am grievously dishonored; my children have forsaken me!' Take comfort, oh earth! For where ten have now arisen in thy behalf a hundred shall follow and out of the hundred shall grow a thousand, and of the thousand a million!"

2. THE SOLDIER OF THE CZAR

The early settlers of Petah-Tikvah were divided into the "Highlanders," who bought plots on higher ground, and the poorer "Yarkonites," who settled in "The Depths," by the river Yarkon. The latter consoled themselves that they would enjoy good fishing and good pasture.

Yaakov "the Soldier" was one of the Yarkonites.

Yaakov did not even know the Jewish name given him at birth. He was one of the so-called "cantonists," the little Jewish boys kidnapped for military service during the reign of Czar Nicholas I of Russia. With hundreds of others he was sent into the interior of Russia and given over to the care of peasants until old enough to enter the army. Under duress, many were converted to Christianity and given new names.

For years Yaakov served the Czar and fought his wars, convinced of the justice of his cause. But one day, when his regiment passed through a small town in the Ukraine, he heard the sounds of a strange tune that came out of a house, which mingled with their own song. It was a sad, heart-rending melody. The soldiers laughed and called it *Zhidovskaya piesnia*—a Jew song. But Yaakov felt attracted to the tune. It sounded familiar. He stopped, and the company commander rebuked him.

The strange melody haunted Yaakov for a long time.

After twenty-five years of military service, Yaakov was given his discharge, married a peasant woman and settled on a plot of land somewhere in the interior of Russia, where there were few Jews. He raised a family of Christian peasants, went in for horse trading and prospered. He almost forgot the melody.

Once business took him to a town in which there were many Jews and there he heard the sad melody again. This time he stopped to listen and followed the sounds until he came into a Jewish prayer-house. He remained in town and went to the house of worship every morning, standing in the doorway and listening to the traditional tunes of Jewish prayers. The soldier never returned to his village or to his wife and children; he went to the local rabbi and asked to be converted to Judaism. The rabbi, who had guessed the soldier's origin, brought him into the Jewish faith, taught him to read Hebrew, to say his prayers and the rudimentary laws of Judaism. He gave him the name of Jacob.

At the age of sixty years, Yaakov went to Jerusalem, the place of which the prayer-book spoke so much. It was in 1878. On arriving in the Holy City, he heard of the purchase of land in Petah-Tikvah, and decided to join the new settlement.

When Yaakov the Soldier settled in Petah-Tikvah, he bought land in "The Depths" and became one of the "Yarkonites." He liked the river and the fertile soil on both sides of the river. But, unlike all other Yarkonites who built mudhouses, Yaakov put up a house of stone. He laid out a large courtyard, bought horses and oxen for plowing, and acquired milch cows, goats, and birds. His barnyard was full of animal sounds. He plowed and sowed his

fields and even rented some of his neighbor's land, and prospered
in his labor.

Yaakov did not marry again and lived alone. From Jerusalem
he brought a Scroll of the Law, which he carried into his house,
and with music and festivities, he made it an informal prayer-house.
A *minyan** of worshippers met there every day for afternoon and
evening prayers. On Saturdays and holidays they held morning
services as well. Yaakov felt an intense desire to lead in the service
at the altar. He knew all the melodies of the weekday and Sabbath
prayers, which he sang to himself at home, in the farmyard, and in
the field. But his enunciation of the Hebrew words in the prayers
made one think of a man walking barefoot over pebbles, and he
did not dare.

There were other Jews in Petah-Tikvah who had come from the
villages of the Diaspora and were hardly better schooled than himself, and yet every one of them had a chance to lead in public
prayer twice a year, on the memorial days for their parents. Yaakov
envied them. He, himself, had no knowledge of the date his father
and mother had died. Finally he decided to make his own *yarzeit*
and fixed it as the date when he first heard the sad melody of the
Jewish prayer in the Ukrainian town. He remembered the day very
well. To be sure, it was the date in the Christian calendar that he
remembered. But a neighbor of his, a Jerusalemite, who was versed
in calendar lore, helped him out. Three times on that day Yaakov
stood before the altar. He did it again the following year. The
melodies of his prayers were sweet, sad, and touching. His congre-
gants, simple rustic Jews like himself, wept profusely. In time the
scholarly Jerusalemites among the settlers, who at first doubted such
Hebrew pronunciation could be used in prayer, changed their attitude. They began to enjoy the musical voice of the ignorant old
soldier, and even offered him the traditional congratulation of
yasher koach on the conclusion of the service. One of the scholars
propounded the theory that if the Goyim were Jews and knew how
to read Hebrew, they might produce great cantors.

---

* Minimum of ten males required for public worship.

Every Saturday, at the conclusion of the services in his house, Yaakov would offer his guests the traditional honey cake and brandy, both of his own making. Yaakov was a good cook, a good baker, and knew how to brew strong drinks. He had brought from Russia, along with the samovar for tea, another kind of samovar—a still which brewed what the Jews called "the bitter drop."

Yaakov was fond of strong drink and believed in its healing qualities. He tried to convince the other colonists that brandy was a better cure for malaria fever than the quinine they used.

The Russian soldier was a powerful, tall, broad-shouldered man. On horseback, with his white flowing beard, he was an impressive figure. The Arab shepherds who threw covetous eyes at the Jewish fields, treated Yaakov with healthy respect and called him "Moskub" —the Muscovite, or the Russian.

Despite his faith in the strong drink, it did not save Yaakov from frequent attacks of malaria, which undermined his strength. But he held out for a long time, as did his stone house, which stood his neighbors in good stead during the floods of the winter of 1879-1880. The whole valley on both banks of the Yarkon River was under water. The settlers' mudhouses were swamped and they could not get out. Their cries for help were in vain, as all the inhabitants of the countryside had fled. Several mudhouses were thrown down. Then Yaakov the Soldier picked some of the strongest men among the Yarkonites and formed a rescue team. Armed with staffs and ropes, they tied themselves to each other, and passing knee deep in water among the houses, they carried out the women, the children and the old people. All the Yarkonites saved from the flood slept on the floor of Yaakov's stone house, ate out of his store, and drank his brandy to keep warm. There, in the depths of despair, they prayed to the Lord.

When all the mudhouses crumbled and most of the Yarkonites moved back to Jerusalem, Yaakov's stone house remained for a long time the only house among the ruins. He was among the last to leave. However, the malaria had eaten into his very bones. A few days after he was taken to Jaffa, he died.

*   *   *

3. THE PIANO IN THE DESERT

Joseph Feinberg was a native of southern Russia, a graduate of a famous school of technology in Western Europe, and an engineer in a large factory in Kiev. In 1881 he joined the BILU movement in Russia, and leaving all behind him, took his young wife and two small children to start a new life in Palestine. As soon as he arrived in Jaffa, Feinberg was elected as land-buying agent for the group. He bought the land on which Rishon-le-Zion was established.

His wife's name was Berta, but she was known by the affectionate diminutive, Bertyusha. Even at twenty-five, and with two small children, she remained the attractive Russian high school girl who had captured Feinberg's heart.

Bertyusha left the sheltered life of a well-to-do middle class home in Russia to face the rigors of pioneer life in a primitive country. She cheerfully gave up all the comforts and the pleasures to which she had been accustomed, except one thing—music. She lived in a primitive shack; her drinking water she drew from the rain pools, water mixed with sand and leeches; she cooked and baked and washed clothes and did all the dreary chores. But she had brought her piano with her to Rishon-le-Zion and played it every night after the children had gone to bed. Those were the first sounds of a piano in the wilderness of Judea.

The settlers lived in tents and shacks. They sowed wheat, but thistles and thorns grew. They dug for a well, but failed to strike water. Their meager resources were depleted. After a few months the colony faced a desperate situation.

Help from the outside was needed. These colonists were the vanguard of the Jewish people. The "rear" was in the Diaspora. Somebody had to go to appeal to the "home-front" for assistance. Who but Feinberg was the proper emissary?

Feinberg was loath to leave Rishon-le-Zion, and even more reluctant to part from his family. But his wife urged him to go:

"I am not the only one to suffer hardship on the soil of Rishon-le-Zion," she told him, and he went.

Feinberg left late in the summer of 1882. The rear, the home-front, failed to respond. Jews in Europe had so many of their own

institutions to take care of; what concern had they with planting
wheat or the digging of a well in a far-away Judea?

But a miracle happened. It was the miracle that saved the First
Aliyah. One day, soon after Rosh Hashanah in 1882, Joseph Feinberg sat in the mansion of the greatest financier of those days, in
the Faubourg St. Honoré in Paris, talking for hours about the story
of Rishon-le-Zion and the vision of the Jewish rebirth in Palestine.
Baron Edmund Rothschild, won over to the man and to the cause,
promised help. But he stipulated two conditions; the number of
colonists must be enlarged and the name of the benefactor must be
kept secret.

Feinberg returned to Rishon-le-Zion in triumph. He was the
hero, and his shack became the social center. That was where friends
gathered in their leisure time to drink tea, to discuss the problems of
the colony, the country, the Jewish people, and the world, and to
sing while Bertyusha played the piano. And woe to him who uttered
a false note!

The Feinbergs planted wheat, cultivated vines, and raised a dairy
herd. The civil engineer and the pianist milked cows, churned but-
ter and did the other chores. They were happy.

This went on for four years. Then, in 1886, came a rude
awakening.

Baron Rothschild had entrusted the administration of his financial
assistance to the Jewish colonies in Palestine in the hands of officials
of his picking. These officials bore no responsibility to the colonists.
In time friction developed between the administrators and the
colonists; the bureaucrats, in an attempt to maintain their influence,
tried to win over some of the settlers to their side.

The Feinberg home became the center of a plot against the
baronial bureaucracy. Bertyusha helped to stoke the fires of rebellion.

"Baron Rothschild and the Jews of the whole world must know
that we have come here to build new lives and to live as free men
and women," she argued.

One night, after a stormy session at the Feinberg home, the
chief administrator of Rishon-le-Zion was asked to leave the colony.
The baronial bureaucrats retaliated by demanding the expulsion of
Joseph Feinberg.

Baron Rothschild came to Palestine on his first visit. He said to Feinberg:

"It is you who got me into this. It was your duty as a man of education to have prevented the squabble from coming to such a pass. The only thing left for you to do now is to sell out and move out of this colony."

"Monsieur le Baron," Feinberg replied, "all your millions cannot get me out of Rishon-le-Zion."

"If this is the position you take," the Baron retorted, "then, as far as I am concerned, you no longer exist." Rothschild cut off all financial support from the colony.

A special messenger brought a letter to Feinberg from two Zionist leaders in Odessa, Leon Pinsker and Moshe Leib Lilienblum, urging him to give in for the sake of the cause. Bertyusha, too, was in favor of submission, "or the colony will suffer and your achievement in Paris will have been lost."

Broken in spirit, Joseph Feinberg left the colony he had built, after five and a half years of devoted, dedicated work. At first he settled in the all-Arab town of Lydda, where he tried to be a pioneer in industry. But the olive press he started had to go to a Christian-Arab creditor to whom it had been mortgaged, and the family moved to Jaffa. Hard times came and Feinberg even tried, unsuccessfully, to become a teamster.

He died in 1902 twenty years after his arrival in Palestine, a poor and forgotten man.

3

THE LAST MEN
ON THE RAMPART

IN THE summer of 1903 three boys of the town of Plonsk, in Poland, stood in the river, reading a newspaper and weeping.

All three boys, about seventeen years of age, were the leading members of the local young Zionist club, "Ezra," and were pledged, among other things, to converse among themselves in Hebrew. While bathing in the river Plonka, they were given a copy of the latest issue of *Hatzefira*, published in Warsaw, and stopped to read the report from the Zionist Congress, then holding its session in Basle. The report made them weep: Herzl, the revered idol of the Jewish masses, the founder of the World Zionist Organization, was in favor of accepting the British offer of making Uganda in East Africa the Jewish Homeland; Herzl was ready to betray Zion.

Forty-five years later, in Tel-Aviv, when one of the three boys, now known to the world as Ben-Gurion, proclaimed the State of Israel, the sins of Herzl had long been forgotten and his memory was an inspiration. But in 1903 the betrayal hurt.

When the three boys got over their crying spell, they came out of the water, dressed and began to discuss the new situation. What was to be done now?

Ever since Herzl became the leader of the Zionists, he had been engaged in diplomatic talks with the German Kaiser, with the Turkish Sultan, with princes, dukes, courtiers, ministers of state—with the purpose of securing international sanction for the rapid colonization of Palestine by the Jews, and the establishment of an autonomous Jewish commonwealth under an open covenant with the Turkish government. He had little patience with the slow, laborious penetration under precarious conditions, with the costly, bumbling methods of colonization that had taken place in Palestine since 1880's and had now come to a standstill.

Herzl fired the imagination of the masses and attracted great Jewish personalities to his cause. He raised many hopes. But his only diplomatic success was with the British, who did not possess Palestine and offered Uganda instead. Herzl was in favor of accepting the offer—at least, as a temporary refuge.

Was all hope lost now?

Not necessarily, the three boys thought. At any rate, one had to try.

Diplomacy might have failed, but not pioneering. If the old colonies in Palestine were deteriorating, then new settlers must come, with new hope and new determination.

But who of the three boys was to be the first to go? Shmuel Fuchs, or Shlomo Zemach, or David Green? (The latter was better known as Duvidl.)

Half in jest, the three boys used the old game common among school boys in the ghetto: you open a Hebrew book at random and look at the first letter of the page: if it is D—Daled—then David is first; if it is Sh—Shin—then it is either Shmuel or Shlomo, depending on whether a Lamed or a Mem is nearest the Shin.

The oracle said Shlomo Zemach.

But Shlomo Zemach's father refused to furnish the money for the fare. He was a comparatively well-to-do merchant in Plonsk and could afford it, but he was not going to help his gifted son ruin his young life.

"I will readily give you money, if it is anything for your good," he argued, "but not for this."

The father was a conservative, observant Jew, who believed that the two main objects in life were to observe and study the Torah and to attend to business. Zionism, in his view, ran counter to tradition, since it presumed to do the work of the Almighty in restoring the Jews to their Homeland, and certainly was not good business.

When his father sent him on some business errand, entrusting him with three hundred rubles, Shlomo Zemach took the money and absconded.

He went to the nearby border and smuggled himself into Galicia, the part of Poland held by Austria, and finally landed in Trieste (then also under Austrian rule), where he took the boat for Jaffa.

* * *

Shlomo Zemach was the first one from Plonsk. Other members of the Ezra Club followed one by one: Shlomo Lefkowitz (now known as Lavi), who was to found Ain-Harod; Duvidl Green, who was to proclaim the Jewish State, and others. But not Shmuel Fuchs, who cried with Green and Zemach in the Plonka river. He left for America that same year.

* * *

They came, one by one, or in groups: from Plonsk in Poland, from Homel in White Russia, from Romny in the Ukraine. No one sent them from Europe; no one welcomed them in Palestine. Most Zionist leaders thought it was madness for green young people to go without preliminary training, without organization, without the right of the Jews to colonize Palestine being recognized. It seemed to be a case of young lunatics dashing their heads against a stone wall.

But four decades later, it was the stone wall that broke.

* * *

The Turkish Government had taken measures to keep out prospective Jewish settlers from Palestine. Russian subjects were more likely to be suspect than, say, Austrian or German Jews. But pilgrims were allowed to visit the Holy Land. The Turks then issued special "red tickets" for pilgrims, who were allowed to remain in the country for three months. What with Turkish inefficiency and corruption, most pioneers of the Second Aliyah entered on those "red tickets" and remained for as long as they could or cared.

Shlomo Zemach, who came from the Polish region of the vast empire of the Czar, employed a different ruse: somewhere in Austria he had made friends with a young Zionist university student and exchanged passports with him. Thus, he landed at Jaffa as an Austrian student, pretending to come to visit the Holy Land during his vacation.

Unfortunately, however, he lost a shoe on the way. The Turkish official in Jaffa, in his broken French, argued that he had never seen an *étudiant* who was barefoot. However, a local Jew who knew his way around, with the gift of Zemach's watch to the official, helped him gain admission to the Homeland.

It was Friday morning. Zemach was anxious to see a Jewish village before the Sabbath made travel impossible. He boarded the primitive stage-coach or *diligence* (deeleezhans) bound for Rishon-le-Zion.

* * *

A quarter of a century had passed since the founding of Petah-Tikvah and over two decades since the founding of Rishon-le-Zion. Other colonies were established at the same time and later in other parts of the country. But these two—Petah-Tikvah and Rishon-le-Zion—were the largest, the best-known, situated nearest to Jaffa. Newcomers like Shlomo Zemach would invariably visit those two places first and compare them.

Petah-Tikvah was founded by pious Talmudic scholars from Jerusalem, some of whom, like Stampfer and Gutmann, were natives of Hungary; Rishon-le-Zion was the first settlement established by Western-educated young idealists from Russia, like Joseph Feinberg; Gadera, to the south of Rishon-le-Zion, was founded by a more radical *Bilu* group; Zamarin in the north and Rosh-Pinah in the Galilean hills were established by Rumanians, simple loyal Jews, who chose Palestine rather than the United States or the Argentine out of an instinctive Jewish attachment.

But all settlers had too little experience, too little capital, too little knowledge of conditions. Soon they were all subjected to the grim test of hunger, disease, Arab attacks and Turkish corruption and misgovernment. Many left, but the stalwarts remained.

"We will eat these stones, but we will not leave this place," cried a Rumanian woman in Zamarin. In Rosh-Pinah, further north, the settlers took a solemn oath in the synagogue that they would not leave, no matter what the hardships. Shortly after this an emissary came from Baron Maurice de Hirsch, the great philanthropist, offering the colonists of Rosh-Pinah resettlement on good soil in the Argentine, with financial assistance to start them off, but refusing to help them in Palestine. The offer was turned down.

Then came another Jewish baron-philanthropist who saved the colonies from ruin. Baron Edmond de Rothschild of Paris began with Rishon-le-Zion and extended his help to other colonies, pouring millions into their rehabilitation.

In Rosh-Pinah the hungry colonists danced with joy when the news arrived of the Baron's readiness to help. For the rest of the Baron's life, prayers were offered for his health in the local synagogue every Saturday. Zamarin was renamed Zichron Yaakov in memory of the Baron's father whose Hebrew name was Jacob. In all the colonies he was revered as a benefactor. Throughout the Jewish world the deeds of the "Well-known Benefactor" were recounted.

Yet Baron Rothschild's help was a mixed blessing. He was a paternal benevolent despot who expected unquestioning obedience not only to himself but to all his appointees. The latter emulated the despotic habits of their master, but not his devotion to, or his belief in the cause of rebuilding Zion. The baronial bureaucracy soon became a petty élite of provincial snobs who tyrannized the colonists and paraded their Parisian manners and French speech.

The colonists had to sign away their freedom of action and even their property (which was returned to them in later years) in order to survive. The farmers in Rishon-le-Zion, in Zichron Yaakov, and in some other colonies were told to give up planting wheat and vegetables and to go in for winegrowing. The Baron, who owned some of the finest vineyards in the South of France, built two winepresses for his colonists, one in Rishon-le-Zion, the other in Zichron Yaakov. The colonists were sometimes ordered by the local administrators not to engage in manual labor in the fields but to employ Arab help. Their wives and children often tended to emulate the manners, the French speech and the ideas of the baronial administrators.

Some independent spirits among the colonists tried to hold out, but few could for very long. Nevertheless, there were local differences. In the far north, colonies like Metulla and Rosh-Pinah kept their rustic character and the farmers tilled their own fields. In the two main colonies, there was a marked difference between Petah-Tikvah, under the leadership of Stampfer, which maintained its independence and individuality, and Rishon-le-Zion, which was affected the most by the demoralizing influences of the Baronial regime.

In 1903, the slump in the world prices on wine aggravated the situation.

When Shlomo Zemach arrived in Rishon-le-Zion one Friday afternoon, the day he had landed, the morale was at its worst. All Rishon-le-Zion, it seemed, was in favor of giving up Palestine and establishing a Jewish Homeland in Uganda. The Jewish workers employed in the winepress were threatened with the loss of their jobs if they voted for candidates for the coming Zionist Congress who opposed Uganda.

* * *

As soon as Zemach was settled in the inn, he went out to look at the village. In front of the synagogue he saw a notice on the billboard announcing a meeting in the house of one of the colonists to discuss the Uganda question. He decided to attend the meeting.

The chairman, who spoke rather poorly in Yiddish, asked a certain Mr. Yudelevitch to read the Hebrew translation of an address delivered by Israel Zangwill, the leader of the Uganda partisans in the Zionist movement. To Zemach's amazement, Mr. Yudelevitch, "a pale sickly-looking man with chestnut hair" had an excellent speaking voice and an excellent command of Hebrew, which he enunciated well in the Sephardi pronunciation accepted in Palestine.

"At first I was carried away by his voice, his style and his manner. But gradually the fog in my mind began to clear. Something was wrong here, I felt . . . When in the whole crowd, the farmers and their wives rose to give the treasonable words a thunderous applause, I felt as if I had been given a blow over the head. I was swept along by the torrent of hot blood in my veins. I was like a young colt suddenly gone wild. I jumped up from my seat and shouted: 'I want the floor!'

"My request silenced the assembly of exuberantly demonstrating farmers. Everyone looked at me with amazement and anger. After a brief consultation between the chairman and the speaker, the former agreed:

" 'Let's hear what those new immigrants have to say.' "

The eighteen year old newcomer then made his maiden speech in the Homeland, in good fluent Hebrew. But he spoke it with the Polish pronunciation, with many oo's and ee's and oi's, which sounded comical to the ears of the listeners.

He voiced his admiration for the past performances of the colonists but remonstrated with them for having forgotten and betrayed their youthful ideas. He warned them that he and many young men like himself would fight them and bring back to life the very ideals to which they, the old colonists, had once dedicated themselves.

Peals of laughter greeted his speech. Nevertheless, when he finished, he thought he noticed here and and there shamefaced looks in the audience.

"Again there was a consultation between the chairman and the main speaker. But before they came to any decision, a man rose from the audience, came up to me, placed his hand on my shoulder and for a while merely looked down at me to everyone's amusement.

" 'So you've come this morning,' he addressed me in Rumanian Yiddish, 'and already you're lecturing us! Well, we like young men with temperament. We were that way ourselves when we were young. But tell me—do you know anything about fever?'

"He paused for an answer.

" 'I am not afraid of malaria.'

" 'Have you ever had a taste of sore eyes?' he persisted.

"Again he waited for my reply. To tell the truth, I felt uneasy. But I mustered my courage and said:

" 'I am not afraid of trachoma or any other ailment!'

" 'Sure, sure, I said you were a hero, and you're ready to fight us all. Would you care to tell us how you are going to fight us?'

" 'I don't know, I don't know! But it cannot go on this way. I will not rest nor be silent. I will fight!'

"There was a renewed outburst of laughter which did not subside for several minutes. With this the meeting came to an end."

* * *

After the death of Theodore Herzl in July 1904, the Zionist movement was divided and demoralized. It had lost its great leader. Some of the illustrious men who had flocked to his banner—Zangwill in England, Mandelstamm in Russia—were now busy scanning the map in search of another homeland for the Jews outside of Palestine. The whole party of Socialist-Zionists (S. S.) in Russia adopted Territorialism as its creed. But many more Zionists left the movement altogether, attracted by the renewed revolutionary activity in Russia and seeking solutions in Europe. The view that Zionism, including its territorial variation, was an impractical, and even a dangerous chimera, gained more an more adherents. The decline of the Zionist movement proceeded parallel with, and probably affected, the decline in the Hebrew press and literature in Russia. Yiddish shared with Russian the resulting literary and intellectual language vacuum. Spokesmen of the Jewish Socialist Labor Party, the Bund, began to deride the "carcass country" and the "carcass language" of Zionists and Hebraists. With their allies, the Bundists raised the banner of Yiddish and secular nationalism in the Diaspora.

Yet out of this despair and confusion, arose a movement which produced the architects and builders of the State of Israel.

The Second Aliyah, which began in 1904 and continued until the outbreak of the First World War in 1914, brought no more than several thousand immigrants, including those who merely sought to escape military service in Russia. Many succumbed—as did pioneers in every wave—to the lure of better climates and more promising economies. Only a minority remained in Palestine for life. Considered as a group, however, these were settlers remarkable for high human qualities; they were dedicated idealists passionately attached to spiritual values.

The average pioneer of the Second Aliyah came from a small town, where the traditional Jewish pattern of life was still the norm, but where it was already set in fermentation by the impact of the West, and by the growing revolutionary movement of Russia. He would be a former student of a yeshivah, certainly one with a good heder education, who had also taught himself or had been taught the Russian language and literature and had had a snatching of modern schooling. Far more than their predecessors, the pioneers of the Second Aliyah were conscious of themselves as the remakers of the pattern of the world—and not merely of the Jewish people: their theories on Zionism and Socialism, whatever their variations and differences, were fully rounded out. They fell to organizing political groups as soon as they arrived—and, as time went on, more and more, before they landed.

*   *   *

"Nobody called us, nobody wanted us. They had no need for our brawn, much less for our brains," wrote Berl Katzenelson, reviewing the history of the Second Aliyah. He was complaining of the hostility shown by both the Zionist leadership and the Jewish colonists in Palestine.

It is difficult to find in the annals of history a movement whose founders were so skeptical and whose ultimate success was so overwhelming. True, a man like Ben-Gurion never wavered. "What a marvelous country this is going to be twenty-five years from now!" he wrote to his father in Poland from his shack in the Galilee in 1909. But Berl Katzenelson, who, during his lifetime (he died in 1944) was far more the spiritual leader of the movement than Ben-Gurion, wrote:

"It was not faith or confidence; it was strength that stemmed from the thought that we may be the last of the Jewish people; that if history decreed our disappearance, we must hold on to the end, that we must not leave the battlefield."

Katzenelson says of himself that he was, like many others, influenced by the call issued by Joseph Hayim Brenner, the brooding moralistic novelist: "We will be the last men on the ramparts!"

Both Brenner and Katzenelson had embraced ideologies different from Zionism before finally deciding that the only course left to the self-respecting Jew was to go down fighting in Palestine.

*   *   *

The First Aliyah, in the 1880's and 1890's, laid the foundations of modern Israel. The Second Aliyah, in the decade between 1904 and 1914, built the ground floor. Moreover, it saved the foundations from disintegrating and set the scaffolding for the whole edifice to rise later.

*   *   *

In the spring of 1903 the Czar's officials organized a pogrom in Kishinev, the capital of the province of Bessarabia. In the fall of the same year, another pogrom took place in Homel, in White Russia. But this time the Jews had a fairly well-organized self-defense unit, which gave a good account of itself. The following winter, in 1904, the leader of the Homel Self-Defense, Hankin, and a group of other members arrived in Palestine and soon took up residence in Petah-Tikvah. This was during the week of Hanukah.

The week of Hanukah, in 1954, the fiftieth anniversary of the Second Aliyah, was celebrated in Petah-Tikvah, in the presence of some 1500 veterans, under the chairmanship of David Ben-Gurion.

Eliahu Even-tov

◆

FROM HOMEL TO PETAH-TIKVAH

IT WAS some time in 1902 or 1903 that we first began to think seriously of migrating to Palestine. There were about twelve or fifteen of us meeting regularly at the Homel branch of the Poalé-Zion (Labor Zionists), including Yehezekiel Hankin and Haya Sara. We knew little about the country, beyond the meager information we found in the Russian-language weekly *Vosshod* and the Yiddish daily *Der Fraind,* both of which we obtained with great difficulty. When a geography book on Palestine by Yehuda Grazovsky made its appearance, we were overjoyed. We spent days and nights poring over the small Hebrew volume and felt happy to learn from it that Rishon-le-Zion had seventy Jewish workers in the winepress and that there was a silk industry in Rosh Pinah at which many Jews were employed. "Not so terrible," we said to ourselves. "We, too, can find work in Palestine."

We heard of a man in Homel named Ginsburg, who was in the habit of visiting the Holy Land once every two years, and went to see him. But Ginsburg had no interest in the mundane life of the country: he merely made a pilgrimage to Hebron where he studied the Torah in the vicinity of the graves where the patriarchs are buried. Hebron, he told us, is a town in which all the Jews are poor and live on the dole called *halukah.* The "Ishmaelites" (Arabs) are savages, clad in long robes, with kerchiefs tied around their heads, working hard for a pittance. The Jews are in subjection there, too . . . The Ishmaelites don't allow them to come near the Cave of the Machpelah (where Abraham, Isaac, Jacob, Sarah, Rebecca and Leah are buried), but you can get everything for money . . .

During one of our discussion meetings, we resolved that before going to Palestine we must train in agriculture. We heard there

[50]

was a Jewish agricultural school somewhere near Minsk, operated
by the Jewish Colonization Association. One of our number, Baruch
Rosen, entered it in the hope that the rest would follow. But after
some time we received a letter from Rosen which was very discouraging: the discipline was unbearable, the singing of Hatikvah
was prohibited and speaking Hebrew was out of the question. The
report elicited the comment from one of our members that there
was no point in hesitating or probing or analyzing—we simply had
to leave for Palestine. Everybody agreed.

But the imminence of a pogrom in Homel delayed our departure:
we had to form a Jewish self-defense unit. Yehezekiel was elected
as the organizer. We asked the Bund (anti-Zionist Jewish Socialists)
to join us, but they refused on the grounds that Jewish self-defense
smacked of nationalism.

Four hundred armed men and women of the Poale Zion defended the Jews of the city during the two days of the riots. At
the request of leading Christians who stood in fear of the Jews,
troops were sent out. The military authorities ordered the Jewish
defense units to disperse and, when the demand was not met, the
troops fired. Four of our comrades fell. Yehezekiel was wounded
and was brought to Kiev for treatment.

After the pogroms we renewed our preparations.

In Odessa, we paid a visit to the local Zionist organization,
known as "The Odessa Committee." We were received by an official
with a glum face who proceeded to cool our ardor for pioneering
in Palestine. On board ship a gendarme stopped us to examine our
documents. He asked us what was the purpose of our journey. Father
said he was a cantor and was going to Constantinople to see if he
could find a synagogue and settle there. "Don't worry," the gendarme
said, "Russia will soon take Constantinople and you won't have to
live in a foreign country."

*   *   *

We reached Jaffa and our feet trod the soil of our Homeland . . .
When the Sabbath was over, we began looking for work.

Of all the settlements, we were especially attracted to Petah-
Tikvah. Rishon-le-Zion had two-story houses, a paved road and

farmers dressed in fine white clothes. In the evenings the women would come out for a walk. We called it "Czarskoye Selo" (The Czar's Village). There were hardly any young people to be seen in the village. They had emigrated.

But Petah-Tikvah was a real village. It had small, mostly frame houses, although some were of mud bricks. The eucalyptus alleys planted by the Baron added to the rustic appearance. The people were simple farmers, and their children, though not imbued with the Zionist spirit, stayed at home. Moreover, it was easier to find work in the fruit groves of Petah-Tikvah, of which there were about thirty at that time, than in the fields of Rishon-le-Zion and Rehovot.

My brother went to Petah-Tikvah; I went to Rishon-le-Zion. I walked to work with Moshe Yekaterinoslavsky who lived in the Neveh Shalom quarter in Jaffa and worked in the winepress in Rishon-le-Zion. Moshe, who in his home-town in Russia had been a Hebrew teacher and devoted Zionist, showed sympathy and understanding for my position. "Don't mention Zionism in Rishon-le-Zion," he cautioned me, "it is anathema."

When we reached Rishon-le-Zion, I saw a long shack, with beds, so-called, made over tins and trunks. It was the barracks of the winepress workers. Moshe Yekaterinoslavsky advised me to go to the foreman, Gershon Levin: "He probably won't give you a job the first time you apply," he warned me, "but don't give up. He likes to give people the runaround."

I went to see the foreman many times, returning disheartened each time. I had no work, the money gave out, and there was no more bread. I became despondent.

My evenings were spent in the shack. But I was given a mattress on the floor between beds. The mattress crawled with vermin. The company of my fellow-workers was far from inspiring: they had no sense of the meaning of Zionism; their speech was vile and everyone was suspicious of the other.

Finally my emaciated body succumbed to malaria. With Moshe's help, I was brought to Jaffa in a fever.

When I regained my health, I went to Petah-Tikvah with my father. We found work. Father then applied to the Village Council for permission to settle, but was refused. The rules of the colony required that each prospective resident own twenty dunams of orange grove or fifty dunams of vineyard, or that he be a skilled laborer.

We consulted the Gissins, a colonist family of somewhat non-conformist views. The villagers looked askance at the Gissins and named the side street at the end of which their home was situated, "The Unholy Lane." The Gissins, unlike the others, welcomed new immigrants and tried to help them. On the advice of the Gissins, we made clandestine arrangements with a farmer named Moshe Chodorow who, for a consideration, rented us quarters. When we brought the family in from Jaffa, it was twilight. My brother wanted to sing for joy, but the landlord entered and told us not to make any noise. We ate in the dark, for fear that our illegal entry would be discovered. In a few days my brother and Chodorow were called up to the Village Council for an explanation. They put the blame on the Gissins, and there the matter ended.

The nucleus of the first labor group in Petah-Tikvah consisted of eight agricultural laborers and three skilled artisans. The eight were: Yehezekiel Hankin, Haya Sarah Hankin, Eliezer Shohet, Israel Shohet, A. D. Gordon, Saul Hartstein, Abraham Eventov, Eliahu Eventov. Of the three artisans, Abraham Krinitzy and Gershon worked as carpenters. Those were the days before the Labor Council and Labor Exchange Bureau. We lived like one large family, dividing the work among ourselves. Each one of us was concerned for the other.

* * *

This is how I obtained my first day's work in Petah-Tikvah:

I arrived at the colony on Friday afternoon. The whole day Saturday was spent in looking around. That same evening, when the stars appeared and the Sabbath was over, I went over to the farmhouse of one I. R., where, as Yehezekiel had told me, I might find some work for a day. I knocked on the door.

"Come in," came a voice from inside.

When I opened the door, I found the household seated around the table, drinking tea. I remained standing in the doorway, while the following conversation took place:

"I was told you might have some work for me," I said.

Instead of replying, the farmer asked between gulps of tea:

"Is it true that there was a pogrom in Homel? And did the Jews really hit back?"

Still sipping his tea, the farmer continued: "Aren't you young fellows foolish to come here? In the first place, this is the Land of Ishmael, not of Israel. And in the second place, young men like you would be better off going to America, where you could make a fortune. Then, when one has money, this is not a bad country."

The conversation—which, of course, was carried on in Yiddish—continued in this vein for about three quarters of an hour. The final outcome was favorable and I was told to report to work the next morning.

I was put to work with four Arabs. At ten in the forenoon, the farmer came and asked one of the Arabs: "How is that Muscovite doing?"

"By Allah," the Arab praised me, "he is pulling like a donkey."

My employer was pleased: "Young man," he said to me, "you may come again tomorrow morning."

I worked for three days and earned my first six *bishliks* in Palestine. I was happy enough, after my unemployment in Rishon-le-Zion, to find a day's work. But the conversation at the farmer's house hurt me and if it had been prolonged just a little, I would have cried out: Are we not all brothers, fellow-Jews? Is this the way to receive me, when I have just come from a distant land?

I was a young pioneer boy when I came to Palestine, full of optimistic dreams, entirely unprepared for such cynicism. I was ready to treat anyone older than myself with deference. The sight of a child in a Jewish village made my heart glad. Any team of oxen, any cow, any red roof on a house, filled me with joy: it was ours, ours. And here, a senior pioneer, who had been dwelling in Zion before me, admonished me to devote my energies to a foreign land, from which to bring dollars to Palestine in my old age, and, as to my work, he asked the Arab's opinion! But what distressed me most was the manner. Today, twenty-five years after that conversation in the doorway, it still rankles . . .

After a period of more unemployment, I was told by Israel Shohet there was work for four men to disinfect trees at the orange grove belonging to Goldenhirsch. A. D. Gordon, Eliezer Shohet,

Israel Shohet and myself worked there for two weeks. When the job was completed, Goldenhirsch paid us at the rate of eight Turkish piasters per day instead of the current rate of seven. We suspected the additional piaster was given us because we were Jews. A. D. Gordon thought we ought not to accept it, as it savored of a dole. We agreed and sent back the extra money with the messenger who had brought our pay. But Goldenhirsch insisted he paid us more money because our work was worth more. His explanation satisfied us and we took the money.

The Jewish worker had to contend with three antagonists: the farmer, who was reluctant to employ Jewish labor; the overseer, who, even more than the employer, preferred to lord it over the primitive serf; and the Arab laborer himself.

The overseer's business was to crack the whip over the workers, to shout *yallah* (come on!), to wink, to cajole, to threaten and in many other ways in which he was skilled, to urge them on to work fast. Whenever he was displeased, he would send the worker away in the middle of the day—and there was no appeal.

The Arab, who had become accustomed to the Jew as a *hawajeh* (lord, gentleman), was puzzled by poor devils like ourselves, whom even the Jewish colonists called Muscovites or Russians. We were "massakeen"—poor things—objects of pity, but not of respect, and not always of sympathy.

It was the time of the Russo-Japanese war, and the Arabs teased us that "the Japanese will massacre all the Russians." Or they would take advantage of our inability to speak Arabic and our inexperience at work.

Our hands were full of blisters, the hoe did not stay steady in our grip, and the Arabs would say to one another: "Let's have a race with those Moskub!"

The overseer would add fuel to the fire: "Murder those Russians, murder them! Go for them, go!"

This would continue for hours. If we persisted in keeping up with the Arabs in hoeing, he would start a new ditty: "Go for them, native sons! Go for them! Oh, native sons! Native sons!"

This always had its effect: the work would proceed with mounting savagery and the hoes would literally fly, as the laborers sped digging pit after pit. Many times we actually fainted in the race to the delight of the overseer.

After about a year, when the Arabs were convinced that we had become real workers and our numbers grew, the Arabs made overtures to us. "Take it easy," they would say when we met on the way to the grove, "why get killed over two bishliks?"

Every ship brought one or two additional workers. Most of them came from Homel, Vilno or Grodno. Before arriving, they usually wrote to us for information. We held consultations on what to answer them.

Hartstein opened one of our early discussions by pointing out that the ordinary worker in Palestine could earn more than in Russia and that the requirements in Palestine were most modest: one could go without shoes for months; there was no need of winter clothes, of heating fuel. He was all for encouraging a large mass migration.

But A. D. Gordon thought differently. "When a Jew in the Diaspora does not do well, he does not blame anyone. But if things go wrong in Palestine, he will hold the Jewish people responsible for all his troubles!" Gordon insisted that a mass Jewish immigration into Palestine must be preceded by a revolution in the attitudes and thinking of the Jews. For the time being only idealists ought to come. Only they could surmount the obstacles of the present and prepare the way for the others.

*   *   *

One day we decided to celebrate our achievements in capturing the first labor positions in the country. We marched out in procession through the main street of Petah-Tikvah—the whole dozen of us—carrying the blue-and-white flag, and singing Hatikvah. The Village Council promptly sent us a letter warning us not to do it again. Gordon was grieved by the communication, but Israel Shohet merely laughed. This was the first conflict between the farmers and the workers in Petah-Tikvah.

At about the same time, we had our first wedding celebration; Yehezekiel Hankin and Hayah Sara got married. Many comrades came from Rishon-le-Zion. The ceremony was performed in Moshe Gissin's farmyard. As bride and groom stood under the canopy, we formed a circle around them and, raising our hands, we sang the Labor-Zionist Hymn in Yiddish:

"We lift our hands towards east and we swear

By Zion, its banner and its holy soil,

By all we hold sacred, by all we hold dear,

By the broken sword of our heroes of old."

Our numbers grew as Hanukah drew nearer. We arranged a literary and musical soiree, to which we invited the local young people who were friendly with us, including some of the girls of the village. The presence of the latter evoked indignation.

Groups of older people stood outside muttering. One Sephardi Jew cried out: "This is forbidden by the Torah!" We were told that we must either let the girls go home or break up. Suddenly four armed Bedouins, who were employed by the colony as night watchmen, approached on horseback. "Get along with you, Muscovites," they said "yallah, get going, no need for the fantasia (sport)."

"What's the matter?" one of us asked.

"Council's orders," came the answer.

This was infuriating.

"We stood up against the Russian cossacks," one of our comrades exclaimed, "we can handle them, too."

But Gordon calmed us and said, "Let's go on with the program for the evening!"

The four horsemen lingered for a while, watching the dancing and listening to the singing, and went their way.

The following day we were the topic of the conversation in the village. Some villagers tried to defend us: "After all, it is the festival of Hanukah!" they said. Others remarked: "Poor devils! They are sure to be deprived of a share in the hereafter. Let them have some joy in this world!" And that was the end of the matter.

Now and then the farmers got into conversation with us about religion. In our discussions among ourselves we had agreed that we ought to be careful not to hurt their feelings in that respect. A. D. Gordon in those days still practiced orthodoxy and prayed

in the synagogue. But he was vexed by the attempts of the colonists
to dictate to us.

A casual talk between a farmer's son and one of our men was
the immediate cause of the famous "boycott" declared by the farmers
of Petah-Tikvah against Jewish labor.

The worker was Yitzhak of Odessa, who had come towards the
end of the second year of our existence.

Yitzhak worked in the grove belonging to Perlin, a pious Jew
who had come from America, a man of domineering character. His
son, Alter, was the manager. One day, at noon, Alter asked Yitzhak
why he did not say his prayers in the mornings. Yitzhak retorted:
"What good does it do you to wind a strip of calf-skin around your
hand and kiss it?" This contemptuous reference to the phylacteries
angered Alter, who reported it to his father.

Mr. Perlin went straight to the Village Council: "Do you see
what we have come to?"

The Council, which consisted mostly of older men, decided to
act promptly and root out the evil at its source. The next morning
the Council issued leaflets announcing: "It is forbidden to employ
Jewish workers. It is forbidden to rent them living quarters. It is
forbidden to have any dealings with them. Whoever disobeys the
prohibition shall be punished to the full rigor of the law."

The situation thus created in the colony was one of martial law.
Some farmers hastened to evict their worker tenants. Others, on the
other hand, were unhappy about the developments. Among the latter
were the Gissins and the Ostashinskys. At seven o'clock in the evening, we gathered at A. D. Gordon's to discuss the new emergency.
As there were thirty-two of us, the small room that Gordon occupied could not hold us and we went out into the fields, where we
sat in a circle.

Gordon opened the meeting with the following remarks: "We
are faced with a new expulsion, not the expulsion from Spain, but
an expulsion by our own fellow-Jews in our own Homeland. What
are we to do? First and foremost, we will not budge from this
place. We will not retreat from the positions we have won here.
We will not give up. No amount of force, no attempt to starve us
out will make us leave this place."

But the question arose: what if this condition continues for months—how were we to exist? It was decided to establish a special relief fund for the emergency. The sum per person in need was set as four piasters a day. Four hundred francs were collected on the spot. Some among us were recent arrivals who still had some of the money they had brought with them. Others had saved up a few napoleons in the bank. We all put our money in the treasury. The largest sum was contributed by Shlomo Zemach. As for evacuating our living quarters, we voted to inform the landlords we would remain where we were until we found other lodgings.

At nine o'clock we broke up the meeting and marched in a protest procession, with Gordon singing one of his favorite Yiddish songs. Windows opened and people inquired: What has happened? Gordon warned us not to give vent to our feelings against the colonists by saying anything or by using our hands.

Two days passed. The ban was in force, but it was not carried out everywhere. We worked in Dr. Mazie's grove. The colonists turned to his manager, Hellmann, threatening him with dire consequences, but he paid no attention. They took up the question with Dr. Mazie himself, but he refused to abide by the ban. Some of the colonists took advantage of the situation and offered us work at so much per job instead of daily wages. The pay was very low and, if it were not for the boycott, we would never have accepted the terms. But, under the circumstances, we did. We undertook to dig a dung pit in Josephson's grove. The Council appointed Baruch Dinowitz as a secret agent to spy on us where we worked. He used to slink through the pathways between the groves to see where we were coming from. As soon as we saw him come, we knew we would not get work at the same place the next day, and so we were on the lookout for him.

Some farmers were called up before the Council on the charge of disregarding the Council's instructions. Often they denied employing Jewish workers.

In the middle of the boycott week our comrade Kunin became the father of a son. The Council quickly warned the midwife and the physician against attending the mother. The midwife obeyed, but the physician, Dr. Stein, a BILU pioneer, who had always been friendly to the workers (he never accepted any fees for treating them), informed the Council that he had no intention of obeying it. The child was circumcised in Kunin's lodgings, in Moshe Chodorow's farmyard. Then A. D. Gordon named the boy Jehoshaphat, meaning the Lord shall judge.

During the boycott we were told we must vacate the library. Since the library was housed in the Baron's Administration building, we paid no attention. Our foes then broke into the library and tore up the books. They vented their fury especially on books in the Russian language. We learned of it immediately, but Gordon kept us from using violence. That evening a cable was sent to the Warsaw daily *Hatzefirah,* signed by Zemach.

Not content with declaring a ban on us in Petah-Tikvah, the Council appealed to other colonies to "fight the evil." When we learned of it, we sent three men who toured the colonies on foot, explaining the nature of this Holy War. The colonists of Rishon-le-Zion and of Rehovot disagreed with the position taken by Petah-Tikvah.

The Council at Petah-Tikvah decided on an amnesty and issued a declaration that any worker who would appear before it and conduct himself properly, would be released from the effect of the ban. None of our members came.

The ban was never repealed, but it became ineffective, since from the beginning some of the farmers did not support it.

*   *   *

David Ben Gurion

◆

IN JUDEA AND GALILEE

AS SOON as I had disembarked and passed through the Turkish customs, I hurried to Petah-Tikvah. Friends pressed me to stay a few days in Jaffa, but I could not restrain an overmastering urge to see a Jewish village, and toward evening of the same day I arrived at the oldest and largest of Jewish colonies.

That night, my first night on Homeland soil, is engraved forever on my heart with its exultation of achievement. I lay awake—who could sleep through his first night in the Homeland? The spirit of my childhood and my dreams had triumphed and was joyous! I was in the Land of Israel, in a Jewish village, and its name was Petah-Tikvah—Portal of Hope!

For a year I sweated in Judean colonies, but I had more malaria and hunger than work. All three—work, hunger and malaria—were new and full of interest. Was it not for this that I had come to the Homeland? The fever would visit me every fortnight with mathematical precision, linger for five or six days, and then disappear. Hunger, too, was a frequent visitor. It would stay with me for weeks, sometimes for months. During the day I could dismiss it somehow, or at least stop thinking of it. But in the nights—the long racked vigils—the pangs would grow fiercer, wringing the heart, darkening the mind, sucking the very marrow from my bones, demanding and torturing—and departing only with the dawn. Shattered and broken, I would drop off to sleep at last.

But the enthusiasm and joy did not fade. Who worried about malaria in those days? The few who did not suffer from it were a little shamefaced before the rest of us who did.

That was in 1907—at the time of the new Aliyah; every ship brought more young people. Most of the new laborers settled in Petah-Tikvah, and although the farmers there had recently issued a ban on Jewish labor, our numbers grew from week to week.

After a day of work, or maybe of fever, we would gather in the workers' kitchen, or in the sandy tracks between the vineyard and the groves, and sing and dance in a circle, sing and dance arm in arm and shoulder to shoulder.

The interminable hoeing and spading did not satisfy me fully. It was too mechanical and monotonous. The ceaseless thumping and thudding smacked of a factory. I yearned for the wide fields, for the waving stalks of corn, for the fragrance of grass, the plowman's song—and I made up my mind to go north to the Galilee.

*   *   *

From Judea I came to Sejera. Here, at last, I found the Land of Israel. Nature, people, work—here everything was wholly different, more of Israel; here one inhaled the aroma of Homeland at every footstep.

Sejera almost monopolized the diverse lovelinesses of created scenery with which the Land is clad. Mountains surround it and enclose it on every side.

The settlement itself is built on the slope of a hill—two rows of houses, one above the other, encircled by thickets of eucalyptus and pepper trees, and looking from afar like rungs of a ladder mounting to the peak. The farm itself stands there.

The people of the village were as diversified as its environment. Among the fifty-odd farmers and laborers were tall, broad-shouldered Kurdish Jews, as unlettered as their non-Jewish neighbors in Kurdistan; thin, bony Yemenites, highly learned in the Hebrew language and in traditional Judaism; young Russians, disciples of enlightenment and revolution; native-born Ashkenazi and Sephardi, who had left the yeshivot of Safed and Tiberias to take up the spade and the plow; Russian farmers from the shores of the Caspian Sea, who had embraced Judaism and come to labor in the Homeland of their new faith; young Sephardim, educated in the schools of the Alliance Israelite. This motley community had

Hebrew, Arabic, Aramaic—(spoken by the Kurdish Jews), Yiddish, Russian, French and Spanish. But this miniature ingathering of exiles was cemented and made one by a firm and powerful bond— the land and its cultivation. In Sejera—and in those days it was unique for its kind—there was nothing but Jewish labor, the labor of the farmers themselves and their children; even the farm, which belonged to the Jewish Colonization Association (ICA), employed only Jewish workers.

The officials and laborers lived on the hilltop; the villagers, the farmers, lived below, on the slope; but the relations between the two sections were very cordial. Almost all the farmers were young men who had formerly worked as laborers on the farm, and when they acquired land of their own, went on working it themselves. We, the workers, would meet them often, in the field and at home. There was no sign here of the rift that divided farmers from laborers in Judea. On Sabbaths and festivals we would celebrate together, and on workdays we would meet in the fields, plow side by side and help one another.

Here I found the environment that I had sought so long. No shopkeepers or speculators, no non-Jewish hirelings, no idlers living on the labor of the others. The men plowed and harrowed their fields and planted the seed; the women weeded the gardens and milked the cows; the children herded geese and rode on horseback to meet their fathers in the field. These were villagers, smelling wholesomely of midden and ripening wheat and burned by the sun.

The work, too, was more satisfying. There was none of the deadening monotony that attend the rigors of the hoe in Judea. You follow and guide the plow, turn the sod and open furrow after furrow; and soon the very soil you plowed and planted would clothe itself in green. Before your very eyes it would bring forth its crop. No sooner were the rains over than the grain would ripen, and out you would go to reap the harvest and carry the yield to the threshing-floor. You felt as a partner in the act of creation.

*   *   *

But even here there was a cloud. True the fields were worked by Jewish hands, but the watchmen were hired Arabs. In Judea we scarcely noticed that we were guarded by non-Jews. The Jewish settlements were large and well-populated; the surroundings were quiet; arms were hardly seen in the Arab villages; there was fear of the government; public security was seldom disturbed. Not so here, in the Galilee, amid the hills. The settlements were new and small. The surroundings were wild, our neighbors all expert and well-armed bandits. "And the caves in the hills and the clefts of the crags are shelters for every seeker after revenge and every hero among his people." Theft and assault were not uncommon, and the authority of the Government was non-existent. The peace and security of the settlement in this vicinity depended entirely on its watchmen. In the settlements of Judea it was difficult to distinguish between Arab watchmen and the numerous Arab laborers. But here in Sejera, Jewish labor was the rule, the place was full of Jewish young people. Could we entrust all that to strange hands? Was it conceivable that here, too, we should accept the humiliation of hiring strangers to guard our property and protect our lives?

We began to plead with the officials and the farmers to engage Jewish watchmen, but they did not take us seriously. At first, they did not believe we really meant it. Did we intend to sacrifice young lives for the sake of some abstract principle? Could enough men be found willing to risk their lives? And would not a Jewish guard be a grave danger to the peace of the settlement? Why, the very Arab watchmen, familiar with every nook and cranny in the settlement, its every approach and egress, would themselves be the first to attack and plunder it! We were weak and few, ringed on all sides by strangers and enemies: the notoriously ferocious Arab peasants of Lubia, the largest village in Lower Galilee; the Christian villagers of Kafr Kana, full of venom and hatred for the Jews; the Zabiah tribesmen, their tents in the forest of Sejera, holding the entire neighborhood in fear, the haughty and reckless Circassians of Kafr Kana. These Circassians, who had settled in the country at the invitation of the Turkish Government, enjoyed a privileged status. Could we afford to challenge them?

But we were determined to vindicate our national honor.

We tried to win over the manager, who always treated us well, and had gradually come close to our views. He admitted that we were right in theory, but he hesitated. The Circassians were the guards of the farm. They were industrious, brave and spirited. No fellah or Bedouin would venture to provoke them. In the Lower Galilee, between Sejera and Yama, they lived on friendly terms with the Jewish settlements. The Circassians had a virtual lien on protecting the Jews.

We spied on a new Circassian watchman for several nights, and discovered that he did not come at all to mount guard, but let his "reputation" do his work. This was a common trick. The watchmen were generally appointed from among the most notorious brigands. They were sure that, once it was known they had taken over a post, no one would have the audacity to come and steal. And even if "something irregular" occurred, it was easy for them, in intimate relations with the underworld, to be able to track down the stolen property and return it to its owner—not, of course, without ample reward. Instead of pacing his beat around the stockade of the farm all night and spending the darkness in the company of the boulders and eucalyptus trees that envelop Sejera, the new man preferred to visit the neighboring Arab village and spend his time carousing.

One dark night, we led the manager's fine mule out of the farm, and immediately informed him of the theft. He ran to the stable—the mule was gone. He whistled frantically to summon the watchman, but not an answering sound. He went outside, ran the length of the stockade—the Circassian was not to be seen. Messengers were sent to seek him in the Arab village, and found him there—lying fast asleep. The manager dismissed him, and gave the job to one of us. We had thus captured the first bastion.

Not many days went by before the manager awoke one morning to find several window-panes broken and a number of Martin bullets embedded in his wall.

We resolved to organize and keep a strict look-out. We set alternating watches of all the workers, two every two hours from dusk to dawn. We used to sleep in the big silo near the mill, our weapons near at hand; every pair, when their turn came, lay

in wait in the cactus hedge or in the crevices of the rocks. It was
the rainy season, and a fierce storm, such as had not been experienced
for years, raged for a week all over the country. In Judea, it destroyed most of the oranges and caused enormous losses to the
grove-owners. In Sejera, it was accompanied by pelting rain; it
was impossible to see a yard ahead. When I stood guard, my
companion and I had to hold on to each other's hands. We could
not even speak to one another. It seemed as though nature had joined
forces with our foes to try our mettle.

Our ambush lasted a fortnight—until the assailants realized
that their threats would not affect us; and they withdrew. We had
won the first round.

*   *   *

The Jewish watchman could not rely on his "reputation" to be
a deterrent against theft or attack. He would have to be on sentry
all night long. To do this duty not only loyally but with success,
a permanent "reserve" was needed. This required the right human
material and a sizeable supply of arms.

Men there were, but we lacked arms. Only a fortunate few
owned pistols.

The manager granted our request unhesitatingly. A special
wagon was sent to Haifa to bring rifles. Impatiently, we awaited
its return; day and night we spoke of nothing but the arms, and
when the wagon finally returned, our joy knew no bounds. The
rifles were of the most inferior type, cheap "Jifts"—double barreled
shotguns. There were much better ones in the office—Martins—
but the management did not yet deign to entrust us with such
dangerous weapons. Not a small thing, a Martin . . . but for us
then, even the "Jifts" were perfection itself. We played with them
like little children; we never put them down for a moment. Reluctantly we went to work next morning—we had to say good-bye
to them for a whole day. As soon as we got home and unharnessed
our horses and mules, we dashed off to our rifles, and they never
left our hands till we fell asleep. Rifle in hand or on shoulder,
we ate and washed, we moved and read and talked.

The big room in the *han* where most of the workers lived was
suddenly changed into a retreat for highway men. Anyone entering

of an evening was startled to see a score of young men, seated on their beds each with a rifle in hand: One would be cleaning the barrel; another testing the sights; one loading and unloading; another filling his pouches—comparing weapons, enumerating the virtues and vices of each, hanging them on the wall and taking them down again, slinging them over their shoulders and taking them off again—and so on until it was time for bed.

Now the farm was in our hands, we cast our eyes on the colony. Here chance helped us. One night a farmer's horses were stolen. When the farmer, who was a member of the village council, discovered the theft, he ran outside and met the Arab watchman returning from the fields. It was quickly proven that this Arab was the miscreant. Immediately we petitioned the council to appoint Jewish watchmen.

*   *   *

From these vantage points our way was open to clear the prickliest thorn of the watch organization—night grazing. This began during the second half of the rainy season, in the months of Shevat and Adar (February and March). At the end of Heshvan (November) the first rain falls, and the hard earth, cracked in the drought and scorching sun for the seven summer months, thirstily soaks up the drops. Then the farmer goes forth to his labor; he plows and sows, harrows and breaks up the loose soil. The bare furrows and pastures now are verdant; the grasses sprout. When the grass in the woods has reached a certain height—in the month of Shevat (February-March)—the night grazing begins.

There was no night grazing without armed guards. A troop of horsemen and a posse on foot, armed cap-a-pied, spread out in the valley, their ears cocked to every rustle and quiver; eyes piercing the darkness to detect the least shadow; sure hands on the butt ready at any moment to greet uninvited guests. Guarding the herds was more difficult and dangerous than guarding the settlement.

To secure the right to protect the night grazing was our third step that winter. When night grazing time came, we managed to place several of our group in the herdsmen's watch—the council and the manager thought it too risky to put the entire job in our hands at once. It was in this night grazing that Jewish watchmen received their first taste of blood-letting.

Dov Schweiger was one of the Jewish herdsmen-guards. He had only come to Sejera a few weeks before, and had won not only the affection of the workers, but also the confidence of the manager. Night grazing, like the other watches, had been the preserve of the Circassians, and they looked askance at their Jewish companions.

Hassan, the son of the Circassian sheikh, was particularly incensed that Dov, who was still only a youngster, should be taking part. At first, he thought the tenderfoot Jew might tire and not muster strength enough. But several nights passed and "Berele" stuck to his guns, diligently, bravely—like an experienced herdsman. Hassan began to tease "Berele"—to mock and insult him. But Dov could give as well as take. Every joke, every sneer, was met with sharp words and stinging retorts, till once Hassan could contain himself no longer and cried: "Damn your religion!" the worst an Arab could say as an insult. Dov lifted his whip and swung it across the Circassian's face. Hassan was dumbfounded at such insolence from a "puny" Jew. In violent anger he fell on Dov— but straightway felt a grip of steel on his wrists. Dov seized and threw him, and while he measured his length, Dov lashed him until he lay still. Ali, Hassan's friend, hurried to the spot, and seeing him all bloodied, made to attack Dov in vengeful ire. Dov levelled his rifle, shouting: "Stay where you are!" And all night Ali straddled his prostate friend, not daring to move hand or foot. Opposite him stood Dov, blood-soaked no less, rifle sighted.

Toward dawn, as we prepared to go to work and were waiting in the courtyard for the return of the herd, Dov entered. We scarcely recognized him. The manager trembled with fear. "What have you done? The Circassians will take revenge," he whispered, and his face was pale as death.

We surrounded Dov. No one uttered a word.

The manager threw a look at the small band of workers, and calmed down. The resolution and courage that showed in their glances gave him all the answer he needed.

The Circassians pursued no vendetta. After the incident, they began to seek out our company more than ever.

The Jewish watch at Sejera had entrenched itself and won a complete victory. After Sejera, Mesha and Yama followed suit and introduced one too.

*　　*　　*

Sejera, the first to adopt the principle of Jewish guards, was also the scene of its first casualty. It happened a year later, during Passover 1909. All through the previous winter the atmosphere had been explosive. Disputes had broken out between ourselves and the villagers of Kafr Kana concerning the boundaries of the land of Umm Jebl. Several times they had tried to plow our fields and we had driven them off by force. The Zabiah tribe was also restive: Government troops had shot its sheikh. In Arab Sejera there were quarrels between the Arabs and the Kurdish Jews who lived there. The fellahin from Lubiah had become particularly insolent, and had taken to molesting travelers on their way from Sejera to Tiberias. This was the first winter after the promulgation of the new Turkish Constitution, which the simple peasants understood in their own way as an end to all law and order. There was an appalling increase in theft and highway robbery.

A few nights before Passover, several attacks ending in bloodshed were made in Sejera, but they did not prevent the workers from celebrating the festival. Many guests came from Judea, for the general meeting of the Poalé-Zion of the Galilee was to be held in Sejera.

The celebration was in the upper *han*, the old Arab staging inn in the farm compound. The large hall, which had first served as a cowshed, and afterwards as workers' dormitory, was decked in Galilee style. The two long walls were draped with branches of eucalyptus and pepper, until they resembled an avenue of trees. On the inner wall, opposite the entrance, hung farm implements and weapons: plows, spades, harrows, and hoes wreathed in flowers at both sides of the window, and rifles, pistols, swords and daggers interlocked above it. The faces of the young men who sat round the great table testified that this arsenal was more than a decoration.

The seder began with song and wine, as usual. The sadness that had oppressed us so long was gradually dispelled. All doubts and cares were forgotten. Joy grew with every new song and enthusiasm waxed from draught to draught. It was the blend of Hassidic ecstasy and wild Arab excitement that prevailed at every workers' feast in the Land. The songs were accompanied by dances—wild, formless and uncontrolled, to the sound of clapping hands, as the Arabs dance.

We were still singing and dancing when an agitated voice reached us from outdoors. The merry-making ceased abruptly and fell silent. An unknown youth burst into the room, his face aflame, his voice trembling. In incoherent words, he told of an assault just made on him. With an acquaintance, he had come from Haifa that day on foot, escorted by an Arab. In their baggage, loaded on the Arab's donkey, was a valuable camera. Toward evening they passed through Kafr Kana. As they left the village, three Arab robbers appeared from among the rocks. Only the narrator was armed—with a Browning pistol—and he defended himself and his companion until his ammunition ran out. The robbers then fell on the Arab, beat him mercilessly, and seized the donkey and its load. He thought one of the assailants had been wounded; when he and his friend continued on their way they saw bloodstains.

We seized our rifles and ran outside. Vainly we searched for tracks. On the scene of the incident we found only bloodstains—a long red line that crimsoned the length of the road, then suddenly disappeared. Angry and anxious, we returned home.

Next day, we heard that a wounded Arab had been brought from Kafr Kana to the Nazareth hospital, and several days later that he had died of his wound. His friends had said that his wound was the result of an accidental discharge of his own rifle. Just before his death, however, he admitted that Jews of Sejera had shot him. We felt that something was brewing.

That was during the Passover week. None of us worked. We gathered in one of the farmhouses at the foot of the hill for the Poalé-Zion meeting. We were all armed. I was in the chair, but my thoughts and feelings were taken up with the local situation more than with the course of discussion, and my hand never left the holster of my Browning. Before the meeting, we had posted sentinels on the hilltop.

While we were still deliberating one of the sentinels pushed his way into the room with the news that Arabs had attacked the herd and carried off several oxen and mules. The meeting was broken off. The members from other settlements were sent away immediately to defend their own homes if necessary. We of Sejera met in the *han* to consider the position. The family of a murdered Arab must avenge his death, and the first seven days after the murder are the most dangerous. In that week the avengers may pillage and plunder; whoever resists takes his life in his hands. We decided during that period to do our utmost to avoid provoking the Arabs.

We did not send the herd to graze in the distant forest; we would pasture it in nearby fields.

The following day, the Arabs descended on the fields between Sejera and Mesha, and harvested the near-ripe barley. No Arabs were to be seen in the colony itself, but suspicious movements could be discerned close to the farm. From dawn to dusk armed men on foot and on horseback were seen on the hilltops. Two of our number who went to Tiberias to buy matzoth (unleavened bread) for the Passover stumbled on a band of Arabs, who attacked and beat them and took their arms.

A black cloud descended upon us—the shadow of death in ambush. No one spoke of it, but each of us sensed it in himself and read it in his neighbor's eyes; the sword of vengeance hung over us all—it must fall on the head of one among us . . . Fate was still to choose its victim. We were all ready, and waiting.

On the last day of Passover, about two in the afternoon, we were at a small gathering of friends at the pharmacy, where we used to spend our free time. Israel Krongold, the watchman at the farm, came in fully armed, his Martin slung over his shoulder, a row of cartridges in his belt, his Browning at his hip. In normal times he carried his arms only at night, when on duty—but in days like these he went on guard immediately after his siesta.

As he entered, he told us that he had sighted two strange Arabs sitting on a hill opposite the graveyard. They had asked him something, but he had not understood——he had not been in the country long, and knew very little Arabic; and he had come to find someone who spoke Arabic well. "Now," he said to us, laughing, "we will drag them in by the ears."

A farmer, who was a native Palestinian, went out with him. We sat and waited. Half an hour went by, we heard a volley of shots. The alarm was sounded on the farm bell. We seized our guns and ran. Behind the hill on the edge of the colony we found Israel, dying. There was a small, dark-red hole in his breast. The rifle was no longer on his shoulder. Only the pouch and the pistol remained . . .

Two of us stayed with him; the rest scattered in the hills to find the killer. We sought in vain and returned downhearted and consumed by impotent wrath. Israel had not taken the Arabs alive for us; we bore him home, dead.

But tragedy did not end there—a second man was to die. We stood on the Nazareth Road, looking toward the scene of the murder—toward Kafr Kana. Suddenly we saw three Arabs in flight, pursued by two of our men.

Evening had already fallen. All the farm workers and the settlers were gathered near the *han*. Among them was Shimon Melamed. He was a carpenter by trade, but had come to Palestine to be a farmer, and had made his way to Sejera for his training. As he was a fine craftsman, the management employed him in his trade for several years. However, he found no satisfaction in carpentry, although he earned three times as much at it than as a farm laborer and even more than an independent farmer; his whole aim in life was to establish himself on the land. After five or six years of work on the farm, the management granted his petition and gave him a parcel of land on a share-cropping basis, in Sejera.

Shimon was the happiest man in the place. His holding was one of the choicest and most fertile in the settlement. No one surpassed him in industry and perseverance, and, although he was a novice, his granary even in the first year was no less full than those of the more experienced farmers. This was his second Passover as a farmer, and his splendid work during the winter and the plentiful rains promised him a fine harvest again. He was as brave as he was industrious and devoted to the land. There was no raid or affray but he was among the first to defend the colony.

He was in his house when the shooting took place. As soon as he heard the shots, he dashed out. In his haste, he forgot his hat and the gun that hung on the wall of his room. His young wife took down the gun, hurried after him, and put it in his hand. She returned home to look after their child and he went on up to the farm. The rest of the people followed.

When we saw the Arabs retreating with our men at their heels, we decided to send several men on to block the escape route. Three went: a Sejera farmer, Shimon and myself. We raced toward the Arabs and fired at them. The Arabs were between the frying-pan and the fire; two pursuers at their heels, and we three in front of them. The Arabs of Sejera village saw their plight, and the entire population of it rushed toward the three of us. When our people realized the danger we were in, they called us back, but in the whistling hail of bullets we could not hear their warning. The Arabs of Sejera closed in on us. In single file, at intervals of several meters, we returned to the farm. We were close to home when an Arab fired from the cactus-hedge, and the bullet got Shimon in the heart.

Mutely we bore our dead comrades from the seder room; mutely we bore them on our shoulders to Sejera's plot of eternal rest, mutely, without funeral oration, we lowered them into the wide single grave.

They had lived together and died together in a Jewish settlement; there they had dreamed their life's dream, dream of rebirth, and there they had fallen. Together now they lay in peace—the watchman and the farmer, in the soil which by their lives as in death they consecrated.

4 THE SONG OF THE HOE

THE PIONEERS of the Second Aliyah were convinced that if Jewish colonists continued to employ Arab farmhands on a large scale, they would merely create a class of petty Jewish barons dominating an alien peasant people. The Arabs some day would revolt and throw them out. The land, the Second Aliyah believed, would belong to the Jews only if they worked it, not if they merely held legal title.

These pioneers were brought up in the atmosphere of the glorification of the peasant and of manual labor then prevalent in Russia. As Jews, they believed that only a return to the land and to manual labor would normalize Jewish life and cure the Jewish mentality of its peculiarities which they considered undesirable.

They came to the land of their fathers to till its soil with their own hands, and were ready to endure every hardship in order to become part of a Jewish peasantry—even, if need be, a landless peasantry.

The conservative colonists, who had become hardened and who were none too prosperous themselves, were reluctant to experiment with these radical young dreamers. At most, some of them agreed to employ a small number of Jews among a much larger number of their Arab farmhands.

A struggle developed. Spokesmen of the workers accused the colonists, among other things, of misusing the money given them by Baron Rothschild and Zionist bodies: financial assistance, the newcomers argued, was intended to help create a Jewish National Homeland, not to strengthen the Arab position and make the creation of a Jewish Homeland more difficult. The colonists accused the new pioneers of being atheists, dangerous revolutionaries who plotted to deprive them of their heard-earned money and possessions and a menace to the Jewish people.

The pioneers of the Second Aliyah fought for employment in the colonies. In that fight they sought to enlist the help of Zionists abroad. But their first steps were to formulate their own aims. In 1904, in a room of a kindergarten teacher in Jaffa, a group of newcomers met to draw up a program. Among them were forty-eight year old A. D. Gordon and eighteen year old Shlomo Zemach. The latter, who had a flair for language, suggested the expression *Kibbush Ha-avodah* as the chief goal. Literally *Kibbush Ha-avodah* is translated as "Conquest of Labor." What it really meant was capturing positions of employment. The phrase was modeled on Herzl's slogan for "capturing the (Jewish) communities" for the Zionist cause. For many years the slogan of *Kibbush Ha-avodah* was the rallying cry of the Second Aliyah in Palestine and of Labor Zionists and their sympathizers abroad.

In time the World Zionist Organization was won over to the idea. Its own resources were very limited, and it did as much as it could; the Jewish National Fund hired Jewish workers to plant its first forests and a Palestine Office was opened in Jaffa. Arthur Ruppin, a promising young German sociologist, was sent to manage the new office, and to assist the pioneers of the Second Aliyah.

The favorable climate of opinion within the Zionist movement probably helped to break through the apathy of the Jewish Colonization Association, the richest Jewish organization in those years, and its representatives in Palestine experimented with farming out plots of land to groups of pioneers. Sejera in the Galilee, where Ben-Gurion worked, was the first such experiment.

Gradually the idea of collective farms evolved as the best solution; it was felt this would ensure the employment of Jews on the land, place effective bars against using Jewish land for employing Arabs, and avoid constant clashes with the Jewish colonists. Two main types developed: the collective *kvutza* and the co-operative *moshav ovdim* (workers' settlement). In time the larger *kibbutz* evolved out of the more restricted *kvutza*.

Parallel with these developments and to some extent incidental to them were the beginnings of consumers' and producers' co-operatives, sick benefits and unemployment benefits, out of which in time grew the mighty structure of the Histadrut (Labor Federation) and its unique system of socialized medicine. The beginnings—ridiculously weak as they were—were made by the pioneers of the Second

Aliyah, under the Turkish regime, and owed more to pressure of necessity than to doctrine.

All this would have been impossible without a certain spirit among the pioneers. Having for the most part lost the traditional faith of their fathers, they nevertheless retained more than their fathers' share of religious fervor in dedicating their lives to hard manual labor. In this they saw the highest moral good for any man, and especially for the Jew.

Many of these pioneers were students who had left their class-rooms to become farmhands. David Shimonovotz (now David Shimeoni) was not only a university student, but a young Hebrew poet of great promise, when he left his native White Russia to labor and starve in the fields of the Homeland. Joseph Hayim Brenner, already a leading novelist and short story writer, traveled to Palestine incognito so as not to be treated as a famous writer but as one of the pioneers. He was extremely unhappy when he failed to develop as a good field worker and was assigned by his comrades to do cultural work, finally ending up as editor of labor publications. Berl Katzenelson, leading theoretican of the Palestine labor movement and founder and first editor of the first labor daily (*Davar*), began in Palestine as a worker in the fields and as one of the founders and members of the collective farm of Kinneret, after a career as a teacher and a librarian in Russia.

The greatest moral teacher of the Second Aliyah was Aaron David Gordon. It was he who coined the phrase *Dat-Ha-avodah* (Religion of Labor). He advocated manual labor as a religous experience. He expounded the tenets of his faith in numerous speeches and articles, which he wrote in the shacks after a day's work in the fields and often after spending half the night dancing and singing with his younger comrades.

Gordon was the only prominent pioneer of the Second Aliyah who was long past his youth when he came to Palestine. He was at least thirty years older than Shlomo Zemach, whom he met and befriended soon after the latter's arrival. Zemach describes his first meeting with Gordon early one morning in Rishon-le-Zion:

> On the morning following Shavuot, I rose early, to go to work on my new job. When I went out into the courtyard to wash up in cold water, I found six young men lying on the floor of the large hall, fast asleep with their bundles under their heads. They must have come on foot from Petah-Tikvah during the night when I slept. By the window stood a bearded Jew of about fifty years, wrapped in his praying shawl, reciting his morning prayers. His

face seemed greener than the old silver crown of his praying shawl and his two cheeks were deeply sunken, forming furrows on both sides of his long thin nose, accentuating the skeletal parchment-like leanness of his cheeks. But his extremely shrewd, quick blue eyes emitted bright sparks of joy and even a soupcon of playful defiance which had the effect of discouraging any incipient compassion that might begin to develop at the sight of such frailty.

Moshe Smilansky

◆

AARON DAVID GORDON

AARON DAVID GORDON, theoretician of the "Religion of Labor" and destined to inspire thousands of pioneers, was born in the village in Podolia on the Feast of Shavuot (Pentecost) in 1857. He studied at home, in Vilno and in a nearby town, until he was about seventeen, confining his learning, as was customary among traditional Jews, to the Bible, the Talmud and related subjects. Not until he was seventeen did he begin studying Hebrew grammar and Russian. He also taught himself German and French and the rudiments of mathematics. Despite the offer of his wealthy and influential relatives, he refused to go to a university to study a profession, insisting that the acquisition of knowledge ought not to be linked with the means of a livelihood. Shortly after his marriage, after having lived the prescribed two years at the home of his father-in-law, he joined the administrative staff of Baron Ginsburg and settled in the village of Mohilna, while his wife and children lived in the nearby town of Haschubata. The Russian laws restricting the domicile of the Jews made it impossible for them to live in the village. Seven children were born, but only two survived—a son and a daughter.

In Mohilna and Haschubata, Gordon spent twenty-three years of his life, devoting his spare time to study, reading and communal activities. Gradually he arrived at the Zionist idea.

In 1903 a crisis developed in the Zionist movement, and a split occurred between those who favored the colonization of Uganda or any other available territory and those who remained loyal to the ancestral Homeland. At the same time Gordon lived through an acute crisis in his personal life, when his only son broke with him. The son rebelled against all modern influences, refused to continue his secular studies and left for a yeshiva to devote himself to a life of piety and traditional learning. That very year Gordon's parents died. Gordon sold the small inheritance he received, gave the money to his wife and daughter, who approved of his decision, and left for Palestine.

*　　*　　*

Aaron David Gordon was forty eight years old when he landed in Jaffa. His worldly possessions consisted of Kohut's Hebrew Lexicon, which he was forced to pawn in order to have enough money to pay a bribe to a Turkish official to be allowed to remain in the country. He refused a position of librarian when it was offered him, saying that he had come to the Homeland to engage in tilling the soil. In Petah-Tikvah he found work as a farmhand, which made him very happy. After a year he went to Rishon-le-Zion to work in the vineyards and in the local winepress. It was during the height of the Uganda controversy, when the colony was dominated by the Ugandists. An official in the winepress slapped Shlomo Zemach in a political argument. Zemach hit back and a scuffle ensued. The administration apologized to Zemach, but Gordon felt the apology was inadequate and led a group of workers out on strike in protest. Gordon went to work in Mikveh Israel, but, he fell ill with malaria and was incapacitated for some time. He went back to Petah-Tikvah, where a poor workingman befriended him and gave him a bed and food while he was ill. After recuperating, Gordon went back to work and, little by little, repaid his benefactor for his room and board. It was at this time that the conflict developed between the extreme pious group among the farmers and the extreme free-thinkers among the workers.*

Gordon was not an orthodox Jew in the accepted sense. But he was a deeply religious person who had a strong feeling for traditional practices and respected the religious feelings of others. He was unhappy when his fellow-workers failed to show consideration for the religious sentiments of the conservative colonists,

---

* See story in previous chapter: "From Homel to Petah-Tikvah."

and was especially incensed against the Rostov group from South Russia, whose extreme socialistic slogans and derisive attitude towards religion annoyed him. But the action of the fanatical farmers in banning Jewish labor made him even more indignant; he told them their conduct was more irreligious than the youthful irresponsibility of the Rostov pioneers. He was more adamant than the rest in insisting on a full revocation of the ban without compromising formulas. In anger he left Petah-Tikvah and went to Rehovot.

When his efforts to work at digging ditches in a grove proved beyond his strength—he managed to dig three a day, where some of the others did fifty—the young farmers of the colony (led by Smilansky) offered him a position as assistant to the colony clerk, but he refused. He was then given the job of a stoker at the oven of the small winepress where alcohol was produced. He was paid two francs a night for his work.

The oven at the winepress became the cultural center of the colony. Young people would gather around the fireman to hear his views on many problems.

When the work at the winepress was finished, Gordon found employment at the vineyards, where he specialized in uprooting parasitic plants. He found a deep sense of satisfaction in destroying parasites and became an expert at his work. At night he mounted guard.

In the summer of 1908 his daughter arrived from Russia to join him. She was frightened when she saw how thin he had grown and how ragged his clothes were. But the luminous spark of his eyes and his cheerful mood gradually effaced that first impression. Gordon took his daughter to the famous Hayim Boruch Hotel in Jaffa, which was the center of the Hapoel Hatzair (Young Labor) movement to which he belonged. During the meal, when Gordon noticed that his daughter was not pleased with the cooking, he remarked to her: "My daughter, in the Homeland one must not be fastidious." She never complained after that.

The following winter, on a cold day, when Gordon walked to Jaffa, he wore a good fur coat his daughter had brought him from home. Three Arabs attacked him, robbed him of his only earthly treasure and left him badly beaten up. He was taken to a hospital where he remained for three weeks. For several months after leaving the hosiptal he was unable to do any physical work and was compelled to accept an assignment to translate a book in order to support himself.

Soon after his return to Petah-Tikvah, Gordon rented a small cottage in a workers' suburb called Ein Ganim. It was there that his wife joined him. Joseph Hayim Brenner who had recently arrived, Berl Kazenelson and David Shimonovitch, three famous men of letters who, like Gordon, were also engaged in manual labor, also settled in Ein Ganim. When too many people gathered in Gordon's small apartment, he would take them outside and suggest they continue their discussion in the open. "Isn't this a marvelous parlor?" he would point to the surrounding hills and the valleys.

The first few months in Ein Ganim were Gordon's happiest days. But soon his wife and daughter came down with malaria. After many months of suffering, his wife died. His daughter lay very ill in the hospital in Jaffa where Gordon nursed her.

He returned to Ein Ganim to which he had become attached. He still hummed his favorite Yiddish melodies, still danced and sang with the workers, still encouraged the young people. But his eyes had become infinitely sadder than they had been.

In 1912 Gordon decided to leave for the Galilee. He worked at Migdal, at Sejera, at Uriah, at Kinneret and finally, in 1915, he settled at Daganiah, where he stayed to the end of his life.

Gordon became depressed by the misfortunes which overtook the Yishuv when Turkey entered the First World War. He went to work for the Turkish army with the labor battalions, merely to suffer the pangs of hunger with his fellow-Jews who had been drafted.

When the Turks began to arrest suspects on charges of spying for the British, Gordon went to Kinnereth to stand in line for questioning. As he heard the cries of the victims of the torture from the adjoining room, he began singing a Yiddish song:

"As they draw my blood, I sing me a merry song."

*   *   *

The war was over. The Third Aliyah began. Hundreds of pioneers streamed from Europe to work on the roads, to join the few existing collective farms, to form new ones. Gordon was happy: the Idea was being consummated; the movement was assuming large dimensions.

The new pioneers who joined the collective settlement of Daganiah admired Gordon. His kindly blue eyes, which looked with affection on the young newcomers, his saintly appearance, his peasant garb—all this was an inspiration to their self-dedication. They were encouraged by his talk and they marveled at his capacity for work. This old man would rise at three in the morning and sit in the passageway, among the bedrooms, in order not to disturb the sleepers, writing by the light of a small kerosene lamp. When daylight came, he would put on his work clothes, go into the mess hall to have his breakfast and leave for his labors in the field, cheerful and energetic.

In 1920, Gordon contracted cancer. When he knew death was inevitable, he merely wished that he could work every day until the end. He continued reading and writing on his sickbed. He felt relieved and cheered in his pains when Jewish workers began to build a bridge across the Jordan near Daganiah. He was happy to see the first bridge built by Jewish hands in the Homeland in two thousand years.

During his last night he kept whispering to his daughter that we must believe in a brighter future for Israel and for mankind. He died in 1922 and was buried in Daganiah.

Joseph Baratz

◆

DAGANIAH

The Jewish National Fund had planted an olive grove at Ben-Shemen as a unit of the Herzl Forest. A group of workers from Russia and one known as the Romny Commune (Romny was a Ukrainian town from which its members came) left Petah-Tikvah for Ben-Shemen to seek work at the nursery and were at once taken on by the supervisor. Later the supervisor asked the members of the Romny Commune to go to Kinneret and settle there.

The first pioneering group of eight arrived in Kinneret in the autumn of 1908.

The work was hard, and the food bad. Accommodations were primitive. Clearing the fields of stones and blasting out the rocks demanded feverish activity from dawn to dark.

* * *

The Palestine Office found the administrative methods at Kinneret inadequate and decided to hand over the land to the laborers themselves. The workers' group was given that part of the Kinneret lands whose working involved special difficulties, since it lay beyond the Jordan. This was the Um Juni tract, now the site of Daganiah.

* * *

A group composed of the flower of Jewish labor in the Galilee occupied the tract. This was in 1910. The group consisted of six men and one woman. Additional labor was to be engaged when seasonal work demanded.

A contract was made for one year between the new pioneer group and the Palestine Office. The first year the farm paid its way.

And at the end of the year the Palestine Office agreed to hand over the tract for permanent labor settlement.

The Romny Commune finally took over the farm at Um Juni during the week of Succot, in 1911. There were ten men and two women.

*　　*　　*

The chief motive of the Romny Commune was to conduct a farm based on the collective responsibility of its members. There was nothing dogmatic about their ideal of the commune. They thought this form of society suited their own needs and desires. They had no aim of imposing it upon others. Neither did they want their kvutza to be an exclusive arrogant sect.

The inner arrangement was different from what later developed. The expenses were divided equally among all members, but all other items, such as clothing, shoes, cultural needs, and assistance to relatives, were charged to each worker individually. Separate accounts therefore had to be kept for each member, except one account kept for the nine members of the "Commune of Romny." The individuals of the latter group had no separate accounts among themselves.

Health conditions, during those early years, were none too good. The site at Um Juni brought on a recrudescence of the malaria which had stricken down workers at Hadera. Many fell ill of it, some even of yellow fever. Death came stalking through Dagania.

Nor were robbery and murder infrequent at first. The farm was close to the ford over which robbers used to carry off their booty to Transjordan. Guard duty in the fields was very exacting. As the two regular watchmen were unable to cope with the task, the comrades took turns with them in the fields after a long day's work. (These watchmen were also members of the group, since hired watchmen could by no means have been reconciled with the principle of doing all the work of the kvutza without outside help.) In those days the slogan was: he who works the land must also be able to protect his crops! At times men watching in the grain fields, revolver in hand, ears attuned to every slight rustle, eyes closing from severe fatigue, would suddenly hear a bullet whiz past their ears. Yet the danger did not deter them. If anything, it added a new zest to their efforts.

That first year at Um Juni was a sort of prolonged honeymoon. The men would go out to the ploughing before dawn. Song would burst from the throats of the six riders who with their six pairs of mules moved along the banks of the winding Jordan, whose forsaken waters had not had such a welcome in many a day.

It was dark again when they returned from the fields. Hurriedly they bathed, ate their supper, and went to the stable to look after the mules. Then to the clay hut that served as an office, where Bussel* had established himself. Bussel would then read out the correspondence to interested listeners; the letters of the kvutza to the Palestine Office; the letters of the Palestine Office to the kvutza.

When a mare died, the misfortune was sorrowfully reported to the Palestine Office, and words of comfort would come in reply. Or, if a wedding or other happy event was reported, cordial congratulations were sure to follow.

For more than a year the group continued to live in the Arab mud huts and in the rickety wooden barracks which rocked every time the wind blew. Once, on a very stormy night one of the barracks was blown down, and the wind carried its remnants far off to the village of Semakh. Meanwhile the all but naked comrades stood about joking over the incident.

After a year or so in the Arab village, the group began to consider erecting permanent structures for their settlement. After all the pros and cons had been thrashed out, the site was fixed at a point where the Jordan flows out from Lake Kinneret, nine kilometers from Tiberias. The location is 198 meters below sea-level. The buildings were planned not for a mixed farm, such as Daganiah now is, but for the usual type of Galilean grain farm.

The group had no liking for the bare Galilean villages without trees or gardens, and wanted their farm to resemble a Russian village with all kinds of shade and fruit trees (plum, apple, pear). A few years later, it was found, of course, that many of these varieties were unsuited both to the soil and the climate, and the trees had to be uprooted. On the other hand, local varieties, such

---

* Joseph Bussel, the leader of the group.

as olive and carob, flourished. Soon rows of cypress and pepper trees grew up near the houses.

* * *

My friend T. and myself, both members of the group, were returning from Damascus on two mules we had just bought. For two days we rode through narrow, stony paths among the mountains of Transjordan, much concerned for the welfare of our animals. As we descended into the valley and neared the shores of Kinneret, we spurred them on and entered the borders of Daganiah after dark, singing, in a happy mood. But a blank silence met us, as we glimpsed our comrades at the entrance to the lane of trees, their faces grief-stricken, guns in hand. They told us that the night before, two comrades—Moshe Barsky of Daganiah and Joseph Salzman of Kinneret—had been murdered.

Barsky was still under nineteen when death struck him down. When his death was reported to his parents in Russia, this is the answer that came from his father:—

"Dear Friends of Daganiah,

"I have received your precious letter, written with tears of blood. I found there true words that had welled up from loving and faithful hearts bound together by an eternal bond. Dear brothers! The unexpected has befallen us. I know that, great as is the disaster that has come upon us, you will not—God forbid!—let your spirits fail you. On the contrary, may the memory of my son inspire you with still greater strength and courage to fight your holy battle until you attain to the great ideal for which my son gave his life.

"Comrades in spirit! It is not only to thank you for your sympathy with my grief that I write you, but also to send you words of comfort. For, is not your grief my own? Come, therefore, and let us hope together that the blood of our precious victim, of my son and your comrade, Moshe, will be accepted, and that he may be the last sacrifice upon the altar of our exalted ideal."

This letter infused the comrades at Daganiah with renewed faith and courage. And soon after, Moshe Barsky's brother came to Daganiah—"to fill the place of the son who had fallen."

* * *

When the first tomatoes were to be planted, two inexperienced young men used huge shovels to dig trenches such as are intended for grape vines. The irrigation, too, was no more expertly done at first.

We bought two Arab cows and gave them a rousing reception. But these Bedouin cows, accustomed to complete freedom and Bedouin supervision, refused to remain confined to the cowshed and to submit to European handling. The members of the kvutza paid the cows more attention that their own needs. But the cows yielded no more milk than before. In 1913 the foundations of the present dairy were laid with the importation of some cows and heifers from Beirut. The kvutza then suddenly found itself with more milk than it could sell. It took a good deal of persuasion to get the Jews of Tiberias to buy our cow milk after they had been accustomed to buy milk from the goatherd who brought the goats to the housewife's door.

Everything was an experiment, the number of which was equalled by the number of errors.

* * *

As long as the farm was restricted to a single crop of grain, it was not possible to have a fixed number of workers for the whole year. During the sowing season, twelve to fifteen men sufficed, whereas when there was weeding to do or the pulse had to be harvested, a large number of temporary workers were required for a few days or weeks. The presence of these temporary workers had serious social implications in a kvutza. Again "farmers" and "hired men appeared." Though the working conditions were identical for all, it was not possible to ignore the existence of two distinct groups with differing rights: the one a group of established settlers, the other of brief sojourns, doing as they were told and then free to go where they would—or could.

This problem was partly solved with the introduction of fruit and vegetable growing, for then it was possible to keep the same number of workers busy throughout the year, merely transferring them from one crop to another with the changing of the seasons. However, the question of temporary hands has not been completely solved even to this day.

To take on permanent workers as comrades also was not simple. There long remained a clear demarcation at Daganiah between the Romny Commune from Hadera and the individual members who had been admitted at different times and who did not, like the original pioneers, form a unified group with common memories. However, as time passed, this distinction was blotted out. There is now no such thing as a group within the group at Daganiah and personal accounts have long been abolished because there is full partnership in all goods. Yet certain essential differences between new comrades and old still persist. The past of the kvutza in which they themselves have had no share, arouses a sort of envy in the hearts of the newcomers, and they feel a strong desire to begin all over again, to become creators in their own right, without following in the established traditions.

This may be the reason for the constant shifting of personnel in kvutzot. At Daganiah farm these changes caused severe losses because, instead of improving its methods and increasing its income, the kvutza became a sort of training school.

*　*　*

With the advent of the first family—when the first child was born in the kvutza—still another problem arose.

What of the mother of the child, she who had been so active and efficient a worker on the farm? What was she to do now? Was she to give up her work and devote all her time to the child? And what kind of care would she give it, having no experienced mother of her own near to teach her how to rear her first child? All were at a loss for an answer.

The theory of the kvutza was, that since the women worked on the farm together with the men, they ought not to be burdened with the sole care of the children. But how was this theory to be applied in real life? No one knew. However, the first mother* herself solved her problem. She simply took the baby with her to the scene of her work—to the barn, or the vegetable plot. And when the baby cried, all Daganiah cried with it. Everyone resented the

---

* Miriam Baratz, the author's wife.

mother's "cruelty." She tried hard to appease her comrades: "Don't worry about him. He'll surely stop. He has nothing at all to cry about." The child became accustomed to this novel method and the others recognized the inevitability of having mothers working in the field while tending their children.

With the birth of the second child, the problem grew even more acute and more complicated. How would the mothers be able to continue their work on the farm? Would any woman be willing to hand her child over to another woman's care? Joseph Bussel said: "The duty to take care of all the children rests not only upon the mothers, but upon all the women of the group, even upon the unmarried ones. If all the women would take a share in the rearing of the children, the mothers would be able to do all forms of work. As for the expense of rearing and educating the children, this should be shared by all the members of a collective. No one should be exempt merely because he himself has no children. All such distinctions undermine the basis of the collective idea."

And by these words of Bussel's the children's mode of life was determined.

Daganiah has been visited by many afflictions—disease, death, famine, and war—but all these have passed the children by. No harm has ever befallen them. In the trying climate of the Jordan Valley, they have been saved by the care and attention they receive in the collective nursery.

To this very day, the attitude of a woman toward the common nursery is still the touchstone of her fitness for life in the kvutza. She can be judged as soon as her first child is born; and not every mother measures up to the test. Age-long habit holds the young mother in its clutches. She has all sorts of fears and suspicions that her child will not receive proper care. These bugbears can be dispelled only by a well-equipped and hygienic nursery in charge of experienced nurses who are patient and kind in dealing with the mothers.

* * *

The children at Daganiah are divided into three age-groups— one, including those up to two and a half years old, remains in the nursery from morning until the evening, under the care of trained comrades. Towards evening these children return to their parents' quarters, where they remain over night. In this respect Daganiah differs from other kvutzot where the youngest children sleep in the nursery.

The second age-group includes the children between the ages of two and a half to six who attend the kindergarten. The kindergarten teacher is a member of the kvutza. These children too spend their nights at their parents' quarters.

The third age-group including children of the age of six and up attends the "Joint School for the Children of the Jordan Valley," which is situated in Daganiah. They spend the largest part of the day at the school.

For many years the children of Dagniah attended the little school which served Daganiah exclusively. In the meantime the number of children increased in neighboring kvutzot, and a spacious building was erected to serve as joint school for all the children of the Jordan Valley.

* * *

During their vacation the children are very happy to work alongside the adults in field and garden. They are superb workers and need no "hachshara"* like halutzim. But their work is productive only when they feel that it is of practical use to the kvutza and on the same level with the work of the adults. When they suspect that their work has been given to them only in order to keep them busy, the results are nil.

Besides formal study, the school curriculum includes other activities: manual work, play and physical culture. It is thrilling to see them in the waters of the Jordan and the Kinneret. Every child—including the very young ones—swims like a fish. Swimming is the best form of physical exercise in the Jordan Valley.

It is difficult to point to a Western type of school corresponding to ours. The direction of the studies is of the technical type, although much emphasis is placed on the humanities: literature, Bible, etc. The objective of the school is to train loyal children of the Homeland and good workers who will continue to build the collec-

---

* Preliminary training.

tive community. It is too early to draw any conclusions about the results of our education. But we are convinced that our children are getting an education which prepares them to follow along the road which we have begun.

* * *

The path of the kvutza has not been strewn with roses. The economic and social problems of the group have always exceeded the powers of the active members to cope with them. Nevertheless, both the kvutza as a unit and its individual members have always taken part in the activities both of the labor movement and of the Yishuv in general. These public activities have interfered with the work on the farm, because it was only the most efficient farmers who were most active in public affairs.

* * *

When the Zionist Organization took over the agricultural settlement work of the National Fund after the war, the original contract between the Daganiah group and the Palestine Office was cancelled. The partnership with the Jewish National Fund ceased, and the farm passed entirely under the control of the kvutza.

As soon as the Daganiah farm came under kvutza control its whole inner organization was changed. All individual accounts were dropped, the small inner group was dissolved, and the entire kvutza went over outright to the collective form of society.

Aliza Shidlovsky

◆

PANGS OF INTEGRATION

Upon my arrival in Daganiah, I was thrown into the peculiar atmosphere of the kvutza—at that time still in its infancy. The climate was one of exacting demands made on each member. Since the whole life was based on ties of comradeship and mutual compatibility, the conscious striving toward these goals caused a constant tension. The slightest manifestation of incompatibility or misunderstanding affected the life of the whole group. Any friction evoked doubts about people's ability to live in a kvutza or posed the question of their suitability before the entire social group. What aggravated the situation was the fact that the group was so small and could ill-afford any disturbance to its delicate balance.

If the comrades did not go to the threshing floor after the evening meal, they would sit around the table, talking little, and singing a great deal. Ever since those days I never heard people sing that way. The melodies were vehicles for the release of the overwhelming feeling of loneliness in the hearts of each of the twenty-four comrades.

There was no contact with other settlements. The periodical *"Hapoel Hatzair"* arrived only rarely. The few books the members had brought were packed away in valises. We felt completely cut off from Europe, from the world, from our own past. We considered ourselves living in a vacuum which we must fill entirely by our conscious efforts. Into that singing were deposited all the doubts and fears that there might not be a tomorrow . . .

Often the singing ended in a weird hora dance carried on to the point of collapse. More than once I saw Yeruham Klebanoff fall down exhausted on the bench after the dance. Joseph Bussel would be carried out of the ring in a swoon. It was not just a dance; it was a wail without words, a bursting forth of all that had accumulated in one's heart. Sometimes the hora had something in it of the reconciliation after a quarrel. Sometimes it showed the insistent longing of a child for a far-away mother. Every hora was to me an open book in which I could read the emotions and hardships of the dancers.

*   *   *

One day the girls went to milk the cows and left me in charge of the lentil porridge. I stood there with a wooden ladle in my hand, stirring. The lentils began to boil and to sizzle, at first gently, then more and more violently, until they exploded and were spattered all over the stove, the wall and my hands. Even when I saw that my hands were burned, it did not occur to me to make the fire smaller. When the girls finally came back, half the stew was already on the floor and covered my hands up to my elbows. I had fainted. For two weeks I went around in bandages.

Following the incident, the comrades decided to let me try my luck in field work. In those times of hardship, human beings were not regarded as individuals, but rather callously in the light of what they could contribute. Each person was under pressure to give his all, whether he had it to give or not.

I went out with Tanhum to gather sheaves after the harvest. This was the first time in Daganiah that a woman went out into the field. I was happy, for this was a dream come true. The first day I was in a particularly festive mood. But it was a hot hamsin day. I suffered from thirst and we had no water with us. And I did not know how to work. I saw Tanhum lift two bundles of the harvest and did likewise. Then he lifted four bundles, so I also lifted four. He started running; I ran too. I was so thirsty that I was forced to face the wind to freshen my parched breath. But I did not ask the man who drove the wagon to bring me a little drinking water next time he came around; I was afraid this would show weakness on my part. And I lived in dread of another failure. At the end of the day I had difficulty getting up on the wagon to drive home. My whole body ached and I had a fever, but I did not dare to tell anybody.

At the end of my six weeks in Daganiah, my membership in the kvutza came up for discussion. In those days such a discussion was tantamount to a sentence pronounced on a man in his absence. The membership of H.Z. was also to be decided at that meeting. H.Z. in a very depressed state of mind during the days preceding the meeting, walked up and down the room singing Bialik's "I wafted my woes to the winds" and other melancholy songs, as if in apology for his life. The evening his fate was being decided, he sat outside, tense and nervous.

When the meeting was over, Tanhum came to me in the barn and tactfully informed me what had been said about me. The comrades had decreed that I was not fit for work. The girls thought it was better for the kvutza to help me get back home.

Before that evening I had already made up my mind to leave Daganiah. Although Tanhum suggested that I stay on for some time and voiced an opinion contrary to that of the girls, I decided to leave immediately.

After my departure I happened to be in Kinneret one day during Passover. I listened to Hannah Meisel making a report on the need for farm work training for girls, and on her own activity on the training farm she had founded two years earlier.

At the end of the report I walked over to Hannah and asked her to admit me. At first she refused: the reputation I had acquired at Daganiah had reached Kinneret. But fortunately for me, all the girls on the training farm suddenly took sick, and the dire need for workers opened the doors for me.

Here begins a new chapter. Here I was given guidance and encouragement. It was Leah Meron, who, in a spirit of simple friendship, taught me how to wash clothes and how to water the garden. I began to see progress in my work. My body, too, became accustomed to a life of labor. When I had arrived in the country I was a thin girl with skinny hands—nobody believed I would shortly become a good worker. Before long, the members of Daganiah sent me an invitation to return. But I had already become acclimatized to Kinneret and would not think of leaving it. When Hannah Meisel left for the Zionist Congress, she put me in charge of the vegetable garden.

Ephraim Auerbach

◆

ON THE THRESHOLD

All the passengers were now ashore, Mendie perspired in the hot sun and contemplated the miraculous thing: his bundle was all there, unharmed, undamaged, with the pillow and the blanket his mother had sewn into the cloth.

A young man came up to him: "Have you any people in Jaffa?" Mendie did not know anybody. "Where are you going to stay?"

"I don't know."

"Then you better go to Pessieh-Leah's. It's in Neveh-Shalom.* It's not expensive. Everybody stays there."

The man called an Arab and talked to him. The Arab soon returned with a donkey, placed the bundle on the animal, and *yallah—* off they trundled. The Arab following the donkey and Mendie walked behind them through winding labyrinthine streets and lanes. The Arab stopped before a house and called out: "Pessieh-Leah, there is a hawajeh."†

A woman came out of the house and talked to the Arab. It sounded to Mendie as if they were quarreling. When the exchanges were over, Pessiah-Leah said to Mendie: "Pay him two bishliks."

"How much is that?" Mendie asked. He took out a Russian ruble and gave it to her. "I haven't any Turkish money."

"You'll get some change out of that," she said smilingly.

She went into the house and returned with two large copper coins which she gave to the Arab. "We'll fix you up somehow," Pessieh-Leah promised Mendie as she took him inside.

* * *

---

* A Jewish quarter of Jaffa.
† A gentleman.

Presently Mendie went out to explore the twisting, winding lanes of Jaffa. He came across an Arab trader standing in front of what seemed like a mountain of oranges. Mendie put out his hand and spread his fingers, as if to ask what the price was.

The trader, who had been peering at him sidelong, suddenly addressed him in Hebrew: *"Yehudi?"* he asked. Mendie confirmed he was a Jew.

"Lo kessef," (no money) the Arab continued in his pidgin Hebrew, and explained his reasons: *"Ani yehudi, atta yehudi, lo kessef"* (Me Jewish, you Jewish—no money.)

So this was a Sephardi Jew. The latter's Hebrew vocabulary was now exhausted, but he found a way of asking another question: "Muscobi?"

Mendie nodded: he was from Russia. His Oriental co-religionist beckoned to him that he take another orange. Mendie took the fruit, waved his hand, said "Shalom" and walked off.

*   *   *

When he reached Pessieh-Leah's hotel, it was already full of people gathered for supper. Some were regular guests, others only came for their evening meal. They sat at the square tables, eating spinach cutlets, onions mixed with oil and thick soup. The conversation was carried on in Hebrew, Russian, Yiddish and in languages Mendie could not decipher. They had emaciated, worn-out faces, their hands were black and bony and full of cuts and bruises. A somber flame flickered in their eyes.

The young man who had met him at the dock came over: "I am Zvi," he introduced himself, "remember me from the boat?"

Of course, Mendie remembered him. What would he have done without him? They sat down at a table near an open window looking out into a small garden.

A tall, lanky man with a pointed lean face and reddish mustache stood in the garden not far from where they sat. He was barefooted. He was not looking at any particular object. His eyes appeared to be covered by a mist and it seemed as though they looked without seeing.

"That's Pessieh-Leah's husband," Zvi explained. There was a note of disdain in his voice.

"I am afraid that man will never be any good. His wife, Pessiah-Leah—that's different. She is a great help to the newcomers. It is she who gives them the first smile, and with that smile they go out to face their first hardship. But he—he plays the violin and writes music. He says he is an artist. Maybe he is—who knows? Sometimes he plays for us. It sounds like something, that's true. But why does he go around idle, letting her carry the whole burden? What is he doing, standing over there?"

The tall man suddenly sensed that he was being discussed and became uncomfortable. He began pacing up and down the garden.

Zvi said, "Nahum, you're thinking too much. You'll never solve the riddle of the universe, anyway. Others before you have tried and failed. What do you expect to accomplish?"

The man drew back. He obviously did not like Zvi and was afraid of him. "I am not trying to solve the riddle of the universe," he retorted. "I am only trying to understand myself."

*   *   *

After supper Mendie went out with a group of pioneers to sing and dance near the seashore. But soon he became tired and went home alone.

Pessieh-Leah's house was still lit up. She sat at the table with her husband, Nahum, and the two conversed quietly in that intimate fashion in which Mendie's father and mother discussed household affairs after the children had gone to bed. Nahum, with his bare feet and his reddish mustache, now seemed altogether different from the way he had looked in the garden. There was no longer that forlorn expression on his gaunt face. His brown eyes looked mild and serene.

Pessieh-Leah rose and welcomed Mendie with a smile: "Back so soon? You must be worn out from the trip. Come, I'll show you where you sleep."

Mendie said he was tired. It was natural to feel tired on arriving in a new country.

"This is not a new country," Nahum contradicted, "this is the Land of Israel."

"But one has to become accustomed to it." Pessieh argued.

Nahum explained: "It is like a man who has never drunk wine in his life and takes his first cup. He gets heady."

* * *

When Mendie woke up, Zvi was gone. He sat down at the same table where he had sat with Zvi for supper. Pessieh-Leah brought him a glass of tea and a slice of bread.

"That's our breakfast," she said apologetically.

Mendie noticed that he was alone in the dining room. He heard a quiet chant coming from the garden. It was Nahum wrapped in a praying shawl, a protruding phylactery resting on his forehead and a velvet skull-cap covering the crown of his head. Nahum chanted his prayers, pacing up and down the small garden. When he reached the Silent Prayer, he stood still as if frozen. When he finished, he took off his praying shawl, kissed it and folded it, then took off his phylacteries from his forehead and his arm, put them together and placed them in the bag. Nahum came into the house, said "good morning," and sat down at Mendie's table. Pessieh-Leah brought him bread and tea and went off.

Nahum drank his tea very slowly and hardly bit into his bread. "I am going away today," he announced suddenly, and let the tea stand. There was a silence. "I am going away today," he repeated. Without waiting to be asked, he explained: "You know, there are sounds inside a man. It is not always that he can hear them, but they are there. But when he does hear them, he feels that the sounds within him crave for other sounds, outside of himself, and he must seek them out. The sounds within must join with the sounds without. He must go out in search of them. Yes, I am going today." He bent over to Mendie, as if revealing a secret.

Without knowing why, Mendie inquired of Nahum whether he was in the habit of reciting his daily prayers regularly. A thin veil came over Nahum's eyes. He began swaying his body as when one studies the Talmud and speaking in a talmudic sing-song, explained: "I do pray every morning. But I don't usually put on my praying shawl and my phylacteries. That I do only when I hear sounds within me. Then I pray as all Jews do."

He made no attempt to explain. He did not seem to be conscious of Mendie or of anything that was visible. He now seemed conscious only of sounds, which he sensed with all his being. Nahum got up, took his praying shawl and phylacteries and went out. Mendie remained seated, without knowing what to do. Ought he to tell Pessieh-Leah that her husband had left? Or ought he to guard the secret?

Pessieh-Leah came into the room, smiled at Mendie and asked: "Is he gone?"

Mendie was surprised: did she know? Then why had not she said anything.

Pessieh-Leah sat down at Mendie's table and explained: "This is not the first time he has gone off like this. He thinks I don't know, but I can tell by his looks when this thing has gotten hold of him. He goes into the hills, stays there for two or three weeks and comes back as if he had just left the house that very morning. 'Pessieh-Leah,' he says, 'have you a bite to eat? I feel hungry today.' So I feed him and don't ask any questions. I just tell him to go and take a haircut, and give him a few piasters. When he comes back from the barber's, you couldn't tell anything had happened."

Pessieh-Leah said she knew why Nahum went off on his tramps. It was because he was in search of sounds. He would some day be a great composer, and would give musical expression to Eretz Israel. Some people thought he was addle-brained. Well, he was a bit queer, but she knew what went on inside him. It was the inner melody of Eretz Israel, which lay hidden in the mountains. Ever since the ancient days when the Levites sang at the Temple, it has been there waiting for a Jew to find it. She knew her Nahum would find it.

Pessieh-Leah now looked much different. Mendie was afraid to meet her eyes, which emitted sparks that seemed to come down on you like a hot rain. All of a sudden she grew silent, rose abruptly and departed.

*　　*　　*

One morning Zvi took Mendie out. "Come, you'll get a taste of Tel-Aviv," he said. The new Jewish suburb north of Jaffa was just then being built. Mendie was trying to get a building job.

"But you must get yourself a wide-brimmed hat to shield you from the sun," Zvi warned. "Have you enough money?"

In the store Zvi examined Mendie with the new hat on and remarked: "You look as if you came from a good home. Is that so?"

"My father is a poor *shohet*"* Mendie said apologetically . . . Mendie's people belonged to the genteel Jewish class in the small towns of Eastern Europe, where scholarship was valued above all else. It was from that class that most of the pioneers were recruited. The artisans in Mendie's town emigrated to the United States; the farmers, of which there were quite a few among the Jews of Bessarabia, chose the Argentine.

"No need to feel ashamed," Zvi reassured him, "we're none of us born laborers. Without quite realizing it, our fathers nurtured within us the yearning for this country—our fathers, our grandfathers, our great-grandfathers. It is they who steered us towards this land. They gave us the strength to carry this land within us. To them it was Judaism, God, "Yiddishkeit" and Ribbono-shel-Olam (Lord of the Universe)—to us, it is the plough, the earth we have to tread rather than the prayers and the biblical verses."

* * *

Mendie spent one day mixing cement in Tel-Aviv and decided to leave for the country. After all, he came to Palestine to work its soil, not to be a city man. Zvi took him to the stage-coach which went to Rehovot.

When he alighted from the vehicle, Mendie was shown to a small lane where, at the very end, near the open field, stood a windowless shack. Inside burned a small kerosene lamp. A few young people sat on wooden crates. There were no tables, no chairs. "Shalom!" someone addressed him, as he haltingly stepped over the threshold, "a newcomer? Shalom, shalom!"

There was a warm welcome in the greeting. The man who first greeted him rose and put out his hand: "You may feel at home here. This is our clubhouse. Anybody may come in. You can eat what there is."

The young man introduced himself as Benjamin and offered Mendie a glass of tea and a slice of bread. He pointed to a crate for Mendie to sit on.

---

* Ritual slaughterer.

There were about twenty or thirty such Jewish workers in the colony which employed about three hundred Arabs. In their club-house they argued about the historic task of *kibbush ha-avodah*—gaining new positions for Jewish workers in Palestine.

Benjamin took Mendie aside: "You won't learn it all in one night," he said, "let me take you to the Seltzerke to see if she can put you up. She does not charge much."

*   *   *

Widow Seltzer was an elderly woman with a shrunken face and sharp, piercing eyes. She was lame and hobbled on a cane. "Her son," Benjamin told Mendie, "is a *pakid* (official). Do you know what that means? An overseer like those the Jews had over them in Egypt. But his mother takes in workers as lodgers."

After the Seltzerke showed Mendie his place, she looked at him intently as if examining him and remarked: "One can tell by looking at you that you come from a nice family." The expression on her face became softer. Her harsh voice now sounded broken. "I'll tell you the truth," she said, "I don't know why you young people come here to suffer so much. What for? Believe me, young man, you will not remake this world. And if you don't find yourself something better to do, you will spend the rest of your life breaking your back and working for others."

She suddenly began pounding on the floor with her cane. Her gray face turned a sickly red like a rotten apple. Her left side sagged, her left shoulder drooped and her head rested on her right shoulder for support.

"My husband, too, was an idealist like you," she said in a dry voice. "He, too, wanted to remake the world. Right here, in Rehovot. Nothing less would do."

She came close to Mendie, fixed her eyes on him, and in a voice suffused with sadness, said: "Young man! Go away from here! Get married and be like other respectable young men in your community."

Mendie feared her. It was not her anger he feared, but the sorrow which spoke out of her eyes. He wanted to tell her that he had nowhere to go back to, that there was no place for him in

Russia, that here he felt he had arrived at his own home. But he could not utter a word.

"What happened to your husband?" he blurted out.

"Young man, he was an idealist, he dug pits here and kept on persuading me that this was how it ought to be." She took Mendie into her own intimate world as she spoke, "He was a weak man. His bones stuck out of his shirt, but he would not stop working. He would not admit that he was too weak to work; he was too proud. Then he fell sick with malaria and burned to death. Do you hear me, young man? He burned to death. Within a few days he burned to death with that fever." Her anger returned to her. She waved her cane over her head: "Burned to death in a few days."

The Seltzerke told Mendie that it was only after her husband's death that she began to believe in what he had preached and decided to continue his work. She went digging ditches, leaving her only son to fend for himself during the day.

"See what became of me," she leaned on her cane. "I got this in a shooting affray with some Arabs. A bullet got me in the leg."

As if wishing to demonstrate what she had said, she began hobbling all over the room, leaning heavily on her cane. She hobbled with gusto.

"But still, your work has not been in vain, has it?" Mendie said. "See how Rehovot has grown."

She laughed. It was a dry, cracking laughter which gave him a headache. It was like sheets of tin being rubbed against one another. "What has become of Rehovot, young man? It is not what my husband wanted it to be. It was not for that he burned to death. It was not for that I got a bullet in my leg. Here I am, an old witch, my son a *pakid* . . . Good night, young man, have a good sleep in Rehovot and go back home."

*   *   *

Widow Seltzer's son, the *pakid,* or overseer, always kept his eyes down. Whenever he had to look at someone, he raised his head just a little and it then seemed as if he were looking not out of his eyes but out of his pointed forehead or out of his bushy eyebrows. He was of short stature, with narrow shoulders and a sunken chest. In the middle of his body his leanness suddenly gave way to a half-round belly which protruded like the belly of a rickety child. But this protrusion was only in his middle and suddenly disappeared in his thin legs and mincing steps. His name was *Shahar* —Dawn. It was a name his father had given him to designate the new era in Jewish history. But no one now called him by that name, except a worker when he wanted to insult him. He would then address him as *Adon Shahar,* that is, Mr. Dawn. The "Seltzerke's son," as he was commonly known, would pretend he did not hear, but towards evening he would say to the worker: "You need not come to work tomorrow."

Shahar was born in Rehovot, in a *tzrif* or shack occupied by his father Zéev and his mother Leah. The midwife was amazed when the infant did not cry. She hit him hard before he emitted a weak wail.

The father, standing outside, stuck in his head when he heard the wail: "Already?"

"A boy!" the midwife shouted to him, "but he won't cry!"

The father laughed out loud. That was good! The young Jews of Palestine were different. They would sing!

The father bought a bottle of cognac and invited his friends to drink with him. He had a son who would not cry, but sing and build up the Galilee. He would call him Shahar, the Dawn.

Who will build the Galilee!

Shahar will build the Galilee!

He danced outside, and he danced into the shack. His wife weakly smiled, as she repeated the words: Shahar will build the Galilee.

* * *

Shahar was four years old, when his father decided to bring him a little lamb. Shahar talked and walked, but did not play with children. Zéev tied a red ribbon on the little lamb, brought him to his four year old son and said: "See, Shahar, here you have a playmate!"

Shahar gave the lamb a sidelong glance and turned away. Zéev brought out a slice of bread and gave it to Shahar: "Here, Shahar, feed your lamb!" Shahar held the bread in his hand and did nothing with it Zéev lost patience. He angrily pulled Shahar's hand and pushed it towards the lamb's mouth: "I'm telling you to feed him!" Shahar held his hand at the lamb's mouth and when the little gray animal began to nibble, Shahar let out a laugh. Zéev began to dance for joy. He clapped his hands and called out to his wife: "Come here, Leah, see our little Shahar laugh. He is feeding the lamb and laughing."

When other children tried to come near the lamb, Shahar drove them off. Even his father and mother he would not allow near his little lamb. Once, when Zéev saw Shahar throw sand at a little girl who wanted to play with the lamb, Zéev became sad. At night he said to his wife: "How does he come to be that way? Why this stubborness of his that the lamb is only his?"

"But it is his," Leah countered, "you gave it to him."

"Yes, I brought it for him. But what will he grow up to be if he is going to fight for his property from his childhood on? Is that what we want in Palestine? Such selfishness! What good is it, Leah? Tell me, what good is Palestine if that is what is going to happen?"

The more Zéev observed Shahar, the sadder he became. He saw that Shahar had no love for the lamb but merely wanted to keep it to himself and not to let other children play with it. He saw Shahar beat the lamb with a relish. He saw how the other children disliked Shahar.

One day he asked Leah to bake a cake for all the children in the *tzrifim* (shacks) of the workers' quarters. He announced his decision to give away the lamb.

Leah looked at Zéev, saw how sad he was and understood. She herself found it distasteful to watch Shahar as he stuck to the lamb without allowing other children to touch it. She even saw him pull a girl's hair because she had pulled the bell attached to the lamb's neck. But she tried to protest: "Let's think it over, Zéev, you see he is not like other children."

Zéev was determined. They were going to let the children draw lots and the lucky one would win the lamb.

He gathered the children on the sand. Leah went around with a plate full of cake serving the children. Zéev led Shahar among the children. The lamb followed them, jingling with the bell. The

children drew back. They were afraid of Shahar. They stared wide-
eyed, timidly put forth a hand and pulled it back immediately.
Shahar could not make out what was taking place. He was afraid
and yet he was pleased to see that he was the object of envy by all
the children. He clung tightly to the string on which the lamb was
tied. He wanted the bell to jingle louder than ever, so the children
should hear it and know that it was his!

Zéev gathered the children around him and entertained them
as if he were one of them. He bleated like a lamb and the children
laughed. He led Shahar to each child, bowed and said: This is
Shahar, this is the lamb and this is me. Then he stood in the middle,
waved a hand and announced: "You see, children, now Shahar has
the lamb, but now you will all have him."

*   *   *

"This was brutal," Leah told Zéev afterward, "the child is ill."
Zéev paced up and down his shack: "I know it was brutal,
Leah," he said quietly, "but our whole life here is brutal. We have
come here to refashion ourselves in a brutal manner. Look at your
own life, Leah! Isn't it brutal? You live in the sand, you eat dry
bread, you work day and night."

Zéev thought that Shahar had fallen asleep. He tiptoed over to
his bed and tried to pat him. Shahar kicked him in his nose. Zéev
let the blood flow over his face and bent over to kiss Shahar on
his forehead.

When Shahar grew up he became an overseer.

*   *   *

Benjamin succeeded in securing employment for Mendie with
a farmer called Novomeysky. In the morning, Mendie walked to
work with Sukhovolin, who also worked in Novomeysky's grove.

Sukhovolin had a candid face and a high forehead furrowed by
deep lines. A sadness glowed quietly in his thoughtful eyes. When
he spoke, his soft voice seemed to be trailed by a vocal shadow.
It occurred to Mendie that his walking companion had the appearance of a rabbi rather than that of a laborer.

"Call me Meir," Sukhovolin said unexpectedly," you remind
me of my young brother."

Mendie was encouraged by the simple warmth of these words.

The sun had now spread over the whole eastern corner of the sky. The air was fresh, the ground sang under the burden of its verdure. Lines of laborers streamed on the roads, most of them Arabs from the villages roundabout. The few Jewish laborers walked by themselves. They seemed isolated, strangers.

"There are so few of us here," Sukhovolin remarked sadly. "We are a tiny island in a large sea. In Rehovot we seem to fill the whole world, but when we get out into the fields, we see how few of us there really are."

* * *

Sukhovolin came from Zhitomir, in the Ukraine, where he was a student revolutionary. During the pogrom in the town he patrolled the streets with a Self-Defense unit in which there were also a few Gentiles. One of the Gentiles, a young idealist named Kholopiev, stood in the middle of the market place to harangue the rabble. His unkempt hair flew in the wind. His delicate shrunken face was aflame. His young voice thundered. Sukhovolin stood by his side, trembling with elation at the sight of a non-Jew appealing to his fellow-Christians not to harm the Jews.

"Brethren!" Kholopiev cried, "don't shed any innocent blood!" The Jews are our brethren! Jews . . ."

A shot rang out and somebody burst into wild laughter.

"There! You can have your damn Jews!"

Sukhovolin carried the bleeding Kholopiev in his arms until he found a doorway in the side line and put him down. Kholopiev was dead. Sukhovolin spoke to the corpse: "You understand, Kholopiev, don't you? My own self-respect is lacerated when I think that you have fallen for my sake. . . ."

This was how his mother, the pious Jewess, had spoken to his dead father when he had been laid out for burial—as one speaks to a living person.

At first, Sukhovolin spoke in Russian, then he changed into Yiddish, the language in which his mother had addressed his father's corpse: "I don't want others to die for my sake. Do I desecrate your death, Kholopiev? Perhaps. But—I want you to understand me—life is more sacred than death. It is a more grievous sin to defile life than to defile death. As you stood among the hoodlums, addressing them, you looked the saint, the champion of the weak and the downtrodden. It was you who thus became elevated, not I, not we, my people. We, on the contrary, were somewhat humiliated. That is just what I want you to know, Kholopiev, that I feel humiliated by the death you died for my sake. . . . "

A few days later, Sukhovolin left for Palestine.

"You understand," Sukhovolin commented on the story he narrated as they walked toward the grove, "I ran away from our helplessness, from our being dependent on the mercy of others. Here it is different. Here, in this country, we have to overcome our smallness by our manual labor. We've got to pluck it out of ourselves as we pluck the parasitic *ingil* out of the ground."

As they walked among the trees, Mendie noticed how different the soil was from that of his native Bessarabia. In Bessarabia it was black and buttery and soaked up the moisture after the rain, so that when the sun shone over it, coils of vapor curled up. But here it was hard, and coated together by the hot rays of the sun.

"I'll tell you the truth, Sukhovolin," he said," I don't understand it."

"Call me Meir."

"Yes, Meir, . . . I can't understand how anything can grow on this earth or why the Bible keeps on telling us it is a land flowing with milk and honey."

Sukhovolin stopped, looked at Mendie's young face with its wondering boyish blue eyes, and laughed: "You would have done the same, Mendie, if you had been in Moses' place, if you had to lead a stiff-necked people through a desert. Our ancestors must have been a greedy people. They like good food: milk, honey. So Moses promised it to them."

They spent the morning working with pick-axes. Noontime came. They ate their lunch: bread and a tomato. Mendie's body ached. His shirt was wet with perspiration. His blonde hair stuck to his forehead.

"The first halfday," Sukhovolin continued, "is like a small door before a large threshold."

"What about the second half?" Mendie asked.

"The door becomes larger. The threshold becomes smaller."

Mendie dreamed of Sonia, the girl he had left behind. At the farewell party given him in his town, she whispered to him that she would not be able to work the soil in Palestine, but he had assured her that all she had to do in Palestine was to love him.

When Mendie woke up, he found Sukhovolin sitting. He told him about Sonia.

"There is always a Sonia on the other side of the threshold," Sukhovolin enlightened Mendie, and went on: "We all come here with yearnings. All of us have left some images behind us, some people we loved, some illusions we cherished."

"What must we do about them?" Mendie asked.

"We sweat them out. We knock them out with our pick-axes. Here we plant fresh yearnings, different from the ones we brought, but yearnings bound up with this land. . . ."

Then he expounded: "The sweethearts we bring here who love only us and not the land run away from here, and we often follow them. They have to love this land as we do."

Ephraim Auerbach

◆

WILD GROWTH

"I hate the parasite," Rotenberg declared, "but it is the *ingil* which I consider my deadly enemy." Rotenberg was the man in charge of the work around the trees in our commune in Ben-Shemen.

I began to understand his sentiments when he explained to me the difference between these two weeds—the ordinary parasite and the *ingil*.

The parasite is a kind of mossy growth which spreads over the grass and devours it. But it has no roots of its own; it draws its sustenance from the earth, the sun and the air. It extends its dark-yellow tendrils over the surface and gradually sucks up the moisture of the green. In time the earth assumes the looks of a scab on a man's head: it is all scorched up. After it has thus gutted up the grass, the weed itself shrivels up and finally dies. When you have once felt you are part of the life that grows, you conceive a personal hatred for the parasite. It is hatred born of anger, of resentment. But, at least, the parasite is all there on the surface and you can get rid of it by trampling it underfoot.

The *ingil*, however, is a far more formidable adversary. It is an herbaceous octopus whose powerful tentacles dig deep into the soil and envelop the roots of the trees in order to strangle it. In appearance it is round and fat: it looks the ravenous monster that it is. The *ingil* is ever ready to twist, to wind, and to coil to no end with the murderous intent of sucking out the life juices. To apprehend it, you've got to find the vital part of it not near the tree, but some distance away, where this evil-doing vampire sticks out its small head. As soon as you've spotted it, a shudder goes through your spine. Then you begin to follow it, digging and

digging. But your adversary is crafty and resourceful: it spreads
out in many directions, it deviates to this side and to that, it
shoots out branches—all to avoid being trapped. You hate it passionately, murderously, but you cannot help having a certain morbid
respect for it.

The dew of the morning was cool and covered the trees and
the grass like frost. In the distance the hills were a bluish white.
Rotenberg had already trampled the parasite underfoot and was now
looking back, surveying the ground, with his piercing eyes. We
walked in silence. Near the almond grove Rotenberg looked intently
as if trying to penetrate with his eyes the grass-clad soil. Wherever
he noticed that ugly head protrude, he stopped and ordered one of
us to start digging. He warned us that it is not easy to distinguish
between the monster that is the *ingil* and the root of a life-giving
tree. "Don't cut any roots," he said, "cut the *ingil!*"

One by one we took up positions to assail the enemy. We
stood bent over, hacking away at the *ingil* with our pick-axes.

Steinkohl dug out a long stem and began pulling at it with
ferocity. His long hair was all over the place, his eye-glasses
seemed to ride up and down his nose as if galloping on horseback.
With his fury mounting, he would not wait until he had dug to
the end of the stem, but insisted on pulling out the weed forthwith.
His face became tense, his veins protruded, and he dug in with
both feet into the ground. He bent backwards, and, with his teeth
clenched, he pulled at the moist stem. His bony hands became
wet with the dew and his own perspiration, the stem slid out of
his hands, and he fell back, his head striking the ground. Then he
got up infuriated, wound the stem around his hand and began
pulling again with all his might and main. "So you'll devour
little trees, will you?" he growled in anger, "I'll see that this is
the end of you, I'll see to it!"

So here was a young Jew come to the land of his ancestors
to battle the desert, to wrestle with the diseases that had leeched
the strength from the land. Steinkohl exuded the determination of
the New Jew to pluck the *ingil* out of himself, to eradicate that
wild growth which had established itself within him because of
his estrangement from the soil of his homeland. . . .

Rotenberg came over. "The *ingil* cannot be extracted like a tooth," he said, "you've got to dig for it."

Steinkohl let go of the stem, his hands full of raw wounds. As he wiped off the perspiration, blotches of blood remained on his face.

We settled down to our pathetic meal and Steinkohl sat down at my side. His face wore a painfully embarrassed smile, like a shy child caught in some prank. He kept his hands palms down to hide his wounds. But his cuts could be sensed—they shone out of his eyes.

"You probably thought I was crazy," he said.

"I don't know," I replied, "I don't know much about how the *ingil* has to be uprooted. But I suppose we've all got to cut ourselves up in order to get ourselves put together again."

"I cannot make out what has come over me," he continued to muse, "it wasn't just the weed; it was something within me. I want to conquer the muddle in my own soul, it was my own inner ingil I wanted to eradicate. . . . You see, the Steinkohls for generations have been scholars and merchants. I am a Steinkohl. It is so hard to pull one's family out of one's self. The *ingil* is within us, within the Jewish people. They are the weeds which have been eating away at our vitality. . . ."

* * *

We heard a chant. It was quiet and melancholy singing which gradually changed first into a groan and then into a wail. The pain in Steinkohl's words was nothing compared to the grief in that wailing chant which now reached our ears. This was a raw human drama that was being enacted in heart-rending accents. It was a naked soul pouring itself out in lament. This was Yihyeh, the Yemenite, who had come out with us to pluck the *ingil* plant. He had been reciting verses from the Psalms all the way in the morning. But now he was lamenting.

We walked over to him and saw him seated on the ground, his eyes shut, his longish face on which the early growth of a beard was spread like young grass, full of anguish and of ecstasy. I could not make out the words in his chant, but one could see that his thoughts were far away.

His lunch was untouched. He had cut up the roots of a tree by mistake while digging for the *ingil*. He had cut down a living creature in the Holy Land. At first he wanted to cut off one of his fingers in self-punishment. When prevented from doing that, he refused to touch his food. He would fast to atone for his sin.

"Yihyeh, eat your lunch," I pleaded with him, "such things happen, it is not a sin."

But he was not even conscious of my presence. He chanted and wept in an ecstasy of agony of which only the Yemenite Jews are capable. His small skull-cap moved up to the crown of his head. In his bony hands he held the fringes of his *tallit-katan*,* fingering them, caressing them. I had never seen such exalted grief in my life.

The bell rang. Yihyeh rose, took his pick-axe and went to cut more of the *ingil*.

---

* The *tallit*, or praying shawl, is worn during prayer. The *tallit-katan*, lit. "smaller garment" is worn by observant male Jews all the time, usually under the shirt, as an undergarment of religious significance. The four fringes ("arba Kanfot") made according to specifications laid down by the Law, are what give the garment its significance.

5 THE GUARDIANS OF ISRAEL

AS MAY be seen from the story "From Homel to Petah-Tikvah" (Chapter Three), the chief organizer of the first self-defense unit in Russia, Yeheze-kiel Hankin, in 1904 migrated with a group of his comrades to Palestine where they finally settled in Petah-Tikvah. (The arrival of the Homel group in Petah-Tikvah, in December, 1904, marks the beginning of the Second Aliyah.)

Two years later, Hankin took part in the formation of a military unit in Palestine, the first such formation in modern Jewish history. The act took place on the initiative of Itzhak Ben-Zvi, who was to become, forty-five years later, the second President of Israel.

The immediate reason for the establishment of the unit was the need for appointing Jews to guard Jewish property against Bedouin, Circassian and other marauders and to eradicate the custom which had grown up among Jewish colonists to entrust this task to the thieves themselves, who proceeded to blackmail them. The long-range purpose was far more ambitious.

Following are a few excerpts from Ben-Zvi's own account:

After a prolonged trip full of trying events, I returned together with Israel Shohet from the Eighth Zionist Congress at The Hague, in the fall of 1906. I came in time for the conference of Poale-Zion, which met in Jaffa during the Succoth holidays. We had from 130-150 members of the party in the country (out of 350 Jewish working men and women, all told), and half of them made their way to the conference, almost wholly on foot. At the close of the conference we agreed—Israel Shohet, myself and a few others,—to call an extraordinary consultation for a special purpose which was not one for the whole party to carry out, but for a more restricted group.

I was living in Jaffa. On the eve of the Feast of the Rejoicing of the Law (Simhat Torah) we met in my upper-story room. The house, which was built among the orange groves, was one in the so-called "Warsaw Court." There was a reed mat on the floor; a few wooden crates, the kind used to pack kerosene cans, served as desk and chairs. Of those present, I particularly recall Yehezekiel Hankin, outstanding for his powerful physique, and his indomitable spirit. Then there was calm and cool-headed Israel Gileadi, Mendele Portugali, the stubborn broad-shouldered youth, with his sarcastic speech, in whom word and deed came to life together. He had but recently arrived in Palestine, brought here, I think, by Hankin, who had fished him out on one of his peregrinations in Egypt. And there was Berele Schweiger, still a youngster, one of the students of the Mikveh-Israel School of Agriculture, the prankster of the group. Then there was Hatzkel Nissanov—that shy young man from the Caucasus, who came with his friend Zvi Becker. Alexander Zaid, in contrast to Nissanov—and Becker, who were natives of the sunny Caucasus, looked the Siberian that he was. Everything about his motions and manners said "This is my place and I am not budging from it!"

A new slogan was born—*Bar-Giora*, named after the great Jewish fighter against Rome, the last defender of Jerusalem.

All of us were new in the country . . . We all felt as if we were standing before Mount Sinai at the Giving of the Law and were ready for heavy sacrifices. Words and debates would not rebuild a nation. "By blood and fire Judea fell; by blood and fire Judea shall be restored."

Here *Hashomer* was born, its program adopted, its constitution worked out, and its principles enunciated. The tasks were distributed—one man to go on guard duty, another to organize and to act as mediator between the guards and the colonies. Some undertook to go and do field work in the employment of old colonists. The Lower Galilee was the first area chosen for our activity . . .

*   *   *

A. Reubeni

◆

THE WATCHMAN AND THE WALL

IT WAS Cain who nicknamed Velvel "the Jackal." Cain liked to pronounce the name "Velvel" in the Arabic fashion, *Weh-weh,* which means Jackal.

Velvel-the-Jackal was a slim youth, of medium stature, with deep green eyes and a thin thread of a mustache over his upper lip, baring gleaming white teeth. He had a supple body which gave the impression that he was about to leap into action and his face always seemed ready to break into a cheerful smile. Yet his motions were languorous and his expression grim and morose. Perhaps it was the result of three years as a watchman standing guard over the Palestine colonies, of sleepless nights, of malaria, of constant tension; perhaps it was just plain disillusionment.

*   *   *

It was suppertime when Velvel the Jackal went out of the watchmen's shack on night duty. The village was deserted: the farmers were at their tables. The night was dark. But the Jackal knew his way over the ill-paved road, deftly feeling the pebbles and the rocks with his feet.

As he turned from the main street toward the wall which encircled the colony, he was met by a strong gust of wind which seemed to have been waiting for him. Everything was in a state of suspended animation, as if biding its time until the storm, whose weird howling swallowed up all the sounds of the night, blew over.

The dogs stopped barking and cowered in the kennels. The night was filled with the roaring of the wind swooping down from the dark skies and wandering over the still darker earth. The night was mute and growing ever darker. The feeble leaden light timidly hovering in the air grew dimmer with every passing moment.

For two years now Velvel had known the path along this wall, in this colony. The wall was his friend. It gave him shelter from bullets fired from ambush. It enabled him to stay in hiding while looking out for thieves. But the *sidras,* the low, prickly bushes, black at night, which grew along the wall, were his enemies—allies of Arab marauders who could lurk there for hours, for whole nights, even for weeks.

He knew the wall and the bushes only as they appeared at night. He never saw them in the daytime—not in all the two years he had been there. When it was dark, the wall seemed pitch black. In the moonlight the color of its stones seemed blood-red lined with shiny black hems. Velvel-the-Jackal liked to think that the wall was as ignorant of his appearance by daylight as he was of the wall's. For in the daytime, Velvel, or Velvele, was a weak man, slovenly clad, shaken with malarial fever, sleepy, listless, sluggish. When the wall met him, he was at his best, armed with pistol and knife, carrying a club, a strange nocturnal being, a hero. . . .

Suddenly Velvel felt a pressing headache. Now he knew why he had been so morose all day long: he had an attack of malaria. . . . If he could only lie down!

At the village gate Velvel ran into his assistant, Alter Schick, who was now resting on a stone. Velvele wrapped himself into his *abaye,** and lay down beside his comrade.

"Has Cain been here?" he asked.

"Not yet."

"Whistle for him. Just once. . . . I am afraid I am in a fever."

"What is new, Alter?" Cain inquired when he arrived. "Are things quiet tonight?"

"I think so."

"You think so? You think too much. . . . It is time to make another round of the wall. I think you've been sitting here too long."

"We know all about it without your telling us," Schick grumbled and walked off slowly.

---

* An Arab cloak.

"Are you really in a fever, Little Jackal?" Cain gently placed his hand on Velvel's chest.

"I find it difficult to walk."

Cain thought for a while. "No, we can't let you off just now. . . . I am afraid you'll have to go on for a while, Little Jackal. . . . It would be different if we had another man, not this fellow Schick. . . . If we depend on him, we may get into serious trouble. . . . In another hour or so the moon will rise. Then you may go to the shack. . . . Now, now, Little Jackal, make an effort. Just one more round of the wall won't kill you. . . . What a time! I can't leave the fields. . . . My man Todrescu is not a ninny like this fellow, but he has no brains. . . . Well, are you coming?"

"O-oh-oh," Velvel groaned, "I am not feeling well."

Velvel raised himself with difficulty and, dragging his feet, went towards the wall. Cain's eyes followed him with great compassion. Then he turned to the other side.

"If one could only depend on that loud-mouthed hero!" He muttered to himself, "Hell, what trash they've been sending us lately!"

*   *   *

It was high noon when Velvele awakened the next day, alone in the shack. Although his fever was gone, he was debilitated, his head was in a whirl, and he did not feel hungry. In the afternoon he rose and walked around a little. He was not to be sent on watch duty that night. Deputy Bear, who happened to be in the colony that day, would take his place.

The head of the Watchmen's Organization, whose name was Berl, was known as The Big Bear. His deputy now came on an errand to buy barley for the mounted guards who patrolled the fields of the colonies.

Deputy Bear spent the afternoon in the shack, with the four regular watchmen. Two workmen who had come in search of employment in the colony dropped in. Two local farmers, taking their afternoon rest in the heat after their midday meal, before going to the barn to resume their work, passed the shack and sat down on the threshold.

The four regular watchmen were Cain, the Jackal, Todrescu, and Alter Schick.

Cain, who was the leader, was of the same height as the Jackal, but differently built. He had a barrel chest, a broad, round Mongolian face of dark complexion and stubborn, hard-looking brown eyes, which won him his nickname. But when he jested, the hard glint in his eyes gave way to sparks of good humor which spread all over his face.

Todrescu was so called because he came from Rumania. His given name was Todros and he was known to be one of the best Jewish farmhands in Palestine. The romantic lure of the new saga of the Jewish watchmen had its effect on him and he joined the organization. He was devoted and brave, but lacked the quick intelligence required for the task. Alter Schick was a young man who had read about the Shomerim (guards) while studying at the Commerce High School in Czernowitz, Bukovina, and migrated to Palestine to become one himself.

That afternoon Alter Schick lay in the only bed in the shack. The Deputy Bear threw sidelong glances at the bed and its occupant.

"Schick!" he appealed to him, "is this the way to receive a visitor? Why don't you give me a chance to rest my bones?"

Cain, who lay on the floor on his *abaye,* tried to spell it out for the Deputy:

"You're not a visitor," he said, "you're going out to watch duty tonight like the rest of us. . . . That's what you're a deputy for—Deputy Bear, Deputy Watchman, Deputy Broomstick, ha-ha! Schick! Hold on to the bed! This fellow is not a graduate of the Commerce High School in Czernowitz like you. The floor is good enough for him!"

"Don't be a fool, Alter!" Velvel came to Cain's aid, "don't give in!"

But the Deputy knew better than Cain and the Jackal how to play on Schick's sentiments. Schick moved over and the Deputy lay down.

"Let me lie near the wall," he asked, "I want to take a nap."

Soon Alter Schick rolled off the bed and lay on the floor. There was general laughter.

One of the local farmers who witnessed the scene, a man in his early thirties, passed his fingers over his red mustache, twisted his fat ruddy cheeks and remarked with venom: "What a crowd of idlers! Living off our necks!"

"What's the matter, Red Bristles?" Cain laughed. "Do you begrudge us? Your neck is strong enough!"

The farmer was offended. His cheeks became even redder. Slowly he uttered:

"Sure . . . we're only the employers, low-down capitalists, aren't we? And you? You're our modern Maccabees, our heroes, Jewish cossacks, our defenders and protectors, aren't you? . . . What is your work, anyway? A stroll in the night air, a little gossip on the corner, smoking, lolling all day. . . . "

"You stupid yokel!" The Deputy Bear rose from his couch. "Why don't you become a watchman, if you think it's so easy? How would you like to be a mounted guard? A rider in the fields?"

Todrescu chimed in:

"He'll be a rider like I'll be a . . . " Todrescu's mind did not work fast enough to find the proper comparison.

"A redhead," Cain helped him out.

"That's right, a redhead!" Todrescu was happy that he could take part in the conversation. He went on: "A year ago, when we had a fight with the Bedouins—I was working on Feldstein's farm then—this man lay under his bed for five full hours."

"Is that true, Red Bristles?" Cain laughed. "Say, Todrescu, you're getting to be good. Some people will forget that you're just a plain peasant."

Alter Schick, who had been pacing up and down the shack in impotent resentment of the treatment meted out to him by the Deputy, now came to life. Confronting the little redheaded man, he knitted his brow and raised his hand in an oratorical gesture:

"Do you know the significance of our work? Do you know what a Jewish watchman is?"

"Bravo, Schick," his comrades applauded.

"Idlers you call them? Do you know what it means to stand guard in the wintertime for thirteen or fourteen hours at a stretch? All night in the mud, in the damp, the wind and the rain blinding your eyes and throwing you off your feet; you can't see even a few inches ahead of you. . . . "

Schick went on in this vein.

"That's right, Schickele," Cain encouraged him half-jestingly.

The older watchmen were glad to hear Schick defend them, although it would never occur to them to speak for themselves.

"What do you know about guarding in the wintertime?" the farmer inquired acidly. "You've only been at it two weeks!"

"I am not talking about myself," Schick declaimed defiantly, "I am discussing the function of guarding."

The following day the Deputy Bear left and Velvel went on guard that night. Velvel had been weakened by the fever and was tense because of reports of Arab attacks in the neighborhood. He fell asleep while gazing at the stars and woke up with a start. The night was quiet and there was no breeze. Bedouins were camping nearby in their black tents. In the nearby fields Arab peasants, apprehensive of the Bedouins, were watching over their harvested wheat and lit bonfires. The dogs of the two adjoining camps barked at one another. One by one in the windows of the houses of the colony, the lights went out.

The moon rose from behind the hills as if breaking free from invisible hands that held it prisoner. The night's thick darkness broke up and retreated and the air was filled with its remnants in the form of isolated shadows.

Velvel stood by the wall, waiting for the three approaching figures. By their voices he recognized the village druggist and the village teacher. But the third voice was unfamiliar: it was the fresh, vibrant voice of a young girl and was accompanied by mirthful laughter. A new girl in the colony? Velvel wondered.

She was small of stature, somewhat plump, and had a wobbly walk. "A duck," Velvel thought to himself.

The girl seized hold of the teacher's hand. "Who is this?" she asked with some fear.

"Must be the watchman!" the teacher answered, and cried out: "The watchman?"

"Is that you, Velvel?" the druggist called. "Shalom!"

Velvele returned the greeting.

"Shalom, shomer!" (Hello, watchman), said the girl, as she walked up to him and proffered her hand.

It was a small, soft, warm hand, with short plump fingers. Velvele enveloped it into his large masculine hand and let go of it with some reluctance. It seemed to him she was in no hurry, either, to take her hand away.

"In the future, don't you dare shadow us when we stroll!" she said playfully. Velvele kept quiet. He could not think of what to say.

"Do you hear me?" she demanded coquettishly.

"I heard you."

"Will you do as I say?"

Velvele laughed out loud: "When three of you take a stroll, or only two?"

"Either way."

"And if you are alone?"

"Then you may." She laughed gaily and ran off.

When Velvele ran into Cain, he asked him who that new girl was.

"So you've already met her?" Cain remarked, "she is worth knowing," and he explained that she was the new stepdaughter of Tellerman, the daughter of the second wife he had recently married. Tellerman was an old well-to-do farmer, and a leading citizen, who was very pious.

When Velvele reached the end of the wall, he suddenly heard the report of a shot. Schick ran towards him.

"What happened?" Velvel asked.

"A man. . . . Something rustled. . . . There, behind the bush. . . ."

"Did he run away?"

"I think so."

Velvel searched the brown distance with his eyes. He could see quite far in the clear moonlight.

"Nobody ran," he said firmly. "I don't think there was anybody there. . . . Come with me into the bushes! You walk ahead!" he commanded.

Schick hesitated.

"Go on now!"

Schick took one step forward, then stopped.

"One does not go into the bushes . . . when thieves hide out in them . . . " he stammered. Velvele came close to Schick and looked at his face. What Velvel saw made him turn away in great agitation.

"Give me your gun!" he said.

"What for?"

"Hand it to me, I am going there myself!"

"But you've got your own," Schick still argued timidly, while taking off his pistol to hand to Velvel.

"I know I have," said Velvel, "but I don't want to be shot in the back."

After carefully examining the bushes, Velvel handed the pistol back to Schick and said contemptuously: "Come, we can go for our meal."

"What has happened?" people asked out of opened windows, their faces pale.

"Nothing . . . thieves . . . " Velvele answered darkly. When they were alone, Velvele said to Schick: "Don't shoot any more, do you hear me?"

Schick became indignant: "How do you know there wasn't anybody there?"

"I am quite sure," Velvel said coolly, "and I am warning you for the last time: don't shoot!"

Later in the night, Velvel said: "Listen, Schick! You ought to leave the occupation of a watchman. It is not for you. Go to Jaffa, get yourself a job as secretary or bookkeeper, and make all the Zionist speeches you want. You're not made to be a watchman."

Schick became indignant at this rude blow to the fondest dreams he had cherished at school in Czernowitz.

"Why," he exclaimed in impotent rage, "do you think that only you are a hero? . . . I'd have liked to see how you behaved the first time under attack!"

"Never mind how I behaved. . . . Not like you anyway. . . . I am not speaking of fear. Everybody is afraid. I am still afraid. But the main thing is that you won't be able to stand it. We can stand it, you can't. . . . "

The next night, in an attack of nervous fright, Schick fired wildly and nearly hit Velvel. Cain stopped him by hitting him with a pebble which he had carefully aimed at his navel.

✳   ✳   ✳

Alter Schick left. His place was taken by a young man with a Russian blouse over which he wore a *toujourka* (Russian jacket), who called himself by a Hebrew surname—Yemini. He had dark smooth hair and bright eyes which he was in the habit of squinting as he surveyed everything around him with an air of cold arrogance. As soon as he came he took possession of the only bed in the shack, which had been vacated by Schick (Velvel slept on the mat; the other two watchmen spread their abayes on the floor when they slept, and then "carried their bedclothes on their backs" when they went on guard). He made sport of the slow-witted Todrescu and boasted to Cain and the Jackal that he had a rich father in Russia, that he had had a long career in the revolutionary underground and that he had come to Palestine to escape involvement with two women who had been pursuing him.

"How do you find this fellow?" Velvel asked Cain when they were alone in the courtyard.

"A braggart, and probably worse. Some bird!"

In the evening Velvel and Yemini sat at the place where they usually rested between rounds on the outskirts of the village, when the new girl passed—Nehama was her name. She again was accompanied by the druggist and the teacher. Velvel had not spoken to her since the first evening they met. She did not recognize him. Perhaps, if he had prepared something to say or if she had suddenly stopped to look at things he would have stopped to talk to her. But she went on and he followed her with his eyes, admiring her childish walk, her blue eyes artlessly caressing the old houses with their red roofs, the bright skies, the dust-covered stones of the pavement. . . . She had little pink ears and little rosy pink lips; she must have been sixteen or seventeen years old. . . .

"Look now," Yemini exclaimed, "you've got some new girls here."

"Why, do you know them all?" Velvel asked.

Yemini enumerated them all, made comments on each one, and suddenly asked Velvel:

"How are you making out with the Arab women here?"

"What do you mean?" asked Velvel.

"Blockhead! Do I have to explain it to you in detail?"

"I don't know of such women among the Arabs here."

Yemini looked at him for a while, then exclaimed: "I'd swear you've never even kissed a girl in your life."

Velvel blushed and mumbled something. He did not like this windbag. But at least he did not speak of his great sacrifices for the cause. Velvel could not endure self-sacrificing heroes. And, anyway, he was doing his job as a watchman, and that's what counted.

Velvel and Yemini parted, each man to make the round of the wall. On returning, Velvel found Yemini talking to Nehama. She listened eagerly as he told her of hair-raising escapades in Siberia when he fled the Czar's police agents who had taken him to do penal service for revolutionary activity.

Nehama greeted Velvel amiably and continued listening to Yemini's tales, while Velvel wondered if she realized he was telling lies to impress her in order to ensnare her later.

"Come, Yemini," he suddenly told him, "it is time to make another round."

*　　*　　*

Velvel had another attack of malaria which confined him to bed for several days. One evening, when his temperature had gone down and he lay alone in the shack, he had an unexpected visit: Nehama walked in.

"What will you do if the Arabs suddenly attack?" she laughed.

He looked at himself shamefacedly. What good was he, anyway? He could hardly move a limb.

"Oh, you've become so pale the last few days! Does it hurt very much when you have the fever?"

"No, only the head."

She sat down on a chair near him. He looked into her eyes with a shy smile.

"Tell me—you won't be angry with me?" She gave him a look which was at once playful and entreating. She could see he was incapable of being angry with her. "Tell me, why do they call you the Jackal?"

He explained.

"And why do they call Cain by that nickname?" she went on—"oh, I know, it is because he is so wicked."

"He is really not a bad sort," he assured her.

"And tell me, Jackal—do you mind if I call you that?—your friend Yemini, isn't he somewhat of a braggart?"

She must have met him many times, Velvel thought, and came here to find out whether her misgivings were right.

"I don't know, these are things which everyone must find out for himself." She felt offended.

"But what do you think of him?"

"I don't know him well enough yet. . . . "

"You don't want to tell me? Ah, you are not so good either. You're no better than the rest!" She pouted her lips and fell silent.

He laughed. "What made you think I was better in the first place?" he asked.

She laughed out loud. She had just begun to feel that men were interested in her. Only a year ago they treated her as a little girl. The discovery was so pleasing.

"Look at him becoming conceited!" she said. "Well, I just made a mistake, that's all. Now listen, Jackal, one more question—do you mind?" She patted his hand. He gave her another shy smile.

"I don't mind."

"Tell me," she asked with a dreamy look in her eyes, "aren't you afraid when they shoot at you? I'd like to experience it sometimes. But I don't think I'd be able to shoot at anybody else. Especially I wouldn't like to be shot at. . . . Ha-ha, what did I say? Well, let it go!"

Velvel laughed. "I've gotten used to it. One gets used to shooting."

"Does everybody get used to it?"

"No, not everybody. But those who stay on, do."

He told her of some amusing incidents of his early days as a watchman, when he mistook the movements of animals and insects for those of robbers and became panicky.

"But didn't you have any real skirmishes?"

He told her of some real encounters. He saw her round fresh face in the dark intent on his words; he saw her tiny rosy lips and felt the warmth of her soft little hand. But then came his misgivings: he feared that she was only interested in him on account of his stories, that she would soon discover some man who could tell them better. . . . But still, who was to know? She might yet come to see him even then. . . . As he thought so, a happy smile flitted over his lips while he gazed into the darkness of the room.

*   *   *

Velvele recovered and went out to watch again. The situation was becoming serious. Cases of theft were increasing. Shots were exchanged in the field. One night Todrescu met a group of Arabs with full sacks of stolen wheat. They fled, leaving their sacks behind, which made it possible to identify them. Representatives of the Arab village then came to sue for peace, promising not to steal any more.

One night, as Velvele turned around the corner of the wall, he saw a black figure detach itself from the wall and make away. He trained his rifle on him—now he never went out without his rifle.

"Stop, or I'll shoot!" he called out firmly and loudly in Arabic. The thief kept running. Velvel fired in the air. The fugitive turned around and fired back. Velvel's left cheek was burned. He became excited, aimed at the fleeing man and pressed the trigger. The fleeing man let out a short cry but continued his flight. The black blood spots found later showed that the man had been slightly wounded. Velvel's wound was little more than a scratch.

During the day an old farmer named Stecker and Cain talked with a few Arab herdsmen in the service of the colony. One of the Arabs, an old grey little man, with small, diseased, cunning eyes, reported that he had met the famous brigand Haj Selim with his hand bandaged up. He must have been wounded the previous night, since he had been seen on the previous day not far from the wadi (creek) with both hands healthy. . . . The Arabs stood looking at the two Jews, searching for some expression, some word, to give them the solution to the riddle. But they saw that the Jews were careful and did not trust them.

One of the herdsmen, a tall, dark-skinned Arab with fierce-looking eyes, a filthy greyish-yellow *abaye* on his back and a very thick dusty *agal* on his head, said: "Haj Selim is not like any other man. Haj Selim is a devil, a killer! He will avenge himself on his enemies and shed their blood!"

The herdsmen watched for the effect of the words.

Cain said mockingly: "Why does he not come in sometimes? My bullet has been yearning to make his personal acquaintance."

The herdsman and the watchman exchanged hostile glances. The old cowherd's eyes flashed with a spark of low cunning as he uttered the ambiguous remark: "No doubt, you too, are a brave man. . . . And if it is the will of Allah, you will yet meet Haj Selim face to face."

In the afternoon the head of the Jewish watchmen, Berl, or as he was nicknamed, Big Bear, came to the colony. The Village Council called a special session and asked him to appear. Big Bear ordered Velvel to accompany him. The farmers had a long list of complaints against the watchmen.

Old Tellerman, Nehama's stepfather, who did a thriving business lending out money to fellaheen and dealing with the sheikhs of the countryside, was boiling: "Is this the way? Bloodshed? To kill and to shoot? What do you expect to accomplish by such methods? The ruination of the colony? Do you think Haj Selim will keep quiet? Next day he will steal a horse or a cow—out of vengeance— and who will order him to return it? And what if he kills somebody? . . . To him it will make no difference whom he kills, so long as he avenges his blood. You don't care, because you are not bound to the land as we are. . . . You can run away. . . ."

"We are not running away," the head of the watchmen remarked quietly.

"But we must stay here: we cannot leave. We have property and land,—we cannot play around! And if you are a bunch of vagabonds. . . ."

"Mind what you're saying!" Big Bear thundered at him furiously.

Tellerman fell silent for a while and then continued with more heat: "Never mind pretty words, I am talking business. Tomorrow or the day after somebody will be killed—one of us or one of them. . . . Don't we know it? And you know it as well as we do. Then there are going to be blood-feuds and lawsuits. . . . What do we want all that trouble for? We are the Council! We are responsible for the peace and welfare of the colony! We must not allow any hotheads. . . . We must not let the colony suffer and come to ruin through them. . . ."

"What is it you wish, then?" Big Bear asked calmly.

"We don't want any 'blood'; we want to settle matters peacefully. . . . One does not shoot to kill at a thief. . . . I've been a farmer here for twenty years now—I know. Are you trying to introduce innovations here? . . . We don't want to suffer on account of you."

Some of the younger farmers spoke up in defense of the watchmen and their achievements, but asked the latter to appreciate the position of the farmers, too. The main line of their argument was that the Village Council should have more control over the watchmen.

Sharik, the redheaded young farmer Cain once called Red Bristles, came up to Big Bear after the meeting and said:

"You claim you never shoot except in self-defense as a last resort—then why did the Jackal shoot Haj Selim in the back?"

"Because the brigand shot at him first and wounded him."

"Do you call this a wound?" Sharik said. "Is that enough to make a man lose his self-control?"

The tall leader of the watchmen stood up to his full height and pierced Sharik with his two grey eyes, with their usual restrained expression, and replied sternly: "Velvel did not lose his self-control. He fired only two shots—one in the air, the other at the robber. The robber aimed at him to kill him. Velvel had a right to return a shot by aiming at his assailant. You don't like to suffer the consequences? Neither do we . . . we are doing our job not to serve you, but to serve the cause. . . . Not to serve us either!"

After the meeting the watchmen went to their shack, where they made tea and spent their time as usual, joking and telling stories. Berl kept quiet most of the time. Presently he declared: "I know Haj Selim. He is sure to try to do us harm, if not by bloodshed, then by causing us some loss of property. . . . You must be careful now to go out in pairs: you Velvele and Yemini. Make your rounds frequently. The first chance I get, I'll send you reinforcements."

"I don't know why we should risk our lives for these farmers," Yemini remarked. "They seem more concerned over their Arab herdsmen and farmhands than over us. We ought to leave them to defend themselves."

Todrescu reported that he overheard Sharik say the watchmen were nothing but a collection of escaped criminals and ought not to be entrusted with the safety of the colony.

"I'd bash his head in, if I were to hear it!" Yemini shouted.

"You'll do nothing of the sort," Berl interrupted him coolly . . . and proceeded:

"Why should you worry about what the farmers think of you, if you have no respect for them? We're not doing it for their sake. When we started out, we were a tiny handful. The farmers ridiculed the very idea that Jews could stand guard over a colony. Now they don't laugh any more. They have respect. True some of them hate us—let's not exaggerate—not all of them. But their hostility ought not to prevent us from doing our duty."

*   *   *

There followed difficult terrifying nights. Strange mysterious movements occurred incessantly in the fields surrounding the colony. The watchmen exercised great caution, walked very softly, listened intently for any sound. One night a furious fusillade broke out between Arab brigands and Jewish watchmen. There were no casualties on either side, but a high-priced mare of one of the Arabs was seriously wounded.

And then it happened.

It was a stormy night. The stars were hidden. Small clouds wandered in the skies. The two watchmen stopped their walk near a small gate of a courtyard. Velvele sat down and raised his foot to knock out a nail in his shoe that had been bothering him. Suddenly he saw a man jump down from the fence about ten or twelve paces from where he was. It was a thief who, while trying to break the lock of the gate, must have been frightened by the noise Velvele had made. The thief did not run very far. It was very dark, the watchmen could not see him, but only sensed his presence. Velvele made one step forward and nearly touched the thief with the butt of his rifle.

"Wolak, wolak" (look out!), the robber cried out a warning in strange desperation.

Suddenly he fired. Velvel noticed the direction of his rifle and had time to turn aside.

"I can't understand why he is so stubborn," Velvele whispered to Yemini, "I don't think he'll come out alive. Fire!"

They fired a few bullets. The Arab fired back from the dark. Suddenly another man slid down from the wall. Now they realized why the first man had lingered. In confusion Yemini fired one shot without thinking. The man who had jumped off the wall fell and rolled on the ground howling with pain. His comrade began firing incessantly, as if gone berserk. The watchmen reloaded.

"Wow!" Yemini cried and fell on his side.

Velvele bent down to him. Yemini groaned and writhed in pain.

Both Arabs fled. Velvele knelt and fired after them shot after shot, but missed.

Yemini was wounded in the right thigh above the knee. Blood spurted out like a waterfall and streamed like a black rivulet. Yemini writhed in terrible pain like a dissected worm, convulsed and shook, buried his hands in the earth, tried to control himself but broke out in terrifying wails.

Soon the whole colony assembled at the place. The druggist and the nurse also came, but they did not know how to arrest the flow of blood. The bandages they applied were without effect. Finally they placed the wounded man on his cloak and carefully carried him to the watchmen's shack. The colony did not have a hospital or a doctor. Cain and Velvel mounted horses and rode off— the one to report to Big Bear, the other to bring a doctor from a neighboring colony.

Three hours later, Velvel, breathless, returned with the doctor.

Berl, the Big Bear also came. Yemini howled incessantly in a low voice. He did not speak except when he cried out a few times "Bring me a doctor." His face had shrunk and was covered with a deathly pallor. The blood still came out in drops from under the bandage.

The doctor examined the wound, bandaged it and stopped the flow of the blood. His face was grim. To Berl's mute question, he replied hesitatingly:

"Very grave. . . . But one must not despair."

"So I am going to die?" Yemini suddenly asked in a loud ringing voice and, seemingly without agitation.

The doctor answered weakly:

"There has been a loss of much blood. . . . Three hours. . . . Still, to be sure . . ."

"So I am going to die?" Yemini asked as before.

The doctor realized his blunder.

"Oh, no, no! It's not dangerous. The blood has been stopped. Now you'll feel better. Just don't get excited."

"No, I'm dying, I'm dying! I can see, I know I am going to die!" the wounded man shouted in a hoarse wild voice.

Yemini began ranting and abusing everyone in the room. He accused Velvel of having pushed him into the way of the bullet which had been intended for him; he called Berl an old grafter; he disclosed that he had seen the nurse walk into the drugstore at night and come out at dawn; he said he had seen Velvel kiss Nehama and that Velvel himself had boasted of it.

Berl silenced the druggist when he tried to return the insults and, after pleading in vain with the dying man to maintain his dignity, he ordered his men to clear the shack.

The doctor and Todrescu remained with the patient.

"I don't want to die! Doctor, save me!" Yemini wailed. . . . "They will inscribe my name in the Memorial Book for the Guards. . . . They'll say I was a hero fallen at his post . . . I don't want to be inscribed in the Yizkor book . . . ow-ow-ah-ah."

*   *   *

The nights were strangely quiet now. The concealed hatred of the mute fields and the dark hills had retreated before death. Velvel-

Jackal remained alone with his stone wall. On the morning after the fatality he had gone out to explore the place and, for the first time since becoming a watchman, he examined the wall in the daylight. It was not at all red as he had pictured it in his nocturnal fancy. Its stones were black, as if covered with ashes, their hems lined with whitish-blue stripes. The wall now appeared more ordinary, more everyday-like. . . . But it did not matter, they were the same friends. He, the wall and the night were now one. Well, it made no difference.

Nehama, after having been castigated by old Tellerman, her stepfather, who believed Yemini's lies that he, Velvel, had boasted of kissing her, avoided Velvel. She now clung to the teacher. Well, thought Velvel, let it be. . . . It made no difference either.

A deadly apathy had descended on Velvel. He was no longer careful about examining the doors, the locks, the gates. He became alarmed.

Big Bear came. Velvel decided to talk to him. They went out into the field.

It was twilight. The setting sun lit a conflagration in the sky. Half the firmament was flooded by fiery waves. Crimson flames spread to the far horizon, where the ends of the skies reclined on the hilltops, and descended even lower. The hilltops, too, were caught in the blaze and burned, weaving golden wreaths engulfed by the sun's waves. . . . The two watchmen lay down on a tall stack of hay, from which could be seen the whole valley in which rose this lonely little Jewish colony, and the dark-red and dark-green hills, surrounding the valley like a fence around a well-kept farmyard. Arab villages appeared like collections of square black boxes on the crests.

"Berl, I want to leave the guard. I can't be a watchman any more."

Berl did not look at him, but only asked: "Why?"

Velvel kept quiet and looked at the fields. The farmers had already finished their day's work. Their white headkerchiefs were seen embroidered with the gold of wheat and hay as they led their horses and mules to the stables in the colony. There were among them lean Lithuanian Jews with dry sharp-featured faces; tall, big fleshy good-natured rustic Jews from the Ukraine; yellow-complexioned Galicians whose eyes were large and naive, and dusky Rumanians whose motions were restrained and whose eyes looked with distrust . . .

Velvel explained that he could no longer trust himself to do his work well. He had lost his interest, his alertness.

"Jackal!" The Big Bear turned to him as he rested his own head on his hand, "we are so few. . . . Are you really that tired and broken? You mustn't leave us!"

Velvele looked at the leader's tired heavy face, his dark eyes with its restrained emotions, which spoke without words; he thought of Cain and his other comrades, remaining at the wall; he pictured to himself the wall itself, at night, when a black silhouette emerged from the darkness—and it would not be his silhouette, not Velvele's.

He said in a low voice, but with determination: "I can't, Berl, I can't trust myself any more."

Berl gave him a quick glance. Suddenly he sensed something. He understood. He gently put his hand on Velvele's shoulder and said: "Go to work! You can stay here, with one of the farmers. Or, better yet, go away from here. Perhaps you ought to work at the Farm?* When you have had a rest, you can come back to us. . . . There will be others who will want a rest. . . . They will have to. . . . Do you understand?"

Velvel did his last night's watch. Towards morning he packed his belongings in his blanket and left the colony. Cain accompanied him and carried his bundle part of the way. As they came to the highway which went up the hill, they sat down to rest and lit cigarettes.

"It is a long time since I've worked," said Velvel.

"And are you really leaving us now, Jackal?" Cain asked, as if he could not bring himself to believe it.

"Yes."

Cain looked at him sadly: "It is a long time since I've worked, too."

Velvele was silent.

---

* Sejera. See Ben-Gurion's "Judea and Galilee," chapter 3.

"Tonight," said Cain, "I will watch at your wall."

Their eyes met, as they once had when they discussed Schick. They rose.

"I've got to go," said Velvele.

"Well, go . . . I hope your nose can stand it."

Velvele touched his nose: "What about my nose?"

"Until now you've used it to plough the skies, now you'll have to plough the ground with it. . . . A peasant's nose needs to be harder . . . ha-ha."

The joke did not catch on. They parted in silence.

*   *   *

Nehama went out for a hike with her sweetheart, the teacher. He was a fine, handsome young man and she loved him—she was sure she was going to love him all her life. But she had already been convinced Velvele had not boasted to Yemini and that the dying man had spoken out of sheer malice. She wanted to see Velvel—just to say shalom, to ask how he was, to see if he still thought kindly of her.

They arrived at the Farm early in the evening. The moon shone and shed a bright light as if it were day. Nehama did not come across Velvele anywhere. Finally she inquired.

"He is outside watching," she was told.

"Watching again? But he came here to work in the fields?"

She was informed that he had worked until two weeks ago, and showed himself to be a good worker, "not at all like a shomer, (guard) ha, ha." But then, when the local watchman was wounded, Big Bear came down and gave orders. "They have their discipline, you know." And so, after two months, Velvel was back at the wall, watching—another wall.

Nehama and her sweetheart came out and saw Velvel's lonely black silhouette walking up and down near the wall.

She suddenly decided she did not want to speak to Velvel. Her merry blue eyes were dimmed.

"Come let's not disturb him," she whispered to her companion.

He did not understand and looked at her inquiringly. But he said nothing and followed her as she wished.

6 THE CRUCIBLE

WHEN WORLD War I broke out in August, 1914, Palestine had a Jewish community of about 100,000. At the end of the war in 1919, hardly 60,000 were left.

Some Jews fled, others were forcibly deported and many died of hunger and disease.

The colonists and agricultural workers could eke out an existence from the soil. However, the pious scholars of the "Old Yishuv" and their dependents, whose source of subsistence was cut off when it became impossible to send money from Russia, starved. The intellectuals, stationed mostly in Jaffa—teachers, writers and office workers—also were ruined.

As soon as Turkey joined the war on Germany's side, all Russian subjects were ordered deported. Zionists were suspect even after they adopted Ottoman citizenship. Among the latter were Ben-Yehuda, Ben-Zvi and Ben-Gurion, who were officially told "never to return" to Turkish soil.

Eliezer Ben-Yehuda, Itshak Ben-Zvi, David Ben-Gurion and many lesser figures, spent the war years in the United States, although they had advocated tying the fate of Zionism to Turkey's star, had become "Ottomanized," and had worn the Turkish fez. Still other Russian-born Zionists, like Moshe Shertok (Sharett), served as officers in the Turkish army.

A German military mission in Palestine induced the Turkish governor to root out the members of *Hashomer*, as a dangerous nucleus of a future Jewish army. Many were tortured; some were hanged. The Turkish governor was preparing to perpetrate a massacre on the Jews of Palestine such as the Turks had recently carried out against the Armenians. But influential

Zionists in Germany prevailed upon their government to intercede. To a lesser extent the United States also helped in this matter, although most of America's help during the war years consisted of economic relief.

* * *

Important developments took place during these years outside of Palestine which greatly affected the country's fate.

Dr. Chaim Weizmann emerged as the world leader of the Zionist movement. In the United States, where the war brought a rapid rise in Zionist sentiment among the Jews, Justice Louis D. Brandeis for a time rivaled Weizmann as the foremost leader. Pinhas, or Peter Rutenberg, a Russian revolutionary living in exile in Italy, hitherto alienated from his people, began advocating a Jewish State in Palestine, a Jewish army to fight for it and a Jewish Congress to establish it. He went to the United States, where he scored some considerable success for a time. Some of his assistants in America, such as Ben-Zvi and Ben-Gurion, exiled from Palestine, were later to prove they had more lasting qualities as leaders. However, Rutenberg was to play a tremendous part in the industrial modernization of Palestine.

In Europe, Vladimir Jabotinsky, a brilliant young Russian writer and the idol of Russia's young Zionists, began advocating the formation of a Jewish Legion. During the first years of the war, Jabotinsky was the most prominent and articulate champion of the Legion idea.

In time, Jabotinsky left for Palestine as an officer in the unit recruited in England, while Ben-Zvi and Ben-Gurion served as privates in the unit recruited in the United States and Canada.

Before the Jewish Legion was formed, a small semi-military unit consisting of a few hundred exiled Palestinian Jews stranded in Egypt saw action in Gallipoli as the "Zion Mule Corps." The leader was Joseph Trumpeldor, the one-armed hero of the Russo-Japanese War of 1904-05 who, after his heroic death in 1920, became the patron saint of both the Socialists in Palestine and their bitter opponents, the Revisionists. (The Zionist-Revisionist movement was founded by Jabotinsky several years after the end of World War I.)

After the first Russian Revolution of February 1917, during the short interval before the Bolshevik Revolution of October 1917, Rutenberg served under Kerensky as Chief of Police in the capital, Petrograd, and Trumpledor led in the defense of the city against a Czarist general.

Trumpeldor had come to Russia to organize a mass movement of halutzim (pioneers) and a Jewish army of 100,000 to invade Palestine through the Caucasus. The Bolshevik rule put an end to his ambitious projects, but thousands of halutzim organized by Trumpeldor did find their way into the Homeland. They were part of the Third Aliyah.

* * *

The Story of the Jewish Legion is eloquently told by Vladimir Jabotinsky, selections of which are given in the following pages.

The book was originally written in Russian, a language Jabotinsky mastered as few in his era did, in verse as well as prose.

Vladimir Jabotinsky

◆

THE STORY OF THE JEWISH LEGION

EARLY IN December, 1914, I arrived in Alexandria, where I unexpectedly found a lively Zionist atmosphere among the more than a thousand refugees from Jaffa.

In Egypt, the British Government provided barracks and money. A special department was created for refugees' affairs, with a kind, friendly Englishman, Mr. Hornblower, in charge. The name of the woman who took care of the largest of the barracks—Gabbari—was Broadbent. The children used to call her the "white lady."

I worked in Gabbari for several weeks. It was a camp of twelve hundred souls, of whom three hundred were Sephardim. We had two kitchens, Ashkenazi and Sephardi (at first there was only one, but the Sephardim rebelled because they could not tolerate Ashkenazi food, especially the soup). We also had a Hebrew school and a chemist shop, and were a completely independent community, even having a regiment of watchmen. There were about twelve languages besides Hebrew spoken in the camp. It was fortunate that all the children, nearly all the men and some of the women knew Hebrew. Otherwise, I cannot imagine how such a community could have been organized—with Bukharans, Moroccans, Grusinians, Spaniards, and Jaffa students who refused to take quinine unless the chemist spoke Hebrew.

Occasionally we received a visit from one of the Australian officers, Lieutenant Eliezer Margolin, who stood and watched, and babbled in broken Yiddish, never for a moment dreaming that in a few years he would be colonel of one of the Jewish Battalions and that these very watchmen would be among his men.

Here in Gabbari the Jewish Legion was born. Two people played an important part in its birth—the Russian Consul, Petrov, and Joseph Trumpeldor.

THE ZION MULE CORPS

I had heard of Joseph Trumpeldor while I was still in Russia. He was born in the Caucasus in 1880. His father was one of those men of iron endurance who went through the hell of Nicholas I's barracks—twenty-five years' service—losing neither their health nor their Jewishness. Joseph became a dentist. Then came military service and the Russo-Japanese War. Trumpeldor's regiment was sent to Port Arthur, and there he lived through eleven terrible months of siege. There he lost his left arm, almost to the shoulder. But no sooner had he come out of the hospital than he demanded to be sent back to the front. After the fall of Port Arthur he was taken prisoner by the Japanese, together with the rest of General Stoessel's Army. While in captivity he organized Zionist societies and collected money for the Jewish National Fund.

After the war he was granted a reserve officer's rank, and until 1917 was, as far as I know, the only Jewish officer in the Russian Army. He entered the University of St. Petersburg, completed his law studies and immediately left for Palestine. There he worked in Daganiah and other Socialist settlements, and all his comrades agree that despite his one arm he was still the strongest and the best of the farm workers.

I found Trumpeldor at home. Rather tall and very slim, with close-cropped hair, he was clean-shaven, with thin lips and a quiet smile. He spoke excellent Russian, though under the influence of Palestine he had developed a slight singsong intonation. His Hebrew was slow, and poor in words—but it sufficed, and his Yiddish was atrocious. He was well-educated, well-read in Russian literature, and apparently gave much thought to every line he read. In Hebrew his favorite expression was "ein davar" (Never mind); and they say it was with these words on his lips that he died, five years later, at Tel-Hai. There was a complete philosophy contained in this "ein davar": do not exaggerate; do not see danger where none exists;

do not regard a man who does his duty as a hero—for history is long, the Jewish people everlasting, and truth is sacred, but everything else, trouble and care and pain and death, "ein davar."

Trumpeldor was served better by his one arm than many of us are served by two. He washed, shaved and dressed, he ate, polished his boots, drove his horse and shot—all with his single arm. His room was remarkably tidy, his clothes were clean and brushed, his bearing quiet and courteous. For many years he had been a vegetarian, a Socialist and a pacifist—but he was not one of those pacifists who sit tight, letting others fight and die . . .

A week later we called a meeting of our young people in the Mafruza barracks. About two hundred were present, and on the platform were the Chief Rabbi, della Pergola, other members of the committee which had charge of the refugees, among them old Mr. Gluskin, and Trumpeldor. We gave the gathering a review of the position. Sooner or later the English forces would leave Egypt for Palestine. From Jaffa bad news was arriving daily. The Turks had forbidden Hebrew shop signs in the streets; they had deported Dr. Ruppin, the representative of the Zionist Actions Committee, even though he was a German citizen. The Turks had arrested the leading members of the Yishuv, and had declared that they would not allow any Jewish colonization to continue after the war.

The document that was signed that spring night is a piece of paper torn out of an exercise-book, on which is written a resolution in Hebrew, "To form a Jewish Legion and to propose to England to make use of it in Palestine." It bears about one hundred signatures.

Next day, as I was coming into the Gabbari courtyard, I saw a big parade. Three groups of young men were learning to march, having chosen their own instructors from among the Russian ex-soldiers; several girls were stitching a flag in a corner and a committee of schoolboys was engaged in translating military terminology into Hebrew. Then Trumpeldor arrived. The three groups formed a column of files and marched past him in a kind of ceremonial procession. He watched with a satisfied smile.

"Good heavens," I whispered to him, "they march like geese."

"Ein davar," he replied.

Several days later a delegation went to Cairo, the winter seat

of the Egyptian Government. The delegation first presented itself
to the Minister of the Interior, Mr. Ronald Graham. He listened,
nodded his head in agreement, and asked, "How many men do
you expect?" He then wrote something in a notebook, and said
curtly, "It does not rest with me, but I shall try."

The second visit was to General Maxwell, who commanded the
small British Force in Egypt. We were introduced by Cattaoui
Pasha, a fine old Sephardi gentleman, one of the most respected men
in all Egypt. The other delegates, besides myself, were Trumpeldor,
Levontin, Gluskin and Margolis. We forced poor Trumpeldor to
put on his four St. George Crosses—two bronze and two gold.
The General looked at him sharply and asked abruptly in French,
"Port Arthur, I understand?"

But his reply to our proposal was profoundly disappointing.

"I have heard nothing about an offensive in Palestine, and I
doubt whether such an offensive will be launched at all. I am prohibited by regulations from admitting foreign soldiers into a British
Army. I can make only one suggestion—that your young men form
themselves into a detachment for mule transport, to be made use
of on some other sector of the Turkish front. I cannot do more
than that."

That night, in Mr. Gluskin's hotel apartment, we sat up till
dawn debating the situation; what should be done?

We civilians felt that General Maxwell's offer must be politely
declined. Trumpeldor disagreed with us.

Next morning, back in Alexandria, I found a cablegram on my
table from Genoa. It was signed "Rutenberg." He wanted to know
whether we could meet "at once" and where.

Having read the cable, I immediately went to find Trumpeldor
and said: "I'm off to Europe. Should General Maxwell change his
mind and agree to form a real fighting regiment, send me a cable
and I'll come back at once; if not, I'll try to find some other
generals."

*   *   *

Toward the middle of April, 1915, at Brindisi, I met Rutenberg.
There was also a cable waiting for me at the Post Office, signed
"Trumpeldor." It read, "Maxwell's offer accepted."

I never took part in the Gallipoli Campaign, and it is therefore not for me to tell the story of Trumpeldor's unit, the "Zion Mule Corps." But I must admit one thing: I had been wrong and Trumpeldor had been right. Those six hundred muleteers actually opened up a new avenue in the development of Zionist possibilities. Until then it had been almost impossible to talk Zionism even to friendly statesmen. At such a cruel time who could have expected them to worry about agricultural settlements or the renaissance of Hebrew? All that was, for the moment, simply outside their field of vision. It was the little transport unit in Gallipoli which succeeded in breaking through, in putting at least a name, a hint, a question mark on the map of that inaccessible, walled-in horizon of a world busy with war.

All through the first half of the war that mule corps proved to be the only manifestation that somehow reminded the "world," especially Great Britain's military "world," that Zionism could also be topical, a part of actuality, and perhaps capable of being transformed into a factor that might prove of some value even under gunfire.

The whole area occupied by British troops was just a few square miles, every bit of it well within the range of Turkish guns on the hilltop of Achi-Baba, which equally peppered the front trenches and the mule camp. Every night under that bombardment they had to lead their loaded mules to the front and back again. Their losses in dead and wounded were hardly different, in proportion, from those of any other section of Gallipoli. It was their courage that especially struck General Ian Hamilton, G. O. C., of the Gallipoli Expeditionary Force, who wrote to me after the close of that campaign, on November 17, 1915: "The men have done extremely well, working their mules calmly under heavy shell and rifle-fire, and thus showing a more difficult type of bravery than the men in the front line who had the excitement of combat to keep them going."

The Commanding Officer was Lieutenant Colonel John Henry Patterson, one of the most remarkable Christian figures our people ever encountered on its way through all the centuries of the Dispersion. Trumpeldor, to whom the military authorities granted a sort of hemi-demi-semi-honorary captaincy, was second in command for a time, but toward the end of the campaign Patterson fell ill or was wounded and was sent to England for convalescence, leaving Trumpeldor as O. C. Zion Mule Corps. The campaign then had to be liquidated; for several months, in Alexandria, Trumpeldor struggled against fate in trying to delay the inevitable disbandment of his corps, bombarding Headquarters with collective petitions to allow them to keep together and train "for the impending Palestine offensive." But it was to no avail. Formed in April, 1915, the Zion Mule Corps was disbanded on May 26, 1916. Not more than about 120 of its soldiers subsequently managed to re-enlist and find their way to London; and this was the nucleus around which the "real" Jewish Legion was ultimately formed; that Legion which, armed with bayonets and Lewis guns, eventually took part in the conquest of Palestine.

* * *

A few days before our departure from England we received a telegram from New York, signed by Brainin, Ben-Zvi and Ben-Gurion, which informed us of the launching of the recruiting campaign for the Legion in America. The Greek Government had announced that volunteer-recruiting would be permitted in Salonika. A message came from Buenos Aires signed by Vladimir Herman: "English consent obtained." A recruiting office already had been opened in Egypt itself.

But the most encouraging news had come from Palestine. Hardly had the train entered the railway station at Cairo, when a khaki-clad young man ran up to me. "My name is Aloni," he said. "I have been sent from Tel-Aviv to welcome the Legion on behalf of the Palestine volunteers."

And he told me of a great movement in that part of Palestine which had already been liberated—Jerusalem, Tel-Aviv and Jaffa, and the colonies of Judea; and even in the north, which was still in the hands of the Turks—in Zichron-Jacob and Hadera, in Haifa, and in the colonies of Upper and Lower Galilee—there was great enthusiasm among the young people, some of whom had broken through the Turkish border patrols and had arrived at Petah-Tikvah asking, "Where is the Legion?"

One morning Patterson told me to pack: "I have been given permission to go to Palestine with you."

We alighted at Beer-Jacob. Not far from the colony, surrounding two large houses previously owned by a German farmer, were a number of tents and barracks—G. H. Q.—General Allenby's headquarters. Here we separated. The colonel went to meet the commander-in-chief, and I was taken to Tel-Aviv. In the evening we exchanged impressions. Mine were pleasant; his were not.

I had found Jaffa and Tel-Aviv in a state of unbounded enthusiasm.

Approaching the town I met a ten-year-old boy whom I took with me, since he had promised to show me the way to my old friends, Eliahu Berlin and Bezalel Jaffe. He told me the latest news: 40,000 Jewish soldiers were coming in English ships; at the head of this army was General James Rothschild, the Baron's son. I did not have the heart to tell him that so far we were but one battalion. But I had to tell my friends in Tel-Aviv, and though their expectations were not so great as those of the boy, I felt that they were disappointed.

But their enthusiasm was created by something which completely overshadowed even our Legion—their own volunteer Legion. Its initiator and leader was Moshe Smilansky, a man of over forty, a well-known Hebrew writer and one of the most highly respected colonists in Rehovot. He was immediately sent for, and he came with a group of workers from the colony—all volunteers. In Jaffa and Tel-Aviv, too, all the volunteers were workers, or college graduates who were preparing to join the workers' movement. Berl Katzenelson, later editor of *Davar,* Yavnieli, who in previous years first brought Yemenites to Palestine, Dov Hos, Eliahu Golomb and many others today prominent in the Labor Movement, were the leading spirits among the volunteers.

Those were the tidings I brought to Colonel Patterson. His story was different.

General Allenby had exhibited much coldness toward both the London regiment and the Palestine volunteers. He had inherited from Kitchener a strong antagonism to "fancy regiments." Exactly what he said about Jewish soldiers I do not know—Patterson

refrained from telling it to me and he says nothing about it in his
book. But he emphasized one thing: it was not Allenby himself who
was the chief opponent, but his Chief-of-Staff, a certain general
Louis Bols—who two years later did nothing to prevent the Jerusalem pogrom.

OUR FIRST FRONT

The actual military history of our battalion falls into three
parts: the summer months at the front at Shechem, the great offensive in the Jordan valley, and the Armistice.

The first of these periods was comparatively quiet. After the
terrific battle of the preceding winter, which had resulted in the
liberation of Southern Palestine from Turkish domination, both
sides decided to rest. The Turks in particular were not at all keen
on taking the initiative, and the few small clashes that took place
during those months were all local English attacks.

Our front was midway between Jerusalem and Shechem (Nablus).

Imagine a long chain of hills, about 2,500 feet high, running
from west to east. North of the hills is a deep valley, and on the
other side of this valley a second parallel chain of hills even higher
than the first. We were encamped on the first and the Turks on
the second. The distance between the summits of the hills was
about two miles. We could not see the Turkish camp even with
the aid of field glasses, for they were encamped two hundred feet
below the summit on the far side of their hill. During the day
we were not permitted to move about on the top of the hill, and
the guards were stationed at rocky observation posts. At night a
strong guard was sent out to the other side of the hill, and they
stationed themselves behind low stone fences called sangars; in
addition, a patrol would descend nightly into the valley and stay
there throughout the night, in order to warn us in case of attack.

It was a peaceful time, the right thing for introducing raw
recruits to the atmosphere of war. Every morning the Turks would
give us the pleasure of half an hour's bombardment, but they
always displayed a marked predilection for a deserted hill far to
our right and much higher up, and at least one-third of their
shells did not even explode. They really fired at our position only

three or four times, but they could not hit us. The hills there do
not rise precipitously, but gradually, in terraces about as wide as
East Broadway in New York. Our tents were clustered together
beneath the shelter of the summit. Our position was thus rendered
inaccessible to the shells of the enemy. Probably ours were just as
ineffective, but we did not waste as many as did the Turks.

The war we conducted is regarded as "small warfare." We knew
nothing of modern scientific horrors. The men had only two dangers
to face during those months: night-patrol duty and the seven days'
watch at Abouein.

Eight to twelve men would go out on night patrol under a
lieutenant. They would swathe their heavy military boots in thick
rags, to lessen their noise; their knees were also covered with rags,
for in the summer we wore shorts, and the hills were covered with
a tremendous variety of prickly vegetation. Before the departure of
the patrol the officer would receive a sealed envelope from the
commander of the battalion, containing an exact description of the
path to be taken by the patrol that night. Very often it was not just
a stroll through the valley, but also a climb up the enemy's hill—
sometimes to within two hundred feet of his observation post. It
was no easy task. First there was the climb down our hill, over
stones and through thorny grass, guns in hand—without noise.
This took more than an hour. Then we had to creep about in the
valley, one mile to the right and one mile to the left, among the
bushes—hastily consulting the sergeant to decide whether some
dark object we had seen was a Turk or just a cactus bush. Then
came the most difficult part: the climb up the enemy's hill, finding
our way with the aid of a compass and with the help of such
directions as "left of a split fig tree," "ten paces to the right from a
ditch," or, finally, "reaching a rock, fifteen feet high, which, looked
at from the north, has the appearance of the head of a hippopotamus!" Who of us had ever seen a hippopotamus, let alone
at such close quarters as to be able to recognize its profile in the
dark? Here we rested, and the men were given slabs of chocolate. And then, back again down the hill for a two hours'
climb. You are tired and footsore, and close to the enemy, and
every step forward releases a whole avalanche of stones. Sud-

denly, you hear a shot from somewhere, close behind the last man in the file. You whisper fiercely, "Down!" The whole patrol goes down. And you see, a hundred yards away, a small point of fire leaping into the air; it resolves itself into a rocket which sheds a rosy light over a long stretch of bushes, a dry river bed, and rocks and crevices in the valley.

It would be a most beautiful sight—if you could set your mind on it. That was the Turkish patrol. Then your own battalion takes your part. From Abouein, from Jiljiliah and from the sangars, there breaks out a wild concert of rifle fire; and a moment later, from somewhere in the distance, the English artillery joins the chorus. Like a railway train at night in the Swiss Alps, a fiery comet makes its majestic way over your head and with a thundering noise explodes on the enemy hill.

Then another. And all for your sake! You would feel really honored—if you could set your mind on it. The tumult lasts half an hour; then silence descends again, and we climb and creep and climb again until we reach camp—and a cup of steaming hot tea, sweet and delicious.

The other danger spot was Abouein. Although it was really in No Man's Land, it had been included in our line. As you descend our hill on the side nearer the Turks, you encounter, three hundred feet down, an outcrop of the hill, in the shape of a great terrace or "table." On this table the Arabs had built a village of about fifty houses.

Each week a new platoon would be sent to Abouein, which it had to occupy for seven days. During the day, of course, nobody could go between the village and the camp, as the intervening ground was visible to the enemy. We therefore went at night. But between the observation post in Abouein and the battalion headquarters we had a field telephone, over which we could sometimes hear one or two words of what was being said at the other end. Through this article of civilization we could "order" whatever we wanted from the battalion—matches, tobacco, quinine, bandages, ammunition and letters—if there were any; at night a small party of soldiers would bring six mules laden with what was needed— or what they had understood was needed!

FROM A LETTER HOME

" . . . Every day I grow to admire our 'tailors'* more and more. Yesterday was a red-letter day. Rishon colonists sent us a gift, which required two mules to carry: grapes, figs, apple-pie and date-pudding. I have a suspicion that there was wine as well, but H. Q. must have decided that wine is unhealthy for men stationed in No Man's Land. . . . About midday, when the platoon had had a refreshing sleep after a hard night's work, the sergeant distributed the good things. We are all living in one house, the sergeant and I on the second floor and the men in three large rooms underneath. The Turks can see only our roof, so I allow the men to sit in the courtyard. Usually they play cards—I hope not for money, for this is against regulations. Today they were also sitting in shady corners of the yard, eating their grapes and playing some game or other—when suddenly the Turk opened a symphony of cannon music. Though he seldom shoots in the daytime, we are well acquainted with his firing: he always directs it at the lofty, totally deserted hill to our right. I immersed myself further in my book, and the boys in the yard went on with their game. But five minutes later the sergeant entered. 'I am afraid, sir,' he said, 'that they're trying to hit us. The sound is different from the usual. They're groping for Abouein.' And indeed the next shell exploded almost in the village. I put my head out through the window and shouted, 'Take cover!' They had heard what was happening themselves, but they did not relish the idea of interrupting their game to go into the gloomy Arab rooms. Slowly, reproachful at my repeating the order, they separated, carrying their cards and grapes and bits of apple-tart in their hands. We waited. Every five minutes an explosion came, first to our right, then to our left, then right again. . . . 'Their shooting is bad,' said the sergeant. He was standing by the window. Suddenly he smiled and beckoned to me. I walked over to him and looked out into the yard. Four of our boys were again sitting outside, absorbed in their cards and their date-pudding, but they were in a corner which could be seen only with difficulty

---

* The Jews of Whitechapel who joined the Jewish Legion.

from the window. Suddenly one of them glanced around and quickly said in Yiddish, 'The officer's watching!' And just at that moment a shell burst right in Abouein, a hundred yards from us. I saw three of them raise their heads, but they did not budge; the fourth didn't even turn his head; he banged his card down on his opponent's—and replied with a note characteristic of deeply absorbed card-players: 'Hob ich ihm in dr'erd.' (To hell with him)—(I hope he meant the shell, not the officer.) I looked stern and made them take cover again but inwardly I am proud of my 'tailors.'

". . . Is the Jew disciplined or not? A difficult question to answer. . . . Here you have an example. English and Australian soldiers destroyed so many trees (unfortunately, from our Herzl Forest as well) that an order had to be sent out forbidding the cutting down of trees on penalty of a substantial fine. Here, around Abouein, are thick woods, and we need wood for cooking. But never will it occur to our men to touch a tree. They know well that I would not make inquiries as to the origin of their wood— for life in No Man's Land is hard enough in all conscience. But they are townsmen, brought up with the idea that a tree is communal property which dare not be hurt, just as one does not destroy a monument. Where do they find fuel? Doors, windows, or they break up the roof of a hut and take out the twigs and roots with which the fellahin make their roofs. But a tree? God forbid."

BEYOND THE JORDAN

On the nineteenth of September, General Chaytor, commander of the Australian and New Zealand cavalry forces and of all the forces in Transjordan, summoned Colonel Patterson and gave him his instructions for the offensive. Our battalion, together with Margolin's two companies, was to form what would be known as "Patterson's Column." Its first task would be to capture both sides of the ford across the Jordan known to the Arabs as Umm Esh Shert, and thereafter to advance on the town of Es Salt in the Hills of Moab, far beyond the Jordan.

Collecting the various units of the battalion occupied an entire night. Our line stretched for a distance of nine or ten miles, concentrated on seven small mountain forts which formed a chain from north to south.

That same night we sent out reinforced patrols to No Man's Land, to find out whether the Turks were still in their forts, for after the blow they had suffered several days earlier at Jaffa, they had begun to retreat from the Jordan as well.

The patrols found only two forts occupied. As we had no artillery, we opened up machine-gun fire on them. They replied. At three o'clock the information that the "ditch"—the deepest part of the valley, where the Jordan flows—was occupied by troops on both sides of the river.

Two days later we were stationed in a long line at the edge of the ditch, and we could look out carefully, over the ridge of improvised trenches, at the Jordan itself.

Malaria had robbed my company of all but three officers and less than a hundred men. Lieutenant Barnes was in charge and I was temporarily second-in-command. Abrahams had to take over the work of the other three platoon commanders. Barnes and Abrahams occupied the rocks with seven of our eight Lewis guns. I was given the remaining Lewis gun and ordered to conduct the main operation. In comparison with the patrol service which had preceded it, it was child's play.

Allenby's report says, "On the night of 23rd September the Jewish battalions captured the Jordan ford at Umm Esh Shert." The ford, the key to Transjordan, was given them by us—a curious commentary on the fact that today Transjordan is excluded from the Jewish National Home.

Among the first infantry troops that entered Transjordan on the heels of the Australian cavalry were Colonel Margolin's Americans. They crossed the Jordan at the bridge Gorania, several miles south of Umm Esh Shert, and marched to Es Salt (believed to be the ancient Ramath Gilead), where Colonel Margolin settled down as commander of the town and its neighborhood. Our battalion followed Margolin's two companies.

This march in Transjordan was the most difficult I have ever experienced; and not I alone. Patterson, who still remembered the Boer War in the hot African sun, at a time when war did not consist, as it does today, of months of waiting in trenches, but wholly of maneuvers and marches, himself said that he had never endured more painful progress.

The march from the river to the foot of the Hills of Moab was difficult enough, through a roadless desert where the Turks had burned the dry grass in their retreat, and the heavy black smoke in the windless heat lay so thick on the ground that our companies often lost sight of each other. But much worse was the climb up the hills. It was about midday. The gradient of the hill was one in about twenty; what this means can be appreciated if one realizes that the maximum gradient on which motor traffic is permitted to travel in Europe is one in from ten to twelve. And the men and N. C. O.'s had to carry, in addition to their rifles and ammunition, bulky kitbags as large as a four-year-old child, full of shirts, socks, shoes and everything else kindly provided by His Majesty, including razors and tins of polish for polishing buttons. And, of course, waterbottles, from which the water had long evaporated.

The officers, who had only kit-bags to carry, helped as much as they could. Each of us carried a rifle on each shoulder.

The dust on the hills was worse than the smoke in the valley had been. It hung over the ground without a breath of wind to disturb it, and instead of air we breathed and swallowed dust.

Man after man would fall out and throw himself down near a rock, with mouth wide open, unable to carry himself farther. "Now they'll laugh at us—Jewish heroes!" I thought to myself, almost ashamed—until I saw two English sergeants, tall, slim, athletic men, who had been sent to us a short time before to replace two of our malaria-stricken sergeants, sitting against a rock with their eyes closed, gasping like fish on dry land.

7 CONTINUATION

FIFTY YEARS had elapsed since Joshua Stampfer, at the age of seventeen, tramped alone across Europe from his native Hungary to Palestine, where he was to found Petah-Tikvah. Now, at the end of the First World War, thousands of young Jews, in singing, dancing, hungry bands, made similar treks across Europe to Palestine.

Some had recently been released, or had escaped the prisons of Soviet Russia, which was still in the throes of a civil war and where Zionists were exiled to Siberia by the Bolsheviks and Jews of all persuasions were killed by the anti-Bolsheviks. Others came from the newly created republics of Poland and Czechoslovakia or the enlarged Kingdom of Rumania; even enlightened, civilized Germany, whose Jews had long apparently been severed from living Jewish tradition, supplied a small quota of these new pioneers. They came by train, by boat, on foot, smuggling themselves across the Caucasus mountains to Turkey and crossing other boundaries, legally or illegally. On their way they worked as stevedores in the ports, as manual laborers and as farmhands, while waiting for their ships.

These were the *halutzim* of the Third Aliyah, fleeing the shambles of Jewish life in Europe and attracted by the dream of the New Zion, now fifty years in its rebuilding, now that the Zionist aim had been officially endorsed by the British and by other great powers. The British were in control of Palestine.

In 1868, when Charles Netter, a native of Alsace, founded the first agricultural school in Palestine for the Alliance Israelite Universelle, he declared it to be an act in anticipation of the time when Jews would be forced to leave Europe and resettle their ancient Homeland. In 1882, Dr. Leon Pinsker, a Russian-born Jewish physician practicing in Germany, published a pamphlet entitled "Auto-emancipation," in which he analyzed anti-Semitism as an incurable mental disease of the European nations which see in the Jews a "walking ghost" of which they have an irrational fear. In 1894, when Captain Alfred Dreyfus was tried and condemned as a spy, Theodor Herzl, who reported the proceedings in Paris for his newspaper in Vienna, was so shocked by the manifestations of anti-Semitism that, without having heard of Pinsker, he arrived at a similar conclusion and published his famous pamphlet "The Jewish State." In 1903, when the Kishinev pogrom took place, Herzl, already the leader of the world's Zionists, fearing these to be merely the preliminary rumblings of a volcanic eruption, was ready to accept the British offer of transferring the Jews to Uganda.

But during all those years Jewish life in Eastern Europe flourished and there were as many signs of progress and of hope as the signs of doom seen by Pinsker and Herzl. However, in 1919, the number of Jews who had lost all hope for rehabilitation in Europe had grown much larger. The civil war in Russia had taken a toll of some 200,000 Jewish lives, mostly in massacres perpetrated by the Ukrainians. The Communist regime had outlawed Zionism, the Hebrew language and, to a lesser extent, Jewish religion. It forbade intercourse between its own Jews and those of other countries. Poland, which held three and a half million Jews, made no secret of its desire to oust them from its economic and cultural life and, eventually from its soil. Bialik's cry that all the earth had become the Jew's scaffold was more grimly true now than it had been in 1903, when he first uttered it after the pogrom in Kishinev.

If the Second Aliyah contained a large proportion of disillusioned revolutionaries who sought escape in a return to their own people, such disenchantment was even more characteristic of the Third Aliyah.

Whatever the variations in their ideologies, these new pioneers were bent on ensuring the continued existence of the Jewish people as a national entity. Their "golden dreams" of a better society were to be merged with the visions of Isaiah and Amos, of justice and equality, and universal brotherhood and peace, and the language of the prophets was to be their daily vernacular, just as, for centuries, it had been the medium of their forefathers' prayers and study. Whatever the differences between them and their fathers in religious practice and belief, they were links in the same historic chain which were not to be broken.

*   *   *

The word *halutz,* used in the Bible for a military vanguard, had gradually become the modern Hebrew equivalent of pioneer. But it was not until the Third Aliyah that halutz became almost a technical term, usually denoting a young man or woman belonging to an organization devoted to building the Jewish Homeland through manual labor on the soil. It was Joseph Trumpeldor, one of the pioneers of the Second Aliyah, the military hero of the Russo-Japanese war of 1904 and the founder and leader of the Zion Mule Corps in 1915, who went to Russia in 1917 to form the first organized body of *halutzim.* His organization survived him by many years.

The halutzim who came after the First World War, despite the warnings of the Zionist leadership that the country was not yet ready for them since the regime of Palestine had not yet been legally established, were faced with hardships. They organized into a Labor Battalion, with companies and platoons and scattered all over the country to find work. Some were given employment on private farms; others were put to work by the British administration to build roads; but many remained unemployed and hungry. Their ideal was to become members of already existing or newly established collective farms, such as Daganiah, or less spectacularly revolutionary co-operative settlements like Ein Ganim, where each farmer owned his own plot of land.

The upheaval of the First World War and its aftermath did arouse a stronger sentiment for Zionism among former opponents and Jews who had been indifferent. The Balfour Declaration of November, 1917, by which the British Government pledged itself to "use its best endeavors to facilitate the attainment of the Jewish National Homeland in Palestine," gave the Jews new hope. The results were greater confidence, more readiness to undertake ambitious projects and a larger flow of funds, especially from American Jewry and from other Jews of the Western world.

The Jewish National Fund, under its director M. M. Ussishkin, negotiated and concluded the purchase of a large tract of land in the Valley of Esdraelon, or Jezreel. The price was much greater than the funds the whole Zionist movement could hope to raise for years, and there was much opposition on the part of realistic-minded leaders, such as Supreme Court Justice Louis Brandeis in Washington. But, after a struggle within the councils of the movement, the purchase was approved and consummated.

The Valley of Esdraelon, once the granary of the Holy Land, lying athwart the strategic highways of history, was a vast marshland desert when the Jews began to settle it after the First World War. Within a decade it became the breadbasket of the Homeland. Among other things, it grew the best citrus fruit in the country, despite the warnings of experts that the soil was not suitable for cultivation.

The saga of building the Valley of Esdraelon became known as the saga of the post-war years throughout the Jewish world. The name "Esdraelon" or "Jezreel" was dropped, and only the name *Emek*—Hebrew for "Valley" remained. It became The Emek.

The largest co-operative small-holders' settlement, Nahalal, was founded in the Emek and flourished. But it attracted much less attention and produced far less literature than the collective settlements of Tel-Joseph and Ein-Harod, in which human nature voluntarily was subjected to the test of new forms of life.

Veterans of the Second Aliyah and of the collective settlements established before the war, recruited pioneers among the members of the Labor Battalion of the Third Aliyah, in order to found new collective settlements in the Emek.

GENESIS

◆

Shlomo Reichenstein

BY MIDNIGHT the storm subsided. A decrepit moon now drifted among shreds of clouds, dodging, hiding and darting out again, shedding its dim light on the large mound which stood alone on the plain.

All day the storm had raged, accompanied by intermittent downpours. Dozens of tents which had been put up that day were torn out by the storm and their canvas and flaps carried away among the rocks and bushes. The young men and women who had come here today were all crowded in the only tent which had withstood the storm. This was the large, square one, intended to serve as a dining room and a kitchen. It was fastened by iron hooks and tied by new ropes to the rocks nearby. Here they brought the bundles they could salvage from under the fallen tents, as, wet and shivering with cold, they huddled together in silence.

Someone tried to sing, but he quickly gave up when there was no response. Someone also made an attempt to speak, wishing to give some expression to the feelings of the young people who had come to build a new settlement in the wilderness, but all he managed were some incoherent sounds. Worn out, deeply agitated, they fell asleep on the cool ground of the large square tent.

Early in the morning, when the valley, surrounded by a chain of mountains on three sides, was still immersed in dusk, from the eastern end of the mound two men came trudging behind a plough. While one led the mules, the other bent over the handles. In the dusk, as the few stars in the sky flickered their last, the men seemed unusually tall. Round and round they plowed through the fields as if harnessed to the wheel of an ancient well.

Presently the eastern rim of the sky grew pale; a livid glow on the mountaintops was soon infused with a dark red hue. The red became brighter and brighter, and turned to gold. Streams of light swelled up, flooding the plain. A golden ball slowly ascended, holding on to the mountain tops, then broke away and remained suspended in the luminous blue.

The plough frequently dug against rocks hidden in the soil. The younger man, who held the handles of the plough, was continuously thrown backward and forward. Panting with his mouth open, his eyes bathed in the morning sunshine; his face radiated beatitude.

"Hell!" he cried ecstatically. "Some devils there must be holding on to the blade of the plough!"

The older man at the reins kept silent. His face was somber and his deep-sunk eyes had a cold glint. He seemed to be a bit of a grumbler. His eyes were intently searching through the bare mountains, as if seeking to burn through their thick rocks.

"Look, earth!" the younger man exclaimed. He bent down, took a handful of soft black earth, rolled it into a ball and handed it to his surly companion.

* * *

Raphael Broshi was now in his eighteenth spring. He had a tall, slender figure, a fresh, child-like face upon which played a bright pink color, and a soft mouth showing two rows of strong well-formed white teeth. His blue eyes shone through the thick hair falling in curls over his forehead. It was only recently that Raphael had left his father's home and the "cell" of young Zionists where he became entranced with the vision of the Homeland.

He could not sleep when he learned that Tuvia who, immediately upon their arrival on the mound, took over the administration, assigned him and Zeev to be the first ones to plough the virgin soil for a vegetable patch. The tent canvas oppressed him. His bed creaked under him and he turned from side to side. Like a hope come true were the footsteps of the guard feeling his way in the dark towards his tent and waking him up to start ploughing. He was glad no one saw him; he was glad it was so dark in the temporary stable made of rags that Zeev could not see

him hugging the warm necks of the mules and kissing them.
And when the plough was sunk into the soil and Raphael felt with
all his limbs that it was penetrating deeper and deeper into the
earth's living bosom, he could no longer contain a shout of joy:
   "Look, Zeev, earth!"
   "What's all this excitement?" Zeev answered, as he kept looking at the mountains all around, "We're ploughing."
   Raphael felt uncomfortable. After each row of furrows he
wanted to shout with joy, but each time he met Zeev's somber
glance and kept his joy within himself.

                    *   *   *

   Raphael was one of the young newcomers who had arrived in
Palestine with the dancing, singing caravans of the Third Aliyah.
Not so Zeev. He was an old-timer, a veteran worker of the Judean
vineyards and the Galilean wheatfields. He had come to Palestine
some time before the war, and, unlike most of his contemporaries,
with a solid background of experience of agriculture in Europe. He
found much in Palestine not to his liking. Mostly, he did not ap-
prove of the way Jews here ran their farms. These youngsters
spent too much time, he thought, in singing, dancing and debating.
   Zeev had joined Tuvia and Aryeh, two old-timers like himself,
who decided to found a new collective farm with the enthusaistic
recruits from among the newcomers. But now that he was here,
he was still displeased.
   It was Tuvia's idea, this new collective farm. He thought the
old one, where he had lived, was too restricted in its membership,
with its atmosphere too oppressive. So he cooked up a new plan
for a large commune, with members free to choose their own
friends, with mixed farming—a little field crop, a little citrus
gardening, some industries. Fine. Tuvia did the planning, and Aryeh
did the recruiting among the newcomers and the arguing with the
Zionist leaders. Fine! But what's the result? Still the same singing
and dancing, still those interminable meetings and debates. Is that
farming? That's playing games, that's what it is!
   And what does this man Tuvia mean anyway? What does he
think he is? A feudal lord or something? Or a foreman of a large

estate? Who is he to tell Zeev, who had had farming experience
in Europe, what to plant, where to plant, how to plant?

It took Raphael a long time to find out from Zeev how he felt
about Tuvia. And when Zeev did burst out one day, Raphael was
shocked: how could anyone talk that way about Tuvia? Tuvia, that
kindly old bachelor with his homely lean face furrowed by years
of hard labor and starvation, with his kindly small eyes which
seemed to look upon you with warm, but unsmiling love, with
real fatherly affection, this Tuvia, who cared little for food, sleep
or comfort, but only, it seemed, for the settlement, its members and,
above all, the cause—the Rebirth of Israel?

Raphael was too young and too naive to explain Zeev's attitude
towards Tuvia as jealousy. He only vaguely sensed a resentment
against Tuvia's authority and popularity. It could not have occurred
to Raphael that Zeev was jealous of Tuvia on account of Rahel,
the cook of the settlement. It would be hard to associate Tuvia with
romance, much less Zeev—and, for that matter, Rahel, the big-
bosomed, motherly cook, Rahel.

Rahel sometimes joined the boys and the girls for walks in
the field, but she was never seen walking arm-in-arm with anyone.
She was more like a big sister or a friendly aunt. As for Tuvia, he
was always too busy with his plants and charts and figures, staying
up until late after midnight, writing, erasing, calculating, planning.
He never had time for anything else. Zeev spent all his free time
in his tent, reading books and magazines about agricultural machinery, with many spare parts lying around, near his unmade bed or
under it. The tent was always untidy and always smelled of lubri-
cating oil. In fact, it was plain dirty. No one liked to share it with
him, and whoever was assigned to Zeev's tent, soon left it on some
pretext or another. Finally he was allowed to have the tent all to
himself—an unheard-of luxury in those days. That pleased him: he
preferred living alone.

*   *   *

Raphael himself was in love with Naomi—or, Naomi-leh as
she was generally called. She was about one year younger than
himself—not more than seventeen—the prettiest girl in the settle-

GENESIS

ment. She had a beautiful face with delicate features, a well-built graceful figure, long blond braids and luminous grey eyes.

Sometimes Raphael took Naomi horseback riding with him. Raphael had been appointed a mountain guard, for which he was duly grateful to Tuvia and of which he was very proud. He would scat Naomi behind him and gallop off through the fields and rocks of the Valley, now and then pointing out to Naomi the nature and historic significance of the places. He wanted to tell her that he loved her, but he always hesitated: now the moment seemed inopportune, now he could not decide whether to say it in Hebrew or in Polish. Naomi knew Polish much better than Hebrew, but how was one to make love in the historic Valley of Jezreel in an alien tongue? When Naomi noticed Raphael's embarrassment, she would start talking about some trivial subject or suggest they ride back home.

Another chance never seemed to come. They were seldom alone. Naomi and Raphael were always in the company of other boys and girls: Hilulah, who liked to recite the latest Russian poets, and Hayimkeh, who told of his exploits in the Red Army and always led in the dancing of the Arab "debka" and the European "rondeau," and Nathan Galili, the only native Palestinian among them, who had once been a member of the famous *Hashomer* and liked to boast about it, and others. It always seemed to Raphael that Naomi avoided being alone with him and sometimes even preferred Hayimkeh's or Nathan's company. Or else, she would cling to her girl-friend, Hilulah.

Raphael would rather not see Naomi than see her in the company of the mean-tongued Hayimkeh or of the braggart Nathan Galili who made it a practice to take the girls out riding with him on his noble Arab mare. He could not stand the raucousness, the vulgarity, the backslapping, the hilarity that went on among the young people. He wanted to be alone with Naomi, to talk to her of the beauty of the Valley and the skies of the Homeland, of his dreams and aspirations and of his feelings for her.

* * *

There was another man who disapproved of the manners at the camp.

Levin, a scion of Talmudic scholars in Lithuania, was a teacher and a writer before he became a pioneer. He had joined the singing caravans of the halutzim in order to till the soil of the Homeland, but he also wanted to preserve the spiritual beauty of the historic tradition of Jewry. He expected that the Hebrew spoken would be good Hebrew, and that the songs would be suffused with Jewish content. Something had to be done about it, and Levin had a plan worked out. Would they listen to him—these youngsters intoxicated by the wine of their new Homeland and by their newly-found undisciplined freedom? After all, these products of an age of upheaval and disruption were trained to scorn the higher values.

Nevertheless, these were not primitives emerging from a jungle, but the children and grandchildren of Jews who had been accustomed to infuse every step of their ordinary lives with high spirituality. The Golden Chain of Jewish civilization must be carried on. Because of the effect of recent changes in history, a link had been severed. A way must be found to reforge the unity of the Chain and to re-unite the last link with the first one. . . . Levin had spent many nights in carefully working out a plan for cultural activities in the camp. It was all written down in biblical Hebrew in his neat hand in his notebooks. Even before he left his native Lithuania, he had published many articles on the subject.

*　　*　　*

On Friday the people left their field work early to prepare for the Sabbath. They were busy airing their bedding, brushing their clothes, polishing their shoes and running to the spring to bathe in its cool fresh water. The scent of delicious Sabbath food floated from the large square tent, where Rahel scurried from pot to pot, stirring, tasting, moving. A large gathering of settlers ready for their Sabbath meal stood near the tent, impatiently prodding Rahel to hasten the serving of supper.

"Get away from here, you gourmands!" she scolded and threatened with the spoon in her hand. "You're keeping me from my work!" But try as she might, Rahel could not make her kindly, motherly eyes look angry.

When Levin entered the large square tent, he found everybody seated at the tables, which were covered with white cloths for the

Sabbath. The flushed faces of the young men and girls were set off against the white of their clean blouses and dresses. The close air was filled with a deafening din of loud singing accompanied by the rhythmic thumping of cutlery against plates. At first Levin saw only a solid mass of pink and white enveloped in the odors of the kitchen tent. It took some time for the scene to become distinct. Suddenly, when he clearly saw the many happy eager faces of these youths, he felt a lump rising in his throat and his eyes were covered by a moist film. He himself had never until now quite understood how great was his effection for these Jewish boys and girls who had come into the wilderness, into this dangerous outpost, to build a Homeland for their people! The singing and the clanging grew louder and louder. Levin could not make out the words. But it all sounded to him like one mighty upsurge emanating from these young boys and girls; from this mound, and from this valley and from the surrounding hills. Suddenly he caught his own voice among the rest. He, Shmuel Levin, the pedantic Hebrew grammarian, who could not bear this raucous noise, he, too, was caught up on the wave of this roaring sea like one of the soldiers in an army storming a fortress.

The curtain was raised and from the adjoining kitchen tent came Rahel, carrying the steaming food. She was dressed in white and washed and combed for the Sabbath. Her wet hair glistened with drops of water from the spring. A boy and a girl helped her serve. Immediately the spoons and forks were set into vigorous action and the sound of masticating jaws mingled with the buzzing of the spluttering Lux lamp.

The fast and ravenous way of eating, always repugnant to Levin, soon took him out of his happy mood. He viewed the scene with chagrin through this thick glasses, and felt no savor in Rahel's delicious dishes. Yes, he was certainly going to say something on that subject. This brotherly repast whose spirit is infused with the highest principles of human ethics must not be turned into a vulgar soup kitchen. Eating must be slow, deliberate, with pauses between dishes and interspersed with orderly singing and intellectual discussion, as had been the custom of our fathers and forefathers for countless generations. . . .

But Levin hardly had time to ponder the question. No sooner was the meal completed than the tables and the benches were shoved aside and Hayimkeh cried out: "Girls—to the left! Boys—to the right!"

Tuvia went out of the tent and pulled at the rope of the bell with all his might. But the wild singing and dancing went on. With difficulty he made his way towards the middle of the tent, stood up on a table and tried to outshout the merrymakers. He raised his hand, but it took a long time before he could command attention. "Tumbah, tumbah, tumbah, tumbah!" an ecstatic sound kept coming from the frenzied circle of the prancing youths.

Tuvia finally opened the meeting, made a short report on the state of the various branches of the husbandry and called upon Belkind, who had just returned from a country-wide tour of the Labor Battalion.

When Belkind finished, Tuvia called upon Levin.

For a while Levin stood silent, passing his hand over his bald pate as if searching for the proper words under the shining pink skin. Then his talk began to flow in his clear resonant voice, in a Hebrew flavored with the style of the Bible, in well-constructed sentences and paragraphs. Red spots appeared in his cheeks as he spoke. He dwelt on the past, on the old wine of Judaism. Then he stressed the need for preserving the old wine in the new bottles. He described the Jewish traditional concept of a communal repast and pleaded against defiling it with alien singing, with songs that recalled the marching of soldiers and the thumping of their jackboots. He appealed for better manners. He painted a picture of a new life, a new civilization, new festivals in a spirit of continuity with the past. Then he went on to make his concrete proposals and unfolded before his audience a complete program for cultural activities.

Rahel, the daughter of a Volhynian *shohet,* sat comfortably relaxed with her arms crossed on her ample bosom, her eyes fixed on the speaker's mouth. She had been unable to follow what Belkind was saying. But Levin's address struck a responsive chord and she avidly imbibed every word. "Wonderful!" she said to herself. "That is what this place needs! It's true, this savage conduct has become unbearable. This noise, this gluttony, this lack of manners! You can't even clear the tables. Sure, Sabbath must be Sabbath! It's a pleasure to hear such talk!"

* * *

Tuvia arranged that Levin should help him in administrative work, keeping the books for part of the day, and devoting the other part to preparing his lessons. In the evening he was to teach.

Yet it was not for this that Levin had come to the Homeland. It had been his lifelong ideal to till its soil. And so, despite Tuvia's protests that he was ruining his health, Levin insisted on spending half a day in the fields. Zeev, watching his nervous, awkward motions, growled that Levin would never make a farm worker. But Levin paid no attention to him. What could Zeev know about the feeling of bliss he experienced when wielding a pitchfork on an axe?

Every evening, as soon as the tables were cleared, the square tent became a school. The boys and girls sat crowded around their teacher, memorizing the forms of Hebrew verbs, studying the rules of etymology and syntax and writing exercises, though their limbs were weary from the day's work in the fields. Twice a week Levin devoted the study period to readings from the Bible and from modern Hebrew literature. Those were the hours when the students felt their weariness leave them, as interest in the lesson imbued them with new vigor. Severed, isolated links were forged together into one chain, at one with the hills, rocks and fields amid which they lived and worked.

Naomi's beautiful eyes looked entranced and full of gratitude as she followed Levin's lectures. What sublime beauty was this, preserved by generations of humiliated and oppressed Jews and handed down from age to age, and yet she knew nothing of it until this man Levin revealed it to her! How stirring were those short simple sentences throbbing with deep human emotions! What a mighty yearning for truth and justice! How much majestic beauty, and splendor and grief in those poetic chapters, which, though not rhyming like the verses of Mickiewicz and Slowacki, were full of music and rhythm!

Raphael had a good knowledge of Hebrew, but he found interest in Levin's presentations and he liked to watch Naomi's progress. Each time Raphael had to attend a Bible class, Tuvia substituted for him on guard duty.

*   *   *

One day, Tuvia, who had gone to the railway station to bring back a shipment of food, found a passenger waiting for him. She was a dark-complexioned very good-looking girl, elegantly dressed, holding a fancy handbag. Tuvia hardly paid any attention to what she said, but took her to the settlement, as she requested. As soon as she alighted from Tuvia's cart, she addressed the first cluster of people she met, in fluent, but rather bookish Hebrew:

"Where does Smuel Levin reside?"

She pronounced "Smuel," not "Shmuel." She obviously hailed from Lithuania, where the knowledge of Hebrew was widespread and where many Jews could not distinguish between "sh" and "s."

At first they thought she was some traveling agent of a business firm who merely wanted the administrative officials and pointed to the hut. But the lady insisted she wanted to see Levin personally, "Smuel Levin, the teatzer, who is also in tzardz of the bookkeeping department." She added: "I am his fiancée."

This caused a sensation, and the report spread immediately.

This was the first time that a person came to the settlement not as a member of a traveling group of halutzim, but as an individual, as a fiancée come to join her affianced. In a world of young men and young women who had turned away from their backgrounds of small town genteel Jewish society to build a new life in the wilderness, this appeared entirely outlandish. Some of the boys and girls on the mound had had sweethearts in Europe, but here the romances had evaporated. Boys and girls met, walked with their arms around each other, embraced, kissed, but they were too busy planning for a new world to cultivate lasting attachments. To think that the hero of the first romance was that pedantic pedagogue, that austere theoretician, that Hebrew grammarian, that Bible-teacher! And what an attractive girl! Where, in the world, could he have gotten her? In a catalogue?

When Levin returned from his daily work in the field, all covered with grime and perspiration, the Lithuanian belle rushed towards him: "Smuel!" But she was taken aback when she saw his appearance, and cried out as her black eyes grew large: "But you wrote me you were a teatzer and in tzardz of the bookkeeping department!"

Levin's hoe dropped from his hand, red spots appeared in his pale cheeks and his eyes looked through the thick lenses of his glasses with embarrassment and shame.

*   *   *

Shoshanna, the attractive Litvak girl who came to marry Levin, had read all his articles and agreed with all his ideas on the greatness of the ideal of a rustic Israel in its ancient homeland, but she had never been in a training farm, never belonged to a halutz organization and her adjustment to life on the mound was difficult. Her first reaction was a crying spell in her tent. Three times each day Levin carried her food from the kitchen given him in generous quantities by the good motherly cook, Rahel. Finally Shoshanna emerged from her seclusion and came to Tuvia asking to be assigned some work. That evening the girls laughingly described Shoshanna's work in the garden: she had wielded the shovel as if it were a croquet mallet, she always kept shaking the dust off her skirt and ran to the spring to wash her hands. What a man this Levin was, to bring this decked-out peacock into the kibbutz!

Shoshanna changed her occupation several times. This job was too filthy, and that was too dusty and there the sun was too strong. Good Tuvia showed patience and sympathetic indulgence. But the community as a whole grumbled and Levin often overheard a remark behind his back about this intolerable attitude towards work.

Still, Shoshanna's arrival had had a beneficial effect on Levin. He was now less irritable; he dressed neatly and beamed in Shoshanna's presence when the two appeared together for the evening meal. She always wore her silk white dress which fitted her dark-complexioned pretty face so well; her shining black hair was done smoothly behind her small white chiseled ears. Hayimkeh sneered and compared Levin to a young scholar in the ghetto whom

a well-to-do father-in-law supported while he spent his time studying the Talmud. Levin pleaded with Shoshanna to take off her
jewelry. "What!" she exclaimed indignantly, "my engagement ring!"
and kept on flashing it in the light of the yellow Lux lamp when
her nimble hands moved gracefully over the table in serving herself and her Shmuel.

But soon Shoshanna adjusted herself. She put away her elegant
clothes and took the ordinary working dress worn by the girls
in the settlement from the store tent. She found work in the kitchen
and liked it, and made friends with Rahel. Shoshanna was a good
housekeeper and worked well, while talking all the time about her
life back home in Lithuania. It was a world the young settlers had
left behind them—the world of fathers and mothers, of uncles and
aunts, established homes and houses inherited from grandfathers
and great-grandfathers, and old furniture and newly furnished
rooms, and family businesses; the world of Zionist meetings and
literary meetings and lectures and balls. Here the tent was the
dwelling place and the army hut was the office. Ploughing, hoeing
and armed clashes with Arabs had taken the place of Zionist meetings. Rahel often felt nostalgic and suddenly discovered during
Shoshanna's chatter that the onions in the kitchen made her eyes
tear.

*   *   *

"We will renounce the old world, we will shake off its dust
from our feet," went the Russian revolutionary song to the tune of
the Marseillaise. It was a song on which many young Jews were
brought up in Eastern Europe and whose spirit they imbibed even
if they did not join the revolutionary movement and even when
they were guilty of "counter-revolutionary" hankerings for the
ancient Homeland and the historic language of the Jews. To the
young men and young women, "the children of upheaval and disruption," who went out pioneering in the swampy wilderness of
the valley and built their settlement on the mound, the idea of
having a synagogue or a rabbi would have appeared partly shock-
ing, partly ludicrous. A marriage ceremony officiated by a rabbi
was unthinkable. Even Shmuel Levin and his Shoshanna did not
think it was necessary. True, Shmuel Levin sought, as he said, to

"pour the old wine" of Judaism into the "new bottles." But the "old wine" did not include a religious marriage ceremony and the "new bottles" would refuse to hold it. True, Shoshanna, back in her Lithuanian town, was a daughter of a respectable middle class Zionist family whose sense of propriety would be outraged by the notion of dispensing with the ceremony for a marital union— but this was The Brave New World, and things were different.

Shmuel and Shoshanna became man and wife when Levin's fellow-occupant of the tent discreetly moved out, leaving it entirely to the couple. Later, when Rahel, who worked with Shoshanna in the kitchen, noticed signs of pregnancy, she spread the word, and the community knew it was faced with a new problem of how to deal with a mother and child.

*   *   *

One night, as the settlers were in deep slumber after a hard day's labor, they were awakened by piercing cries. The young men and young women quickly tumbled out and ran to take up their posts, hugging the cold steel, as their eyes tried to penetrate the darkness enveloping the hills. Soon they realized that this was not an attack by Arabs. The cries were coming from Levin's tent.

"Quick! Quick!" cried Rahel the Cook, "Somebody heat up some water!"

"Is it Shoshanna? Already?" The shadows moved helplessly among the tents. Why hadn't she said she was so close to confinement? Why hadn't she gone to a hospital in town?

Not one of the women knew how to care for a woman in labor.

In the morning the camp rejoiced with Levin at the birth of his first child. It was a boy and he called him Yigal—He who will redeem.

*   *   *

The time came to celebrate the first planting festival and Levin was asked to direct the festivities. It turned out that the large trunks Shoshanna had brought with her on her arrival contained the costumes for the biblical play Levin had planned for the kibbutz a long time before this.

Nathan Galili and Shoshanna played the main parts. Nathan played well. As a native of the country, he pronounced his Hebrew naturally and successfully impersonated the ancient Hebrew. Shoshanna, too, showed unexpected talent. Her diction was good, even though occasionally she lapsed into the "s" for the "sh." Besides, she was very beautiful, in the flowering of her first motherhood.

Levin was pleased. But something worried him about the too intimate contact between Shoshanna and Nathan. He recalled that at first Shoshanna had kept this native Lothario at arm's length and rebuked him sharply each time he attempted any familiarity. What had happened?

After the play and the choral singing there was a banquet. Belkind spoke, and Aryeh, but when Tuvia was asked to say a few words, he rose and mumbled: "I can't, I can't" and sat down in embarrassment. They drank wine and Hayimkeh tried to amuse the gathering by his mockery of every member. At the end they danced and danced and danced.

"Vetaher libbenu leovdekha be-emet"—And purify our hearts so that we may worship Thee truly, they sang the verse from the Psalms, as their fathers and forefathers, the pious *Hassidim,* sang when they danced.

Raphael dropped out of the dancing circle. He was all wet with perspiration and unsteady on his feet. He panted heavily. The circle had been surging for hours, and some who had dropped out rejoined it after a brief rest. Naomi had been dancing, spinning all the time. "Where does she get so much strength?" Raphael asked himself as he watched her. Her supple young body was lightly tripping, as if carried ever higher by an unseen power. Her thick blond braids, wound around her read, had fallen over her shoulders and her face, tossing in the stormy dance. Her eyes were overcast with a moist film of delight.

But the circle broke and Noami sank down on the bench near Raphael. "I'm so tired," she said, and put her head in his shoulder. Raphael, feeling the warmth of her body, sat immobile, not daring to make the slightest motion.

"Come," said Naomi, "let us take a walk in the fields." She put her arm through his.

They reached the palm tree which stood alone in the field over a little stream, surrounded by a thick growth of verdure.

"Let us sit down awhile," Naomi said. She placed her head in his lap and shut her eyes. The silence rang in his ears with myriad sound. The heavy clouds froze in the low skies. . . . Suddenly she raised the upper part of her body, entwined her arm about his neck and drew him to herself: "Come here, you silly boy."

Thick drops began falling on them and, after a slight pause, increased in frequency. Soon the drops grew into a heavy rain. They rose, took each others hands and ran towards the mound. Their faces and clothes were streaming with water. They felt like jumping, splashing, singing:

"The spring rain!" cried Raphael.

"Yes, Raphael, that's the spring rain!" she laughed.

*　　*　　*

From sunrise to sunset Raphael and Naomi were bent over the tender seedlings to rid them of the malignant parasitic plants. But neither of them seemed to see or hear what went on around them. They worked and thought of each other and the labor now was easy to bear. When not at work, Raphael took Naomi to the fields, telling her about every plant, teaching her to perceive the nocturnal sounds, all of which he had learned while working with Zeev and while patrolling on horseback at night. Naomi had now nearly forgotten the loud rustles of the Polish woods and the noisy splashing of the waters of the Vistula. Together with Raphael's marvelous love she had acquired the gift of the love of the Homeland. She loved that little country with the sharp changes in weather and in scenery, which suddenly came rushing with the heady effect of strong wine. How precious was every tender seedling, every stalk of corn in the golden field, planted in land that but recently had been a swamp. . . .

*　　*　　*

When Naomi became pregnant, the two youngsters felt lost. The pioneers on the mound had learned how to make the wilderness produce corn and fruit, how to hold out against the Arabs; they were highly skilled in argument about this or that theory of social living. But they did not know how to translate into terms of the reality of their lives the customs and traditions of their fathers lost during the troublous periods of war and revolution, of upheaval and disruption.

Naomi remembered that Levin and Shoshanna shared the same tent and Raphael duly collected his belongings and moved from the tent he shared with Nathan Galili into Naomi's. Naomi fixed up the beds, the clothes, the books and put a few flowers on the table. So this was their home and this was the first night in their home. Suddenly both lovers felt gloomy and lonely.

Somebody seemed to have scraped at the flap of the tent. It was Tuvia, good old shy Tuvia. He stood there, his small eyes flickering with a light of boundless affection for these two young children, but he could not utter a word. Finally he made an effort and just walked away. When he left, Raphael and Naomi noticed a bunch of blue cornflowers on the bed. Naomi threw her head against Raphael's chest, struggling to hold back her tears. . . .

Tuvia once came into the tent occupied by Raphael and Naomi and, after speaking of this and that, asked them to accompany him into town. "We shall be very happy if you are present with us at that little ceremony. . . . I am very grateful to you. . . . Rahel, too, wants you to come. I got some money from the treasurer for traveling expenses for the four of us. . . . I am very grateful to you. . . ."

The four settlers wandered aimlessly through the streets of the sleepy town, arousing the curiosity of the idlers sitting in the stores. Tuvia, accustomed to the open spaces and to simple working clothes, felt tired and uncomfortable in the summer heat beating against the white walls of the narrow streets, wearing the finest clothes Rahel could fish out of the supply tent. Rahel was dressed in her Sabbath finery she had brought from home. Well, Tuvia comforted himself, it would soon be over and he would be back at work.

Their knock was answered by an old man with a long white beard and with a pair of childish blue eyes.

"Come in, my children, come in," he welcomed them in good Hebrew. His kindly eyes were flooded with affection when he learned of the purpose of their visit.

"Sit down, my children, sit down, where are you from?"

It transpired that the old rabbi had been closely following the development of the kibbutz in the valley. He inquired about the progress of agriculture and about the security situation, viewing them all the time with open affection and admiration.

"Neche, Neche!" he called in his wife. A wrinkled yellow-faced old lady came hobbling in from behind the partition.

"Haven't I been telling you?" his childish blue eyes beamed, "haven't I been telling you that there were unplumbed depths in the Jewish soul. Here are these dear boys and girls from that burning wilderness among the savage Ishmaelites, here they are come to me for a religious ceremony. I always knew they'd come, I knew it! These dear children, our flesh and blood. Who can plumb the deep recesses of the Jewish soul? What did I tell you, Neche?" His face glowed.

The old woman passed her trembling wrinkled hands over the cheeks and hands of Naomi and Rahel, muttering with her old cracked voice:

"Dear children! Dear children!"

*   *   *

Sometime after the pioneers settled on the mound, they noticed in the distance another group of white tents and men ploughing in the fields. This was the only intimation they had of another Jewish settlement. Communication with these neighbors was difficult and infrequent, despite the proximity. There were also Arab neighbors—villager fellaheen and nomad Bedouin. On the surface relations were friendly, but whenever opportunity seemed to present itself, the Arabs stole. Veteran shomerim, experienced since the pre-war days in the guarding of Jewish settlements, trained some of the local boys in patrolling and organized the general defense. Raphael was one of the first to be trained, tested and found to be a good shomer. Later, when a group of Crimean Jews arrived to settle in the community, little Mishka was inducted. He guarded together with Nathan Galili, a former shomer who had joined the kibbutz and who was now in charge.

Both Raphael and Mishka showed themselves to be brave and

cool but reticent. Nathan Galili sought to overawe his fellow-settlers by his tales of former prowess as a shomer and by a show of bravery now. He had more success with the women than with the men.

Mishka did not like such goings-on. But he did not like to talk, and, besides, he knew that Nathan was his superior, and that in military matters, discipline was of paramount importance.

One night Mishka heard twelve shots and galloped in the direction of the fire. He found Nathan Galili caressing and kissing his Arab mare, who had a light wound in her cheek.

Because there was some dispute with the neighboring Arabs, Galili was ordered to keep to his tent. Soon suspicion arose that Galili had faked the attack and wounded his own mare.

Shoshanna, who worked with Rahel in the kitchen, once brought Nathan his food.

"Where is Rahel?" Nathan asked in surprise.

"She is busy now. The police are here again, making investigations. Tuvia is entertaining them. Rahel is busy feeding them. . . ."

Nathan asked Shoshanna to sit down for a few minutes. She said she was very busy and that she was afraid Rahel would be angry. Yet she sat down on the edge of the bed.

"Do you like horseback riding, Shoshanna?"

"I am afraid of horses."

"Of my horse, too? How would you like to try?"

"That mad one? She is only for wild brave riders!"

"Would you be afraid if you rode her with me?"

Shoshanna blushed: "I am sorry, I think I hear my name." She gathered up the dishes and left.

*　　*　　*

The police investigation of the case of the shooting of a Bedouin, who meantime died of his wounds, led to the discovery that he had been shot at close range in a quarrel over a woman, and that the assailant was a member of the same tribe. The impression gained ground that Galili, having heard a shot from the direction of the Bedouin camp, fired twelve shots on his own, inflicted a slight wound on his mare and pretended he had fought off a formidable attack. He explained to the few people who might want to listen that he was the tragic victim of malicious slander. Shoshanna believed him and lavished her sympathy on him. Everybody felt sorry for Levin, but Levin was too busy with his work and with his first-born son to notice anything. He merely wondered what kept Shoshanna out so late at night. She did not even go to the children's room to visit little Yigal.

One night, as Levin walked out into the field, wondering if he was not guilty of spying on his own wife, he saw her ride out with Nathan Galili. From then on his life became a nightmare. Eventually Shoshanna moved to Galili's tent and lived with him openly. Levin tried to see that his visits to the nursery tent, where little Yigal lived, should not take place at the same time as Shoshanna's, but that could not always be managed. The moments when the two met in the nursery tent were extremely painful.

Levin became untidy and careless. He could no longer conduct his classes and begged Tuvia to let him be a night watchman.

Galili, meanwhile, became tired of the unfriendly looks of his neighbors and of Shoshanna's love. One day he told her he was leaving the settlement. She offered to go with him, but he left alone.

* * *

Thus, Galili was the first settler to defect. The second one was Zeev. More were to follow.

Zeev, who had always objected to the singing, dancing and debating in the settlement, was especially outraged by the controversy which had broken out almost from the beginning of the existence of the settlement and had become more virulent as time went on.

The leader of one faction was Belkind, the head of the Labor Battalion, whose first loyalty was to the Battalion. The leaders of the opposite faction were Tuvia and Aryeh, the founders of the settlement. Belkind was primarily interested in a world revolution carried out by the working class of which his Labor Battalion was the outpost in Palestine. Tuvia and Aryeh were first of all Zionists.

At one time, during the early part of the settlement's existence, Belkind succeeded in convincing the majority of the settlers, over

Tuvia's and Aryeh's objections, to admit a group of new members. The group consisted of young Crimean Jews who had recently completed an assignment on road-building and were now out of work. In time both Tuvia and Aryeh realized they had made a mistake, since the Crimeans turned out to be a valuable asset to the economic development of the settlement.

*　　*　　*

Few among the individual members of the two opposing factions followed all the intricate reasoning of one or the other spokesman, but, in time, nearly everybody took sides. What else could Yashka, Mishka and Abrashka and the other Crimeans do but to follow Belkind? They knew that it was because of Belkind that they had been admitted into the settlement. The language he spoke about class solidarity sounded more familiar to them than this talk of Judaism by ghetto-bred Tuvia, Aryeh and Levin.

The leadership of the Jewish Labor movement in Palestine was on the side of Tuvia and Aryeh. But the membership of the Labor Battalion, led by Belkind, objected to the leadership's interference. This involved jurisdictional problem added to the acrimonious nature of the debate.

The conflict grew more and more bitter. Some branches of the work were taken over by members of one faction, others by their opponents. There were jobs which were "neutral," that is on which the members of both factions worked, with the result that the work suffered, because opponents were hardly on speaking terms. There were a few outbursts of physical violence, which were quickly suppressed. But the conflict grew.

*　　*　　*

And so Zeev made up his mind to leave this collective life forever. The life he chose for himself was one in a *moshav-ovedim* (workers' settlement, or co-operative colony), in which each farmer was given a long lease by the Jewish National Fund and conducted his own husbandry.

"Can't you see the brighter side of our life?" Raphael argued with him. "To be sure, there is want, poverty, congestion—but what do you expect? It is only two years since we first came to settle on this mound. Look what has been created here in spite of all the hardships! Don't you remember the swamps, the weeds, the rocks? We have had a good crop this year. . . ."

"What's the use of all this talking? Each one has his own way of seeing things." Zeev spoke reluctantly, "It may be that the commune will become established and will thrive in the midst of all these debates and controversies and quarrels. All right, some day you will have temples of culture in this place. I am not at all sure that some will not feel cold in those temples of culture you are dreaming about. . . ."

"But the fields, the plantations, the hills, the people—how can you say these things?" Naomi pleaded, "How can you forget them? How can you leave them? You have been among the very first here! Don't you remember the waste that we found? You, you have taken part in all that has been created here—how can you part from it?"

"Really, Naomi-leh, I can't carry on any more," Zeev replied, "I don't know how to explain it. And there is no use anyway. It will be very hard for me, too, but what is the use? . . ."

"If you ever feel lonesome, Zeev," Naomi said as tears streamed down her cheeks, "write to us! We will receive you back with open arms!"

"Shalom!" was all Zeev could reply in a voice that had suddenly become husky. He walked off with his knapsack on his back.

Zeev knocked at the tent of Tuvia and Rahel. They had already gone to bed.

"Excuse me," Zeev stammered, "I have come to say good-bye."

"Are you going anywhere?" They were surprised. "For how long? And why in the middle of the night?"

"I am leaving the settlement," Zeev explained.

Tuvia tried to argue with Zeev. Rahel became flustered and offered to prepare something for Zeev to take along. "Just turn away for a minute, Zeev and I'll get dressed and run over to the kitchen," she pleaded with him. Zeev refused.

After they spent some time in arguing, Tuvia said: "Well Zeev, if that is your decision, go and be of good strength! . . . But if

you ever change your mind, don't be ashamed to come back. You'll
be as welcome as you are now. . . ."

"Write to us Zeev, write to us," Rahel sobbed.

"Shalom!" said Zeev and walked off.

*　　*　　*

There was one more person whose hand Zeev wanted to shake
before leaving. The figure of a lean tall man was silhouetted in
the dark.

"Levin!" called Zeev.

The figure did not stir. Zeev called again. Levin still stood
as if frozen.

"I came to bid you farewell, Levin," said Zeev, as he put his
hand on the man's shoulder.

"What's that?"

"I came to say good-bye, I am leaving."

"You're leaving," Levin repeated mechanically.

Zeev's heart was contracted with sorrow.

"Shalom, Levin, I wish you health and luck!" He shook his
hand warmly, but Levin's hand lay in his limp and cold.

"What a stupid idea it was to let Levin do night watch duty!"
Zeev thought to himself. "Something may happen to this man."

Some time after Zeev left, Levin committed suicide.

*　　*　　*

As the controversy grew in bitterness, the adherents of Tuvia and
Aryeh realizing that they were in the minority, moved out and
joined the neighboring settlement. Belkind's followers remained in
the old kibbutz on the mound but the leader himself, with a small
handful, eventually left to go back to Russia.

With the passing of the years little survived of the old differences between the two factions and the two settlements got along
in a neighborly spirit.

Many years passed.

*　　*　　*

As the day grew to its close, Aryeh walked home through a
path flanked on both sides with vineyards and orchards. He walked
slowly, with the large hoe on his shoulder carried lightly, like

something dear to his heart. His face was all wrinkled now. His hair was gray. His tall figure slightly bent towards the good earth. His thin-lipped mouth, formerly closed with a mien of defiant determination, was now slightly open, as if ready to greet anyone who happened along the way. The dense foliage of the trees formed an arched roof over his head and some twigs and branches rubbed against his clothes. He gently moved them away to pass, a kindly indulgent smile playing on his lips. Aryeh remembered every seedling, every plant, its age and its history. He recalled the swamps, the desolation of the valley, the bitter debates, the defections, the painful division and the emigration of the minority to another settlement. But what did it all matter now? They were all servants of the soil and servants of the landless people yearning for redemption.

Aryeh sat down on a rock. The supper gong had sounded and young men and women dressed in white must be seated around tables, discussing tomorrow's work and the problems of the country and many other things. There was no hurry. Aryeh would eat later. He looked down the valley and observed its fields, its groves, its settlements. Quietly he sang a Psalm:

> The heavens declare the glory of God
> And the firmament showeth His handiwork
> Day unto day uttereth speech,
> And night unto night revealeth knowledge.

Aryeh looked at the sunset, as if this was the first sunset he had seen in his life.

When Aryeh entered the settlement grounds, strong light was pouring out of the windows of the largest buildings situated in the middle—the dining hall and the children's home. The smaller buildings containing the residences shed fainter light. He took a shower, changed his clothes, went into his room and played with his children, then took them to their beds in the children's home, and with his wife went into the dining hall. He saw a solid mass of bodies entwined by their arms, rising and descending, in a circle—young people dancing, as in the days when Aryeh had been young and his comrades danced.

"Am Yisrael hai, am Yisrael hai!"—the people of Israel lives, the people of Israel lives—went the refrain. The words were not very distinct. All that Aryeh heard was *"hai, hai, hai"*—lives, lives, lives. . . .

* * *

Raphael, too, now had gray strands in his hair, once golden-colored. His deep blue eyes no longer exuded that youthful exultation and his body was no longer as supple. His gait was slow and heavy, his calloused hands hung by his sides like full pails of water. His forehead was furrowed with wrinkles, his face was tanned with the sun and the wind.

Raphael, too, was returning from his day's work in the fields. He was sure to be met on the way by Naomi and their children. His heart still leaped at the prospect of the meeting, but he no longer ran. He was very tired and very sad.

These tempestuous years on the mound and later on the slope, where the new settlement was situated, with all their bitterness, had had a depressing effect on him. So much had passed over Raphael, first in his lonely tent, later in his lonely room. Naomi, too, was worn out. Her once blond, thick, sweet-smelling braids were now much thinner and sprinkled with white.

Indeed, the achievement was great: the wasteland had become a garden; the once desolate valley was teeming with Jewish settlements. But Man had not been purified, as he, Raphael, had once hoped. Perhaps it was a vain dream. One must accept life, with its inevitable conflicts, and strive only for betterment, without expecting the absolute good. . . .

As Raphael slowly climbed up the slope of the hill, he met face to face the flaming ball of fire which scorched the whole settlement by its heat.

He stood looking at the burning bush, uncertain whether he faced the passing of a dying day or the dawn of a bright morning rising over the valley. . . .

8 STRANDS IN A PATTERN

THE FOUNDATIONS for the remarkable rebirth of the Hebrew language were laid in the pre-war years. The first two decades under the British Mandate saw its consolidation. Tel-Aviv now took the place of Warsaw, Vilno and Odessa as the world center of Hebrew literature.

Despite occasional bloody encounters with Arab rioters and despite conflicts with the British authorities, the Jewish Homeland grew and expanded, enjoying a large measure of internal autonomy. A pattern of national life emerged, which soon found its expression in literature.

For the first time since the days of the Second Jewish Commonwealth the written word and the spoken word were of the same language.

As a spoken medium Hebrew began to lose ground to its sister-language Aramaic before the Jews were deprived of their independence. But a small determined band centered in Jerusalem maintained the Hebrew speech until about 1,500 years ago. As a written language, however, Hebrew never died.

Throughout the ages of Jewish Dispersion a rich body of Hebrew literature evolved, developing new styles and new vocabularies, often subjected to the influences of other languages and literatures. Most books produced in Hebrew were of a religious nature, but much of the literature was devoted to the cultivation of arts and sciences. The first Hebrew grammar was written in Morocco over a thousand years ago. The greatest poetry in Hebrew since the Bible was produced in Spain two centuries later. The first novel came out of Southern France somewhat later. A contemporary and friend of Dante in Rome introduced the sonnet into Hebrew before it was known in English. In the seventeenth century Amsterdam was for a short period the center of secular Hebrew literature;

in the eighteenth century it was Berlin and Leipzig, where the disciples of Moses Mendelssohn published periodicals, treatises and collections of poems. From Germany the movement spread to Eastern Europe, where the large Jewish masses steeped in traditional Hebrew lore provided a fertile soil for the flourishing of a modern literature. The period immediately preceding the First World War was the one in which modern Hebrew literature reached its flowering stage, with the two great poets, Bialik and Tchernikhovsky, as its towering figures. The best years of Hebrew literature in the Diaspora were the years of the growth of Zionism, on which it exerted a profound influence and from which it drew great strength.

But as a spoken language Hebrew was used on rare occasions. Some pious Jews insisted on speaking only Hebrew on Saturdays and holidays; Jews of various countries whose daily vernaculars were different, used Hebrew to communicate with each other by word of mouth. (As far as communication by mail, most literate Jews carried on their correspondence in Hebrew, even with people speaking the same vernacular.) In the Holy Land, where Yiddish-speaking Jews from Eastern Europe mingled with Jews from the Balkans, Africa and Asia, whose daily speech was in other languages (Ladino, Tat, Arabic, Persian, Tartar, etc.) there was more occasion for speaking Hebrew than in any other country.

Such was the situation when Eliezer Ben-Yehuda arrived in 1882 with his young bride and settled in Jerusalem. Ben-Yehuda was determined to introduce the use of Hebrew in daily conversation for all occasions among all Jews and he started with his bride who hardly knew a word of the language. The ultra-orthodox in the Holy City were outraged by what they considered such sacrilege. But the young Zionists took up Ben-Yehuda's call with enthusiasm and began forming Hebrew-speaking circles, which, in time, spread to the Diaspora. The teachers among the Zionists fought hard to introduce Hebrew as the language of instruction and oral communication in the schools where they taught. In time, they enlisted the support of the parents and the children for the idea of the language rebirth. They did not succeed in exerting much influence on the old traditional type school, such as prevailed in Jerusalem in those days. But they did penetrate quite easily into the schools maintained by the colonies, by Baron Rothschild, by the Alliance Israelite Universelle and by the Hilfverein den deutschen Juden. Since the schools maintained by the French and German Jews vied with each other for the good will of the Palestine Jewish population, the Zionists, led by Ben-Yehuda and his followers found it comparatively simple to induce them to employ Hebrew for most subjects and to allow the teachers to converse with their pupils in Hebrew. A system of kindergartens and nursery schools helped to disseminate the daily use of the language.

The old colonists were slow to give up Yiddish or Russian for Hebrew. But the young pioneers of the Second Aliyah, ever ready to sacrifice comfort to principle, took up the question seriously and, finally decided in favor of Hebrew after a vehement controversy. The controversy raged around the rivalry between Hebrew and Yiddish.

The impact of the modern West on the ghetto which stimulated the unparalleled development of Hebrew literature in Eastern Europe also gave birth to a modern literature in Yiddish. Intended, in its first steps, only for the masses unschooled in Hebrew, Yiddish literature, in time, acquired more self-confidence and demanded a place of honor. As the most widely spoken and most highly developed Jewish vernacular, Yiddish found its own champions who proclaimed it as the national language of the Jewish people. Hebrew was to be relegated to a place similar to that of Latin among the Christian nations of Europe.

As a rule, Zionists championed Hebrew, but some of the pioneers were Yiddishists. Of the two main labor parties the non-Socialist *Hashomer Hatzair* was committed to Hebrew, while the Socialist Poale-Zion was divided, a slim majority favoring Hebrew. In time, it became a rule at every Jewish labor meeting in Palestine to use only Hebrew from the platform. Exceptions were made only for newcomers.

The support given by the Second Aliyah to Ben-Yehuda's efforts to revive the Hebrew language was probably decisive in enthroning it as the language of the Homeland.

Thus, by the middle 1930's, Tel-Aviv, having displaced Warsaw, Vilno and Odessa as the center of Hebrew literature, was the seat of writers who wrote primarily for an audience living in Palestine and speaking Hebrew. A very large portion of the reading public consisted of young people whose mother tongue was Hebrew, who had been brought up in Zionist-controlled schools where the language of instruction was Hebrew for all subjects and who had been nurtured on Hebrew classics produced in Eastern Europe and dealing with a pattern of life remote from their own experiences. These readers demanded material which portrayed the life and the problems around them. But the time when the native sabra was the writer and the subject of literary work was still some two decades away.

Moshe Smilansky

◆

STORY OF A LOVE

IT WAS twenty years ago, in the wintertime.*

In midwinter our Homeland's skies are as blue as her eyes, as pure as her soul and as deep as the bottomless recesses of her spirit.

The sun was warm and healing; the air was pleasingly mild, permeating one's being with a quiet, gentle delight. There was a profusion of light; the hills were decked with countless flowers and the trees were clothed in green; there was a riot of colors.

It was on just such a luminous day that I first entered her father's house.

The house stood on elevated ground in the colony of Pisgah. Through the windows the Mediterranean could be seen in the distance, lapping the sands of the Valley of Ephraim, its serene grandeur enhancing the beauty of the day.

But it was the house of an official and I entered with reluctance. From the moment I set foot on the soil of my forefathers I conceived a dislike for bureaucrats. And the man, who was the school administrator in Pisgah, behaved like a typical bureaucrat. He insisted on receiving petitioners in his own house.

I always had an interest in schools and in teaching and I wanted to visit the Pisgah school. For that I required his permission. And that is how I came to his house.

Monsieur le directeur received me well, asked me to sit down and engaged me in conversation. His wife, a rather young woman, entered the room and she, too, gave me a friendly look. I wondered whether it was because they knew I had a certificate of matriculation from a Russian high school and was the son of well-to-do parents.

---

* The novel was published in 1911.

But I came to Pisgah to be a worker in the fields. I could not tolerate their talk and ignored their overtures. As my host spoke to me,
I was looking out the window. A faint smile flitted over his intelligent face. Suddenly I sensed the presence of a new person in the
room and turned around. In the doorway leading from the adjoining room stood a little girl of about five, with a crown of curly black
hair and a tall white forehead. The freshness of her little face was
inundated by a bright light. Her azure blue eyes looked in wonderment, now at me, now at her father.

"This is my daughter, Shifra," the host introduced her with a
proud happy smile.

"To think that they, the bureaucrats, have such a beautiful little
girl!" I thought with resentment, "Why isn't she a farmer's daughter?"

After that first visit I had to fight the temptation to go to the
house where that beautiful child lived. To be attracted to it was
against my principles. I hated "aristocrats," that is, people who had
comfortable homes, fine clothes and fine furniture. My ideal consisted of home-spun clothes, simple wooden tables and chairs in a
small peasant's hut, such as I had seen in my native village in Russia.

                              *   *   *

Soon I left Pisgah to go to Imkiyah, a newly-founded settlement,
where I worked hard and where I outgrew some of my fondest hopes
and beliefs. Bitter disillusionment injected its first drops of poison
into my soul. My faith in mankind began to waver. Overcome by
human wickedness and by the ravages of malaria, I left Imkiyah, as
did other pioneers like myself—I was among the last to leave—still
hoping to return some day. In the meantime I went back to Pisgah,
back to the work in the vineyards which I loved. It was the work
I had learned during my first year in the Homeland, in that very
village of Pisgah. It had been my finest year in Palestine. Now,
after an absence of two years, I was back.

Not long after my return I was seized with an attack of the green
fever and hovered between life and death in the Baron's hospital
in Pisgah. It was already winter when I came out. It was the peak
of the season for the work in the vineyards. I learned that the school
administrator, Shifra's father, had died and that the Baron had

granted his widow a life pension, a large house and a substantial sum of money for little Shifra's dowry.

But I had no interest in Shifra, her mother or in their position. At my age of twenty-one years, I already felt old in spirit, a disillusioned man. Meantime, however, I took up a light flirtation with the blacksmith's daughter across the street. For hours I would sit at my window, trying to meet her eyes. Those were two burning black eyes set in a comely dark-complexioned face. She was about fifteen years old. But the spark in her eyes was not one that one usually finds in a fifteen year old girl. That spark I thought was kindled in those eyes by the young clerks of the administrative offices who danced with her at every festive occasion and who stared at her as if she were much older. I hated those fops with their long mustaches, Parisian manners and French speech. . . .

I kept to myself. The landlady in whose house I stayed and took my meals was friendly and so were her daughters, but I hardly talked to them. I was very shy in their presence. One day, as I sat at my meal in the dining room, embarrassing my landlady with my stubborn silence, Shifra suddenly appeared in the doorway. She had grown during these two years. Her face was much paler and her curls were gone. The sight of her evoked in me a feeling of displeasure. I knew that her mother belonged to the circle of Baronial bureaucrats who led an easy life, that the two of them occupied a house large enough for two farmers' families. . . . Or did I perhaps resent Shifra's haircut?

While I hated those "aristocrats," I myself was receiving money from my parents in Russia to whom I kept writing that I was studying agriculture. They believed my tales and urged me to accept larger remittances. . . .

In Pisgah, as I watched the Jewish colonists work their land seemingly as a mere pretext for qualifying for the Baron's bounty, I lost my enthusiasm for manual labor. I decided that this generation of farmers was lost and that the only thing left was to save their children. That could be done through education. I resolved to become a teacher. With that in mind, I left Pisgah again, this time for Jerusalem, to spend a year in training.

This was the time when the movement for speaking Hebrew got under way. It gave me a new inspiration. I was beside myself with joy when I met the leader of the movement, Eliezer Ben-Yehuda, and he praised my Hebrew speech.

At the end of the year I returned to Pisgah, went directly to Monsieur Alatin, who was the chief administrator, and offered my services. He gave me a job and even agreed to let me use Hebrew as the medium of instruction.

"But," he gave me a friendly warning, "don't feed on too many ideals. People ought to respect their benefactors."

(The benefactors, of course, were the Baron and his appointees —including Monsieur Alatin).

Shifra now became my pupil. She was ten years old. I was twenty-four. It could not have occurred to me that I was in love with her. She was merely my favorite pupil. I thought so much of her abilities that I often reprimanded her for lack of application. She showed quick intelligence, interest, enthusiasm, but she never made an effort to win high marks at the final examinations. My strictures always seemed to annoy her more than I should have expected. I began to think that she liked me as a teacher, but not as a person and therefore resented any attempt on my part to tell her what to do. However, she was only a child.

I was wrapped up in my work. I managed to infect my pupils with the love I had for Palestine, the Hebrew language and for the study of Jewish history. My pupils certainly were fond of me and followed me with enthusiasm. The only exception seemed to be Shifra, who as I said, liked me only as a teacher.

After some time, I overcame my prejudices and began visiting at Shifra's house. Her mother, who obviously had found it strange that I should have avoided them, received me with cordiality and showed no signs of feeling offended. She encouraged me to come and to hold long talks with my pupil. Shifra always showed a lively interest in talking to me about school work or books, but withdrew darkly whenever I tried to banter her or showed any sign of familiarity.

But—she was only a child. Time passed. She was twelve years old now. I was twenty-six—still unmarried. That seemed to worry some people.

One evening, as I walked along the main street of Pisgah, I ran into Shifra's mother who stood chatting with Madame Alatin, the wife of the chief administrator.

Madame Alatin wondered why I was not getting married and began singing the praises of a certain young lady of her acquaintance. "I don't like big girls, Madam," I said jestingly.

"That is right," Shifra's mother confirmed laughingly, "you'll wait for my Shifra to grow up, won't you?" It seemed to me I detected a grave note in those words spoken in jest.

"Of course, I'll wait," I said. "But will she want me then?" Shifra was twelve years old at the time.

Time rolled on. Shifra was graduated from school. I now saw her only at her house. But soon something happened which made me stop seeing her. I overheard a conversation by two women:

"That little girl," said one, "fancies herself a grown up lady. That silly mother of hers has ideas of getting the teacher as her son-in-law. Yesterday I was in their house, and what do you think that hussy said to her mother? 'Why does Lurie follow me around?' she said. 'He is not my teacher any more . . . I'm not going to marry him!' What do you think of that for a fourteen year old?"

It did not occur to me then how obvious it was that the words were spoken with the malicious intent for me to overhear them; that the woman who spoke them was the very one whom Madame Alatin tried to talk me into marrying. Of all that I thought much later. At the time I merely lost all desire to see Shifra and her mother and suddenly stopped coming to the house.

Meantime a crisis developed at my school. The Paris office sent us a lady who had connections in the right places but I did not consider her teaching qualifications sufficiently good. Certainly not the qualifications for educating a young generation of Palestinians to build the Jewish Homeland. I spurned her friendly overtures and she began to hate me. Using her influence in the Paris office, she sought to re-establish French as the medium of instruction at the school.

The atmosphere at the school became oppressive and did not give me the satisfaction it once did. I looked for an outlet elsewhere. The idea then occurred to me to organize my former pupils into a reading club. We already had organized a library at the colony. I found a ready response for my idea. The library was our meeting place and we read and discussed Achad Ha-am and other Hebrew classics. I read to them in Hebrew, translating at sight some of my favorite Russian authors. I prescribed readings in French literature, since they knew enough French to read by themselves. Shifra became one of the most active and interested members of the Club.

I began visiting their house again. Her mother received me after the long interval as if I had been there only the evening before. The house visits were only a continuation of the meetings at the library; we talked of literature. One evening, when I was at the house, a book fell off the table and both of us, Shifra and I, bent down simultaneously to pick it up. My hand inadvertently touched hers, and I felt as if my hand had been scalded. An electric current passed through my brain, my heart, my soul. It suddenly became clear to me that this fifteen year old girl was not just my favorite pupil, but that she was a woman, the woman I loved.

It was just then that the lure of the Galilee became strong. I went to spend the summer in that legendary land of rugged beauty, where Jewish pioneers were carving out new settlements. At the sight of them my faith was renewed. Full of fresh inspiration, I returned to Pisgah, to my school. But a rude shock awaited me: the teacher from Paris had been appointed principal and my position at the school was now untenable. I decided to go to Europe. The band of my faithful disciples, including Shifra, went all the way to Haifa to see me off to the boat.

I paid a short visit to Russia to see my parents. It was a difficult reunion. My parents, good middle class Jews, concerned over the career of their son, reproached me for throwing away my youth in the wilderness of Asia while so many of my boyhood companions were doing well for themselves: some had become doctors, others lawyers; some had married well and had fine homes. Was it not time for me, too, to settle down? The prodigal son announced his decision to complete his studies in Switzerland and the parents felt somewhat reassured.

From Switzerland I wrote to Shifra twice. At first there was no reply. A boy who had once courted Shifra, wrote me that she was spending a good deal of her time in the company of young Alatin, the son of the chief administrator of Pisgah, while the boy was home on furlough from his studies in Paris.

Another year passed. Then suddenly a letter came from Shifra. She apologized for her long silence and then apologized nearly as much for her writing. She wrote she felt it was presumptuous on her part to treat me as her equal. The effect of that unexpected humility on me was that the very next day I left for Trieste where I took the first boat to Haifa.

Soon after I came to Pisgah, young Alatin came from Paris. He was now a graduate civil engineer and had come to stay. I went back to Switzerland.

I maintained a correspondence with several of my pupils, but not with Shifra. I heard that Alatin père had been promoted and had moved to Beirut, where the Baron's main Levant office was located. His son took his place in Pisgah and married Shifra. I received an invitation to the wedding, but could not bring myself to send her a warm friendly greeting. My message of good wishes was dry and stereotyped, although I felt guilty about it and was angry with myself for doing it. Shifra wrote me to thank me for my letter, but her reply was full of reproach for my aloofness and for my absence from the country. What a pity, she wrote, that people like myself who have so much to contribute to the Homeland were not there when they were needed. There was a note in her writing suggesting unhappiness. This was rather puzzling. Certainly, my impression of seeing them together during my brief stay in Pisgah was of a happy couple, in love with each other. He was a handsome, vivacious young man, a provincial Sephardi boy, it was true, but well-educated and evidently eager to become one of us, devoted to our ideals. He even studied Hebrew. Why should she be unhappy?

I did not write to her, nor to anybody else in Pisgah and gradually lost touch with the colony. Another two years passed. Presently a letter arrived from Shifra's mother, from Haifa. The widow had remarried soon after Shifra's wedding and had gone to live in Haifa where her husband had a thriving business. The letter in-

formed me that Shifra was in Paris, at a sanatorium, and urged me
to go to see her. I took the next train to Paris.

The French nurse who received me smiled and made some broad
hints about the patient's affection for me and assured me that my
visit would have a healing effect. Shifra evidently suffered from a
nervous breakdown. As far as I could gather, she was pregnant.
I was sure that was the cause of her condition. She received me
with obvious pleasure, but, to my wonderment, kept on apologizing
for her conduct.

I went back to my studies in Switzerland, and Shifra soon left
for home. When, after some months, I was informed that Shifra
had given birth to a little girl, I knew I had been right.

When I returned to Pisgah, I became a frequent visitor in
Shifra's house. I learned that it took some time for young Alatin
to get over his disappointment with the fact that his firstborn was
a girl and not a boy. He was heavier. As a self-satisfied bureaucrat,
he had long since given up any attempt to acquire a speaking knowledge of Hebrew and was a typical Levantine Jew who had risen
in the Baron's service. Shifra spoke Hebrew to the child and the
husband treated the foible with good-natured indulgence. He was
a good-natured man, treating me in a friendly though somewhat
condescending fashion, as a "Russian." He laughingly referred to
his wife as a "Russian," meaning that she had been infected with
peculiar ideas, like speaking Hebrew. He often urged me to come
to the house, to spend time with his wife, since she was so interested
in my talk, but seldom found time for me—or, for that matter, for
her, either.

Shifra and I spent much time together, walking and talking.

It gradually became clear to me that Shifra did not love her
husband. She probably fell in love with him for a brief time, when
he courted her during his vacation from Paris. But the disillusionment came very soon after the wedding.

Did she love me?

There was no doubt that I loved her. I told her so, and she
kept silent. She struggled when I kissed her, but she always pleaded
with me not to cease visiting. A few times I felt it would be better
for my peace of mind to stop seeing her, or, perhaps, to leave Pisgah.

She would come to seek me out, she would send me notes to come to see them, or Alatin would ask me to come keep his wife company.

One evening, as we walked through the vineyards alone, she whispered to me: "It is too late now." I gradually pieced together that she would have been ready to leave her husband and go with me, when I saw her in Paris. It was only shortly after her return from Paris that she became pregnant.

"Shifra!" I pleaded with her, "Either come with me, or let me leave this place!"

"Then you will have to leave Pisgah!" she uttered in quiet resignation. Before leaving, I burned all my papers.

Yitzhak Shenhar

◆

ISRAEL ZVI

ON COMING to Palestine, Israel Zvi looked around and found a group of people from different countries who wanted to cultivate the land, each man by his own efforts. Having found what he wanted, he paid his share of the group funds and, when the day came, he and his fellow-members settled as smallholders on a stretch of land that had been allotted to them in the vicinity of an old established 'moshava.' They each erected two huts—one to live in, the other to serve as a cowshed—planted vegetables, and brought in some poultry.

"You ought to complete your household by taking a wife," his fellow-settlers used to tell Israel-Zvi.

And Israel Zvi would listen and nod his head.

At first he schooled himself to hold his peace, until he had quite forgotten the secret of the rapid flow of chatter that had once been his, in the days when he had worked in a haberdashery shop. He used to wear heavy hobnailed boots that seemed to weigh down his feet and restrain the hurried jerkiness of their motion. Then he applied himself to learning how to speak to the animals, birds and plants—snatches of talk, throaty noises and shrill twitterings.

All day Israel-Zvi used to toil away, and at night he slept on a couch whose legs sank into the earthen floor. His little hut was wrapped in darkness, silence and loneliness. His fellow-settlers smiled whenever they spoke about him. They used to say that the first time he went out to work in his fields he wore a suit of immaculate white, and that when he came back in the evening it had become a dirty gray.

Yehezekiel the Watchman, in particular, used to delight in re-counting amusing episodes in the life of "Israel Zvi, Tiller of the Soil."

"One night I saw from afar a light in Israel Zvi's yard. It was after midnight, all the stars were moving in their course, and I was mounted on my mare. 'What can the matter be?' I asked myself. I drew near, and saw Israel Zvi coming out of his hut with a lamp in his hand. He was going towards the vegetable garden. . . . What for? Oh, to see how the young tomato plants in the nursery were getting on. Yes, and then he went into the cowshed. 'What on earth are you doing here at this time of night?' I asked. 'I'm worried about the chickens,' he replied. 'They climb up among the rafters of the cowshed and stay there all night. Suppose they should start laying their eggs there—why, they'd fall down and break.' Those are the very words used to me by that 'Tiller of the Soil,' honestly. But there's something more: do listen. On Saturday I found him standing motionless in the field, with his hands out-stretched, looking like a scarecrow. He wanted to frighten away the birds that came to peck at the seeds."

The settlers listened with enjoyment and burst out laughing. Israel-Zvi listened too, smiled and shook his head in silence.

Once Israel-Zvi went out to plough. It was shortly after the rain. The earth was moist and sticky, and the horses drew the plough along with difficulty. Israel-Zvi continued to drive his fur-rows from end to end till sunset, his body tired and broken. The heavy clods of earth, with thorns and briers sticking to them, clung to his boots until he could not move an inch. He removed the plough from the furrow and turned it over on its side. Farmers passing by at that moment saw Israel-Zvi, his legs wide apart, standing as if rooted in the soil of his field. The disc of the setting sun had become a sphere behind his back and looked like a wide-open gate of flame. In the field there was utter silence. Night was drawing on, and lights began to appear in the nearby 'moshava.' The sweat-ing horses stood where they were, half closing their eyes and lowering their heads in rest. Then, when they began to feel the pangs of hunger, they started off of their own accord and made straight for home. Once again Israel Zvi was left alone, smiling, the blackness of the earth beneath him, and his toes aching painfully among the damp clods.

The years passed. The old-established 'moshava' continued as before, but in the new 'moshav' members came and went. Some did not have sufficient strength to hold out, and had to leave; they went to the towns with the lament of the vanquished upon their lips, while new-comers came in their place and occupied the little huts. Young trees sprung up in the farm-yards, and flowering creepers began to cover the fences. The youngsters brought a new song with them into the yards; the faces of the old-timers were covered by a multitude of wrinkles. All the affairs of the settlement were managed by the old-timers. Only Israel Zvi did not cease to be young, even though his face had shrunk, his hair thinned out and his legs became like spindles.

Yehezkiel the Watchman still would move about from yard to yard, aiming his shafts at Israel-Zvi as of old. The old-timers were silent and did not listen, but the new-comers were highly amused, and they slapped Israel-Zvi on the back as if he were one of them.

"You ought to complete your household by taking a wife," they told him.

He nodded his head, his gray eyes looking like opaque mirrors.

In the 'moshava' on the hill-top there lived a very aged but active woman by the name of Hannah-Leah. She was known to the inhabitants of both 'moshava' and 'moshav' as "Granny." Some time before she had handed over her farm to her son.

"Israel-Zvi, I shall find you a wife," Hannah-Leah once said to him when they were alone.

Israel-Zvi's face by then had become completely tanned by the sun, save for two patches of white skin behind his ears. These promptly turned a deep crimson as Granny made her offer. He, however, waited patiently, the only step he took being to pile up some planks in his yard with which to partition his little hut into two rooms.

Hannah-Leah looked round among the local girls, but did not find a wife for him. She explored a distant village in the hills of Galilee, but was no more successful.

"I shall walk all the way from Dan to Beersheba on my tottering legs," Granny comforted him. "I shan't give up. Soon, please God, I shall be going to Tiberias to bathe in the waters. There, no doubt, I shall be able to find what I'm looking for."

She was still engaged in making preparations for the journey when death came and closed her kind eyes. The days passed by in regular succession; the sun blazed away in the firmament, the horizon was blue and very desolate.

One day Israel-Zvi received a letter from foreign parts. It was from a young girl, a relative of his step-mother's and she had written at greath length from her distant township. She wanted to get away from there; there was no point to her life; there was not a single ray of light; no purpose in it at all. She was longing to devote all her energies to building up Palestine and to helping those who stood in the front line. She said so explicitly. And as Israel-Zvi was a veteran farmer, surely he would stand by her in her need and would not withhold from her the benefit of his advice. The letter contained a postscript in tiny letters to the effect that the writer lacked money for the fare.

Israel-Zvi read the letter and re-read it, and looked out of the window at the horizon. He recollected that, while he was still quite young, he had seen a little girl who had come to visit his step-mother, and that her name was Mira. She had been dressed in white, and her slender plait had been tied round with a red ribbon. That had been many years ago. At that time the skin of his face had been altogether soft and white, there had been no callouses on his hands, and it looked as if he might still grow in stature. And now Mira wanted to come here.

Israel-Zvi went along and applied for a loan from the local "Loan and Saving Fund" and immediately dispatched the money to the far-off little town in the Diaspora. Once again, he waited patiently, the only step he took being to take the planks from his yard and put up a partition in his tiny hut. A few weeks passed, and Mira turned up at his place in the 'moshav.' She brought her two tightly packed trunks, two dimples in her cheeks, and a sunny laugh that welled up from deep down inside her.

Somewhat confused, she entered the hut, but on seeing Israel-Zvi's face, she burst out laughing:

"Oh, how funny you are. Are you Israel-Zvi? I expected to find someone quite different. Why, you haven't grown at all. You look like a little 'Goy,' ha-ha-ha." Then she raised her eyes, looked around the room and said, winningly: "You won't mind if I stay in your hut for the time being, will you?"

Israel-Zvi nodded his head and turned his gray eyes upon her, which now looked like fallow fields that had never been ploughed.

The first evening she sat alone with Israel-Zvi and told him about the old town, about people who had already faded from his memory, about his stepmother and her misfortunes. Only one thing did Mira omit to tell him: how she intended to help those that stood in the front line. Israel-Zvi sat opposite her, short and straight, catching his breath and smiling.

Next day Mira rolled up her sleeves and began working on the poor assortment of furniture littered about the hut. Mattresses were aired, and cane mats were spread over the wooden walls. For the first time since the settlement was founded the sound of singing was heard from the farm of Israel-Zvi. From early morning a red kerchief fluttered about among the green of the bushes and trees. Yehezekiel became a frequent visitor at Israel-Zvi's. Following the partitioning of the hut, it seemed to have become very spacious. Yehezekiel, with a kerchief on his head, Bedouin style, would stand his rifle between his knees and sit there drinking tea.

"Israel Zvi, Tiller of Soil," he would say, "how long will you continue to imprison your fair visitor in this place? Heavens, man, you should let her see the country, so that she can know where she is in the world."

Israel Zvi was busy and pre-occupied and never had the time, so Yehezekiel used to offer his services to Mira and would tour the neighborhood with her. They would walk in the hills and stay at the nearby kibbutz. At the kibbutz there was dancing by the light of the moon; the large huts pulsated with the vitality of youth and the scent of the fields around was very near and very full.

"I wonder why you chose to join the 'moshav,' " Mira would say to Israel-Zvi on returning to the hut. "The 'kibbutz' would suit you

far better. That sort of place was specially designed for the likes
of you." And she would break off suddenly with a roguish laugh:
"What a pity. . . . "

Night after night Mira would disappear from the hut and
would return at a late hour.

"Now that you have brought a woman to the household," the
old-timers used to say to Israel-Zvi, "you ought to hurry up about
it. . . . "

Israel-Zvi would nod, and the patches of white skin behind
his ears would turn crimson.

The summer passed, and the rainy season came. One Sabbath
Israel-Zvi turned to Mira and said: "Mira, to my way of thinking
we can't go on like this any more . . . " and then he fell silent.

"So?" said Mira laughing. "Well, if you don't want me any
more. . . . "

"No, no, I didn't mean that." Israel Zvi mumbled and lapsed
into silence. For the first time he was sorry that he had gotten out
of the habit of being talkative. Otherwise he would have told Mira
about his way of life, about his intense loneliness, about the idea
that he had once thought out so completely. Perhaps he might then
have plucked up courage to tell her that since she had come, no
other thought had crossed his mind. But he did not say anything.

Mira cleared the things off the table and went over to her side
of the hut. From behind the partition she said: "You are right,
Israel-Zvi, we really cannot go on like this. Actually I ought to
have told you this before, but for some reason or other I didn't.
Well, the fact is that I'm going over to Yehezekiel in a few days'
time. I know, you're a goodhearted fellow, Israel-Zvi. I shall
always be grateful to you, really I shall. After all, you got me into
the country and altogether. . . . One day we shall pay you back the
money you laid out for me."

"Yes, yes," Israel-Zvi replied and nodded his head in the
direction of the partition.

The wedding celebration took place in the nearby 'kibbutz.'
Carts laden with guests left the 'moshav,' and a number of youngsters from the 'moshava' accompanied them on horseback.

"Aren't you coming with us?" Mira asked Israel-Zvi. "After all, you're the only relative we have in the country. You really won't come with us?"

"I?" asked Israel-Zvi in amazement. "No, no . . . I can't leave the farm. . . . "

Yitzhak Shenhar

◆

STREET SYMPHONY

FIVE HOUSES stood along the asphalt roadway, two on the one side, three on the other. The pavement did not quite cover the full width of the street and was lined by two parallel strips of desert sand, on which were strewn old papers, orange peelings, and other rubbish. When the litter became too thick, an east wind would come to the rescue and cover it with a layer of fresh sand. The street reached a dead end at a fenced yard filled with scrap iron and rusty utensils; the other end tapered off into a chain of low sand dunes stretching far on the horizon.

At one time nothing stood here but an abandoned Arab building. Then Ezra Sassoon came from Baghdad and bought it at a ridiculously low price. He had it repaired and then let it out to Aharon Hayimovitch for his iron working shop. In time Sassoon had another building adjoining the old one.

Across the street stood the Nesher Taxi Company, a small building with a makeshift sloping roof made of shingles. Iron bars reached from the eaves in every direction like arms uplifted to take on the burden of another floor. But the builder, after a year in Palestine, had gone bankrupt and returned to Poland. The bank took over the building, and Sassoon, when the time came, obtained it from the bank by paying the liability. He let it stand as it was, until something turned up.

Next to it was the "estate" of David Mirsky, consisting of a house and a garden. The walls of the house were painted blue and its roof was red. Except for the shell-paved pathways, every foot of ground on the "estate" was taken up with flowers, vegetables and trees. It was the only plot of land on the street not owned by Ezra Sassoon.

Last came a tall narrow building the upper floor of which was supported by four crude pillars of concrete. The pit at the bottom of the pillars formed an obstacle to the construction of the lower floor. All day long the upper floor resounded with the clatter of the sewing machines operated by the Geulah Dressmakers' Co-operative.

The two-story house in which the Sassoons lived was of mixed architecture: a Babylonian balcony, Persian beams and two Greek columns. The ground floor was occupied by Mr. Etzioni's cabinet-maker's shop, with two rooms left to Joseph Stein for a bachelor's apartment. In the turret-like attic in a corner on the flat roof Eliyahu the night watchman lived.

These were the habitants of the Lovers of Zion Street. Whether mere chance had brought them together, or Providence, in its inscrutable wisdom, after careful selection and elimination, placed them here by design, they made up a remarkable assortment. The Tel-Aviv Municipal Committee on Street Names, looking for a street to commemorate the forerunners of Herzl, decided to call this street Rehov Hoveve-Zion, that is, Lovers of Zion Street. It was only when they hung up the sign that they realized what a fortunate choice had been made.

It was a short street on the city's edge. The breezes from the Mediterranean took a long time reaching it and they lost their tang in the many streets and alleys along the way. But the east winds came directly from the desert, carrying fine sand which penetrated every crack and settled in thick layers on the window sills and on the floors.

It was dark and cool where the Sassoons lived. The shutters were closed all day and the walls were hung with tapestries. One room was furnished in Western style. In the others, the floors were covered with mats over which were strewn many small pillows. Madame Sylvia sat all day in a corner on a pile of pillows exhaling cigarette smoke.

Ezra Sassoon was a dark man with an aquiline nose and an unctuous look of innocence in his protruding eyes. His wife was quiet, short and stout. Her forehead was very wrinkled and in her daughter's presence she looked more like the girl's grandmother than her mother. The two sons were at the American University in Beirut, Lebanon, and only the daughter, Jeanette, lived at home. She was a well-formed rosy-cheeked girl who, like her mother spent her days in the house in silent preoccupation with nothing in particular.

Towards evening mother and daughter came out for their daily promenade, Madame Sylvia rolling from hip to hip, her Oriental sandals clattering on the pavement, Mademoiselle Jeanette traipsing gingerly at her side, her arms obliquely held out in the air to protect her silk dress and carefully stepping around any hole in the ground to guard against a speck of dust falling on her lacquered shoes.

The street was quiet and deserted, machines and workers having finished their day's labor. It was just then that Joseph Stein would come out of his apartment to go into town. Stein was a young man whose fat made him look much older than he was. His complexion was very fair; his hair was flaxen-colored and his eyebrows and eyelids so white that they were almost invisible. His pink face was so well groomed that one got the impression he treated a shave like a religious sacrament.

Somewhere in a small town in Poland, Joseph Stein's widowed mother and aging maiden sister ran a small store. He was the only son and a doting mother and adoring sister still expected him to become a great man some day. In his mother's house, Joseph Stein used to sleep late, lying in a soft featherbed, while his mother and sister would hover around on tiptoe. As soon as he awoke his mother would rush to his bedside with a towel, while his sister would prepare a breakfast of tea and eggrolls for him. He was never permitted to do any chores in the house or in the store and knew nothing of his mother's worries. When the time came for Joseph Stein to go out into the world, his mother fainted in the railway carriage, and his sister wept. Joseph settled in Germany in a large city, where he obtained a post in a travel agency. Although he had never traveled much, his well-groomed appearance, his glib tongue and persuasive manner were perfect qualifications for his work.

Joseph would actually cast a spell over his clients by his descriptions of the heights of snow-capped St. Moritz, of the pleasures of Florida, the eternity which speaks through the silence of Rome's glorious thoroughfares, of the age-long riddle of the sphinxes. When the political climate in Germany became menacing, inquiries about Palestine grew more and more frequent. Never at a loss, Joseph Stein waxed rhetorical in his mellow voice, about the sacred magnificence of biblical scenery. Then came the first anti-Jewish decrees and the operators of the travel agencies were ordered to inquire into the racial origin of their employees. Two Jews were found—the manager and Joseph Stein. The manager had money and succeeded in getting an American visa. Stein left for Palestine. This was his first sea voyage, his first opportunity to partake of the marvelous experiences he had so glowingly described to his expectant clients from behind the counter. But the seas were rough, and Joseph kept to his cabin all through the trip.

Ever since Joseph Stein's arrival in Palestine, he had not worked; he could not get what he wanted and he would not take what was offered. The owner of a bakery shop in Tel-Aviv, impressed by Stein's manner and appearance, offered him a job as a pastry salesman, but he refused. Occasionally, an acquaintance would try to make Stein understand that the notions of the old country could not be applied to Palestine and urged him to take a job in some construction work, while the building boom was on. However, he was determined to find employment in a travel agency—or nothing. When the little money he brought with him gave out, he wrote to his mother in Poland and she began further stinting on herself in order to send him a monthly allowance. Joseph rented two spare rooms in Mrs. Etzioni's cabinetmaker's shop, bought a table and a damaged arm-chair with a high back, a bed from Mr. Etzioni, and curtained his street window with a big poster of the travel agency in which he worked in Germany on which a large colored ship was painted. He became a resident of the Lovers of Zion Street. Every morning and every evening he prepared his meal at the gasburner. With every sunset he walked into town to visit the travel agencies and watched the way the incompetent provincials mishandled their jobs.

On coming out, Stein would run into Madame Sylvia and Mademoiselle Jeanette. Gallantly bowing, he would address the daughter in French: "Tout va bien, mademoiselle?"—"Is everything all right?"

Jeanette pleasantly bared her lipstick-tainted white teeth.

"Today I saw a party of messieurs et dames at the tourist office. The poor clerk did not know what to advise them. What is there, after all, in this poor country? He should have suggested a trip to Lebanon."

Jeanette's almond-shaped eyes beamed at him from behind their pointed eyebrows, while her mother, sullenly standing at some distance, furiously cracked melon seeds.

In the morning Ezra Sassoon would come out of his apartment clad in a white robe over which he wore a brown cloth jacket. As he walked down the stairway, he pressed the weight of his whole body on every stair to test its strength. He passed among the street buildings, scrutinizing everything. Then he would take a chair and sit down on it in a shady nook at the entrance to his house, between Stein's apartment and the cabinetmaker's shop. He placed a white handkerchief under his skull-cap to wipe the perspiration. For some time he would listen to the humming of the wheels in the iron working shop, the wheezing of the plane in the cabinetmaker's shop, and the clatter of the sewing machines in the Dressmakers' Cooperative, nodding his head, feeling he was the Grand Master of the Lovers of Zion Street.

Presently he would lift up his eyes to the turret-like attic, calling: "Liyahu, come down and fetch some coffee."

"Liyahu"—that is, Eliyahu—would descend from his abode on high, carrying a fancy network tray on which a dainty demi-tasse of hot Turkish coffee was steaming. Eliyahu's eyes were bleary, his back was bent and he had a large Adam's apple. It was almost impossible to tell his age from his lean face—he might be twenty years old or he might be forty.

When Eliyahu came to Palestine with one of the early waves of pioneers after World War I, he first went to work on the roads, like so many of his comrades. Then he was a night watchman in an old colony, where he had his fill of romancing in the vineyards.

Those were the days of youth in the country, carefree, singing youth, extolling poverty and hunger in the glory of nation-building. Those were the days when the barefoot halutzim reigned over the desert sands and the rocky wastes of the Homeland. It was customary then to call each halutz by a pet diminutive, and so Eliyahu was known as Ellik. In all the Jewish settlements, from Rohama in the Negev, to Mettulah in the North, Ellik's name was a household word, and they used to say about him that there were three things of which he was unconscious—fear, old age and private property; also, that he never experienced two kinds of feeling—enough dancing, or tiredness. Ellik wandered all over Palestine, loading bricks here, leading a camel caravan there. Sometimes he would disappear for months, spending his time with a tribe of Bedouins, as their cattleherder or shepherd. But one night, while on watch duty in a new settlement, he was attacked by Arabs armed with knives and clubs; they crippled him and even took his gun away from him.

For many days Ellik lay in the hospital, hovering between life and death. When he left, his body was dry and lean, his once-flowing hair was shaved off, he could no longer sing or dance, his back was bent. Ellik now became silent and morose, and some of his friends feared he would lose his mind or do away with himself. When the Labor Federation offered to take care of him, he refused. Yet no one knew that as he went around tattered and hungry, he continued to write cheerful letters to his old father in Europe who spent his days in prayer and study, and to his younger brother who was in training as a halutz, intending to follow in Ellik's footsteps. Then Ezra Sassoon came along and offered Ellik a job as a night watchman. The Lovers of Zion Street was not, strictly speaking, within the municipal jurisdiction of Tel-Aviv, and only once every night a team of mounted watchmen passed it on their round. Sassoon's tenants demanded protection before they would rent the premises and that condition was written into the leases. Sassoon, who always looked for low-priced merchandise, discovered Ellik. He gave him a corner in the turret-attic, put a whistle on his shoulder, a club in his hand, and paid him a tiny salary. In case of trouble, Ellik was to run behind the house and strike the iron bar which hung there, serving as an alarm bell.

The understanding was that Ellik was to watch Sassoon's houses from dark to dawn. But Mr. Sassoon found a way of making use of him in the daytime as well. Now and then he would remark: "I can't understand you, Liyahu, you see the yard is dirty, and you won't take a broom to sweep it up." Or he would reprimand him, in the Arabized Hebrew of a Baghdadi: "Liyahu, you're a young fellow, and you don't have respect for elders. Here I am, an old man, standing, and you won't bring me a chair to sit down on."

So Ellik bowed his head and ran to sweep the yard and to bring a chair and to fetch Turkish coffee and to go to town to fetch a spool of wool for Madame Sylvia. Ellik went around in the daytime like a somnambulist. His head was awhirr from lack of sleep, from the uncomfortable position on the hard bench in his attic. His clothes were ruffled and his mood resentful, his lips tightly sealed between two grooves of grief in the corners of his mouth. At night he slowly made his rounds, checking the locks in the workshops, walking between the dark junkyard filled with cats and dogs and the moonlit expanse of sands, and back again. When he wanted to take a little rest, he bundled up in his worn-out ragged overcoat and sat down by the pit under the pillars of concrete on which the Geulah Dressmakers' Cooperative was situated, placed his club between his knees and rested his hand on it. And Ellik sat motionless, his heart as vacant as the night that stretched before him, feeling so unbearably lonely that he wished he could split himself into two so that one-half would keep the other company.

Ellik had nothing to do with the people on Lovers of Zion Street and did not even associate with his fellow proletarians who were employed at the workshops. But whenever he could escape the watchful eye of Ezra Sassoon, he would sneak through the courtyard and enter the Mirsky "estate" by the small back gate. Here, he sat down on the wooden stairs of the porch, which were drowned in clinging vines, to enjoy the peace and quiet. The noise and the hubbub of the Lovers of Zion Street seemed to be muted by the tall, stately sycamores rising gracefully in a row along the fence, and reached this spot only as a dull rumble of distant waves on the sea.

David Mirsky, the "squire" of the "estate," was always dressed in a wide Russian blouse, such as Count Tolstoy wore in his old age. The blouse fluttered over Mirsky's tall, thin figure. His gait was so straight that his head was tilted backwards. His bald pate was tanned like parchment, but on the back of his neck long white tresses flowed down to his shoulders. His thick, bushy eyebrows over his blue eyes reminded one of the sage of Yasnaya Polyana, whose portrait hung in a gilded frame in the dining room. Mirsky spoke Hebrew with an atrocious Russian accent, and was known among his townspeople, even when they did not speak in his presence, as David Moyseyevitch. Rarely did people come to visit him, and the estate lived its quiet isolated life like a world unto itself.

Mr. Mirsky was a confirmed vegetarian. He was proud of his diet, which was made up exclusively of vegetables grown on his own soil. All morning long, he puttered around the garden, pruning the trees, watering the flowers, or working at the vegetables. Now and then he would announce, as if speaking into space: "The lettuce is just beautiful; the spinach is a joy to behold." No reply came, but, without turning his head, Mr. Mirsky knew that his wife smiled on him from the porch. She waited for him to pick her some fresh roses and bring them to her side to place them in the glass vase by her arm-chair.

Manya Mirsky was a sick woman who, because of a heart ailment, had reclined in an arm-chair on the porch all day. Her face was transparently pale; her moist black eyes looked upon the world as if in childish wonderment, as if something had happened a long time ago to strike her with amazement for the rest of her days. Her right arm was as thin as a stick. She usually kept it on her chest, like a small, helpless kitten, stroking it gently with her left arm. As she did that, her thick grey hair looked like a halo of grief around her suffering face, and the earrings hanging from her ears, like large tears.

Mrs. Mirsky had taken sick in Siberia, where she was banished in her youth for revolutionary activity. She moved around and talked very little. Esterke, a girl of about sixteen, whose father's salary in the City Health Department was not enough to provide for the whole family, looked after the Mirsky house. On account of Mrs. Mirsky's illness, Esterke slept there six nights a week and went home only on the Sabbath, when she could enjoy a slice of meat. At the Mirsky's, she walked around without uttering a sound, attending to Mrs. Mirsky, sweeping the floors, and preparing meals according to Mr. Mirsky's recipes.

Of the two Mirsky boys, the elder got married and emigrated to America. From time to time he sent his father a little money, which was enough to buy medicine for Mrs. Mirsky. The younger son, Menachem, was a member of one of the kibbutzim in the Emek. Whenever some urgent task was completed or, as they say in the kibbutzim, when a "burning" season came to an end, Menachem would ask for leave to go visit his parents in the city. He would come to Tel-Aviv dressed as he was in the kibbutz—blue shirt, khaki shorts, heavy shoes and a sleeveless leather jacket. He never announced his arrival, but suddenly appeared in the doorway, exuding the brightness of youth.

Walking carefully, he would walk over to his mother and plant a kiss on her forehead. Then he would turn to his father, talking shop, as one farmer to another: "Well, *abba,* what about your intensive cultures this season? What did you plant? I see you haven't an inch of uncultivated ground left."

David Moyeseyvitch knit his thick eyebrows to feign a frown and did not budge from his work, while Menachem stood smiling, like a grown-up man used to doing a man's work confronted with a child playing at the same occupation. Ellik, sitting on the side, watched the scene with a semblance of delight, the shadow of a smile passing over the cracked lips of his thin face.

When Menachem came to town, he had many errands to attend to for his kibbutz—for individual comrades, for the farm committee, for the cultural committee. Yet now and then he would find time to sit down near Ellik at his mother's feet on the porch stairs. Then while Mr. Mirsky walked around imperturbably in the garden among his shrubs, his wide-rimmed hat on his head, his pruning hook in his hand, singing and talking, cutting the vegetables, he would address his audience in his Russian-sounding Hebrew:

"Vegetarianism, you know, is not just the pacifism of the kitchen and the stomach; it does not merely concern the palate and the pot. No, ladies and gentlemen, it is something of a much higher order. It is physical cleanliness as a hallway to spiritual purity. No man is born a vegetarian, you know, and he cannot get there just by reading books. They did not teach me vegetarianism when I went to school. On the contrary, I ate plenty of meat and drank plenty of vodka. . . .

"You might say that vegetarianism is a master plan for solving all social problems. The world will never be saved, you know, until every individual is seized by a paroxysm of disgust such as seized me, that day, in Odessa, when I saw the cartload of bovine heads in front of the butcher shop. . . . And I cannot understand what a strange generation this is! Its basic fallacy is that it seeks to change society without first re-making Man, you know, in its own midst. If you just examine every social revolution, you will find it came as a result of despair from the individual person. If I were not afraid you would kill me, I'd say, ladies and gentlemen, that at the basis of every revolution is lack of faith in the future. . . . "

Again there was a clip of the pruning hook and a leaf fell down to the ground with a thump. The old man laughed at his own words, and shrugged his shoulders.

Manya Mirsky would listen attentively, slowly stroking her tubercular arm resting in her lap. There was a time when she used to argue with her husband, until the vehemence of her own speech would drain her strength. But now it had become stereotyped, and she was happy to see her husband immersed in these things which savored of a distant past. With moist eyes, she regarded the two young men at her feet, one of whom was broken and dwarfed beyond all theories of social revolution; the other, a youth, whose innermost being was fermented by these very theories and who viewed them as the final destination of his life's labors.

Mrs. Mirsky held out her hand and took a flower from the vase, saying in a weak voice: "Take a flower from me, Mr. Ellik!"

Ellik blushed as he accepted this gift of life's supreme loving kindness and brought the flower up to somewhere between his nostrils and his lips, so that one could hardly tell whether he was smelling it or kissing it.

"Tztztz," the old man suddenly cried out, and put his finger to his mouth.

A bee in its flight had descended on one of the sunflowers in the flower bed and began to suck at the bud, the lower half of its body aquiver with ardor. "Ah, now, my little hedonist," the old man softly murmured to it. "Ah you gourmet. You like the beverage, don't you? Is it sweet?" David Moyseyevitch stood there motionless among the sunflowers so as not to disturb the bee from its frenzy. With his wide-rimmed hat, he himself appeared like a tall sunflower looking up to the skies.

Mr. Etzioni was a tall, large-framed, somewhat portly man. He had a healthy red hirsute neck and did not seem to have a single wrinkle. When he spoke, his voice sounded as if it emerged from the depths of his abdomen. His hands were always busy with the skull cap on his head, trying to put it in its place. In the late hours of the morning, when work was in full swing, he liked to step out of his shop to breathe the fresh air, to take a look at the old Yemenite worker upholstering furniture, and to talk to Mr. Sassoon. In his native town in Eastern Europe, Mr. Etzioni was a pillar of the Jewish community, who subscribed to a Hebrew newspaper from Palestine, contributed to various Palestine funds, planted trees in the Herzl forest and was one of the leaders of the moderate Zionist faction. From year to year he postponed his intended trip to the Homeland, until a pogrom in which his house was wrecked took place. He then moved his whole family to Palestine. As soon as he arrived, he went to the appropriate government office, paid half a pound and had his name changed from Holzmann to Etzioni. Next he sought out the leaders of the General Zionists who gave him a picture of the situation in the country. He never found time to tour the country and to see its agricultural settlements. He went into business, opening his shop on the Lovers of Zion Street where labor could be obtained at lower wages than in other parts of Tel-Aviv.

No sooner had he taken off his jacket and rolled up his sleeves than his feuding began. First he engaged in a long-drawn-out fight

with the City Council about the taxes. He felt that, as a veteran
Zionist who had come to build up the Homeland, he was entitled
to different treatment than an ordinary businessman interested only
in profit. Mr. Etzioni would address long memoranda to the Council and seek out the individual councillors to argue his case. Finally
he gave up and started a new crusade, this time against labor.

It all began with a relative of his wife, scion of a good family,
but a helpless-looking fellow with a face which always looked ready
to cry. When he came to Mr. Etzioni to ask for advice and assistance
in finding a livelihood, Mr. Etzioni slapped him on the back and
assured him:

"You needn't worry. Just stay with me and work. At first you
won't get any wages—only your board at my house, then, when
you've learned the trade, you'll get paid, too."

The workers raised a protest: the new employee was not a member of the union. Mr. Etzioni retorted that he was the owner of the
shop and he was going to run it as he saw fit. The workers threatened to call a strike. Mr. Etzioni threatened to declare a lockout.
After some futile negotiations, the strike broke out. Newspapers
wrote about it; the Histradruth raised a special fund to help the
strikers; pickets with banners took up positions at both ends of
the street. Every day Mr. Etzioni would emerge from his shop to
heap abuse on the strikers. However, since his warehouse was well-
stocked with furniture, he was in no hurry to settle.

After some time the workers returned to their jobs. Although
the strike had been lost, Mr. Etzioni's relative was so impressed
with this show of labor solidarity that he joined the union.

Mr. Etzioni exploded at his wife: "It was you who made me
take that viper into my house, that good-for-nothing kinsman of
yours. I saved him from starvation. I taught him a trade and now
he has joined my enemies! I won't have it!"

When he fired the young man, the workers protested this discrimination against organized labor. Mr. Etzioni glowered at them
and his neck became redder than ever.

Again there was a strike at Mr. Etzioni's shop with pickets
at both ends of the street. The conflict between Mr. Etzioni and
his employees continued after his relative with the weeping face

had found another job, with new reasons for the new strikes. Matters became more complicated as time went on. Mr. Etzioni, now filled with hatred against organized labor, became the symbol of anti-labor sentiment. The workers coined a new word—"Etzionism" —to designate the trend against them.

Each time there was a strike Mr. Etzioni would run around, shaking his fist at the pickets and growl: "Look at those heroes of Israel, look at them! Stand there, stand! I'll show you, I will! I'll make you starve! I'll have you lick the dust! I won't rest until I've rooted you out!"

Then he would go over to Mr. Sassoon, who was sitting in front of his house: "Utter lawlessness!" he would shake his head. "In my own shop I am not to do as I want! Are those scoundrels going to tell me what to do?"

He would roll out his belly, beat his chest and shout: "Every year I used to contribute to the funds for Palestine! Those bloodsuckers—they've fed on my blood and marrow and they've grown fat! Now they're my oppressors! To think that they are our masters, our overlords! The workers! Workers—pshaw! These are not workers! They are college students, yeshivah boys, star-gazers, ne'er-do-wells, good-for-nothings, that's what they are! Do you think they knew anything when they first came to me? They couldn't tell a tree from a stick! I'm the one who taught them—and now they are my bosses!"

Mr. Ezra Sassoon, who was concerned only with the rent he received from his tenants, sought to pour oil on the troubled waters.

"Yes, of course, of course, Mr. Etzioni, you are right. An owner is an owner, he is the boss. But, after all, a workshop is made to work in, isn't it? Wouldn't it be better to give in a little, to argue a little and find some compromise."

"Compromise?" Mr. Etzioni was indignant, "I should look for a compromise? Why, these blackguards are ruining the country, that's what they are doing! Just let somebody ask me for a donation for any of the funds for Palestine—I won't give them a penny! Can a man exist here? Can he make a living in this country?"

"Ai, ai!" Mr. Etzioni's tone changed and he began speaking in a wistful reminiscent vein, as his eyes assumed a dreamy far-away look: "Where are those *goyim* who used to work for me over there, in Europe, with that smell of tar from their boots and the smell of vodka on their breath? Those were workers—real workers, not amateurs, fussing around with all kinds of nonsense. Ai, ai!"

It was siesta time, the men felt sleepy and bored, as perspiration rolled down their temples and between their shoulder blades. The drivers of the Nesher Taxi Cooperative had had their afternoon tea and cookies and had looked at all the illustrated movie magazines. There were no telephone calls from the city and no one felt like cruising the streets for passengers. They wrestled, joked and teased one another, and made a great deal of noise. Ezra Sassoon watched them and laughed so hard that the handkerchief under his skullcap shook and his eyes filled with tears. Although these drivers were his tenants, Mr. Sassoon could not distinguish one from another and did not know their names. They all seemed alike to him—fellows with round faces and bare thighs, each twirling a bunch of keys around his finger. He would not permit his daughter Jeanette to go near them.

During the recent disturbances these eagles,* wrought wonders and were the objects of admiration in the Jewish community. They were fearless in the face of danger, traveling in their bullet-ridden cars along paved roads of trackless fields, maintaining communication among the Jewish settlements. But once things had quietened down, their courage relaxed with the tension. They no longer insisted on speaking Hebrew but lapsed into Yiddish with a mixture of Arabic and English. They put on weight and became a distinct breed of men—half aristocrat, half labor.

When the taxi drivers shouted, the curtain shook in the window of the Geulah Seamstresses' Cooperative. Adinah peered out on the street, singing as she always did.

Adinah always sang Yiddish folk-songs of sadness and nostalgia: songs of an irretrievable past, songs of a broken heart, of a lover who had gone overseas and had forgotten to write. Adinah's shrill singing was the only manifestation of any capacity she had for

---

* *Nesher,* the name of the Company, means "eagle" in Hebrew.

sentiment. Otherwise, her large body, with its broad shoulders and heavy hips gave one the impression of immunity to pain.

Adinah sang the same songs in her father's house in Europe; she sang them when she left it as a ripe fig falls from its fig-tree; she sang them in Palestine where for a year and a half she worked on the roads breaking gravel, in workers' kitchens, preparing meals, until a letter came from America. It was from a widowed relative who wrote and asked her to come and marry him. She left the shores of the Homeland with the same apparent absence of pain or regret as she had left her father's house. But on the very day that Adinah arrived in the United States, her relative died. For two years Adinah struggled alone, working in sweat shops, and then returned to Palestine with the same songs on her lips: songs in which fate is likened to a stepmother, songs in which the sweetheart overseas betrays his vows of love. But she brought back something new in her mouth: half a row of gold teeth, and English words and phrases in her talk. It was at this time the seamstresses' Cooperative was being organized. She joined and was soon elected its business manager.

The front part of the shop was the store, where customers came to select a blouse from the stock on hand. Behind a wooden partition six tired, pale, girls sat over their needles and sewing machines. The clientele consisted mostly of working people. Sometimes a *vatik* would come in, one of those old-timers whose face had been wrinkled and whose hair had been strewn with silver during his years of pioneering. He would come to order that well-known Sabbath blouse with its silken girdle and embroidered collar, usually worn open so that only part of the embroidery was visible. In such a case, Adinah would assume the grave mien of a solicitous housewife, advising him how to use his hard-earned money to the best advantage. But when a young worker came in, one of those who had a smooth neck and laughing eyes, one who wore either a new blouse or a torn blouse, but never a mended blouse, Adinah would dissolve into her golden smile. She would take the measurements with obvious relish and shower him with heavy-handed motherly affection. The store would be filled, as it were, with her full-hipped gait. The seamstresses, watching the scene through the

wooden partition, would wink or smirk at one another or else
grow sad and apathetic with weariness.

Whenever Adinah heard the din raised by the wrestling "eagles"
at the other end of the street, she would bend over the window
sill and leer at them coquettishly, sending forth her song into space:
The snows of the winter in the sun are dissolved,
But my pain is still fresh, my heart is still cold.

                    *   *   *

S. J. Agnon

◆

IN A JERUSALEM CAFE

THEY ENTERED the cafe and seated themselves. Herbst sat like a man who is not used to women's company, while Shira sat like a woman who is resting and has nothing particular in mind. When Herbst saw that she was in no hurry to start a conversation he felt more at ease and allowed himself to look at her as she sat without any particular familiarity, without crossing her knees—sat and simply drank tea with milk, sat without staring round this way and that, but just gazed at the small area of space directly ahead of her. But that space gradually began to fill up with her wordless essence. Although that cannot very well be said, seeing that the area was only an area and she was only herself, so how could it very well fill up merely from the fact that she was gazing into it? . . .

While Herbst was doing his best to clear his thoughts, the cafe owner came along, bowed to them and asked whether they were satisfied with what they had received. When they answered that they were quite satisfied he went on and made his request, "I hope that from now on you will not merely pass my house by." And when they answered, "We shall come and come again," he started explaining that his was a new face here in Palestine, and certainly in Jerusalem; that never in all his life had he thought of coming here, and certainly not of living here.

"When I came to Palestine," he said, "I wanted to open a cafe in Tel-Aviv like the one I used to have in Berlin. But when I saw that in Tel-Aviv half of the cafe is out in the street, I gave up my intention. For my dear madam and sir, I regard the cafe as an institution into which a man escapes from the street, and not one into which he brings the street with him. In Tel-Aviv they sit themselves down in the street and drink their coffee as though it were 'gazoz' (soda-water).

"Every kind of drink demands its own surroundings. Wine prefers to be drunk in a pleasant dining-room with fine lights shining, where you can see the wine gleaming cheerily from the glass and you enjoy what you see and it seems that both of you are singing together. Tea likes to be drunk between greyish-yellow walls, while it reclines in the cup like a mandarin who holds sway over the land. Cocoa prefers to be served on a white table-cloth decorated with roses and butterflies, while beer has a wish for a gloomy old cellar with heavy oaken tables on which no cloth is spread. The cocktail should be drunk standing bent over the buffet or the bar. And so it is with all the drinks, each one of them prefers its own setting, according to the kind of drink it is. And more than each of them, coffee, particularly prefers a building in its own right, where everybody who comes to drink a cup of coffee can rest and gather his strength again.

"But down there in Tel-Aviv a man sits in the street and drinks without knowing what it is that he is drinking and stops any and every passer-by and argues with him and shouts and complains, and neither of them hears what the other is saying; and meanwhile a little dark Yemenite shoeshiner comes crawling along and passes his brushes backwards and forwards over their shoes. And I can say that he is the only one who is consistent, for he polishes a man's two shoes at a time when you could change the head of that man with the head of another without his even noticing it.

"To tell the truth, everything isn't in order in Jerusalem either. It is hard to find a good spot and hard to find waiters. So whether you want to or not you have to use waitresses and they haven't the patience that guests require because some of the customers don't know, to begin with, what they would prefer; and the waiter has to know what the proper thing is to suggest to them; and sometimes it has to be suggested to them hypnotically. But the waitresses stand over them and confuse the guest by their cheeky way of standing. And I have to watch this and be quiet, because the minute I say a word along comes the Histadruth.

"If you will permit me to, my dear lady and gentleman, I shall tell you a story. On one occasion I dismissed a waitress from my cafe. I do not claim that I was a hundred per cent justified, but I was annoyed because, while I was talking to her, she yawned in my face. I told her off and said to her, 'Take your rubbish and get out.' No sooner was she out of the place than her fellow-waitresses left their work and went out after her; that is, they went on strike. I laughed to myself and said, 'Strike, my girls, strike, by your lives such poor chicks as you aren't even worth the expense of slaughtering.' Well, I go looking for other waitresses but I can't find any, because they are all members of the Histadruth and don't want to have anything to do with a man at whose place a strike has been proclaimed; and meanwhile a certain gentleman comes along to me, sent by the Histadruth, with a briefcase in his hand like a lawyer; and he begins talking to me as though he is the owner of my cafe. In brief, he talks and I answer. I talk and he answers, and meanwhile the guests are bursting and there's nobody to serve them.

"For lack of any alternative I agreed to pay the waitresses compensation and to take them back to work, apart from the piece of impudence. What did that gentleman who was sent by the Histadruth answer? He answered like this, 'If you don't want her, we don't want you.' Ha-ha-ha, I'm the owner and that impudent thing's only a little employee of mine. What has happened, my dear lady and gentleman, such things don't happen anywhere except in Palestine.

"That gentleman had meanwhile taken a fancy to that waitress and she had taken a fancy to him as well, so they married one another. And as for me, believe it or not, on their wedding day I sent them a large cream cake with 'mazel tov' written on it in chocolate. Needless to add that we made it up, and furthermore, I won their hearts and they have become regular guests in this cafe. He comes to drink coffee and she comes to eat ice cream. A thing of that kind can't happen anywhere except in Palestine. Good night, worthy lady, good night, sir. I am your servant. Au revoir."

✳   ✳   ✳

S. J. Agnon

◆

THE MINYAN

IN TIBERIAS there lived a fine young man, the son of a widow, learned in the Torah and perfect in the fear of God, who all his days was swift as a deer to do the will of his Father in Heaven. But, just as the skin of a deer can hardly contain its body, so the body of the youth could not hold in his soul, and one day he fell ill and was likely to die. All kinds of remedies were used, and all kinds of doctors were called, but to no avail. If the Holy One, blessed be He, does not send healing from Heaven, what can men do?

In those days, Tiberias was full of pious *hassidim* and men of good deeds, who knew how to pray. And when they heard that this young man was likely to die, they were filled with pity for him, and they said to each other: "Let us pray for him, so that he may recover from his sickness."

So they all gathered together in a certain House of Study within whose walls the sound of learning and prayer never ceased, and they allotted a large sum to charity, which they divided into seven portions, so that the youth might be delivered from the seven punishments which are written in the Torah, and that there might be fulfilled for him the verse, "And charity delivers from death"; and they stood all day and all night in prayer and supplication. Then they went to the tomb of Rabbi Meir, the Worker of the Miracle, and to the tombs of other rabbis and sages and righteous and pious men, whose bodies were buried in the earth of Tiberias. And they prostrated themselves upon the graves with great weeping, and lit lamps, according to the number of years of the sick youth and according to the number of years of man in this world; till

the holy city was lit up by these lamps. But the soul of the young
man's life sank lower and lower, like a wick without oil.

When the *hassidim* saw this, they said to each other: "Beloved
brethren, what more can we do for this sick man that we have not
yet done?" And they answered each other: "Beloved brethren, all
that we are able to do, we have already done."

So they took their prayer-books and returned home in despair.

But the Holy One, blessed be He, still wished to enjoy the
learning of the young man in this world, and he planted in the
hearts of the relatives of the youth the idea of going up to Meron
on Lag Ba'omer, to prostrate themselves upon the grave of Rabbi
Shimon Ben Yohai, that the merit of this divine sage might stand him
in good stead and help him to recover from his sickness.

They took him, in his bed, and carried him all the way until
they reached Safed. And since Safed was full of many physicians,
expert in books of healing and the ways of the human body, they
brought the sick youth before them. When the physicians saw him,
they lowered their heads, with a sigh and said: "We despair of
him, we cannot lengthen his life even for an hour. But in the west
of Safed there is an old burial ground with many caves; and in
that place many righteous and holy men are buried, double the
number of those who came out of Egypt. Take the sick man, and
make the circuit of the burial ground with him; perhaps they will
have pity on him and beg mercy for him." So the relatives went
and made the circuit of the burial ground with weeping and supplication, but they saw no sign of improvement in the sick man.
Then they went up to Meron with him, but when they reached
Meron there was no life left in him. So they put down the young
man's bed, and laid him down in front of the cave, and wept loud
and long, until all the companies of pilgrims who came to prostrate
themselves upon the grave of Rabbi Shimon Ben Yohai wept with
them.

At that moment, all the sages of Safed arrived with scrolls of
the Law in their hands, dancing all the way in great joy, singing
songs and praises and playing all kinds of instruments. And the
Rabbi of the Sephardim walked before them, an old man and
righteous, all the years of his life adorned with learning and prayer

and good deeds. He saw all the people weeping and asked: "Why are you weeping?" They said to him: "A certain widow from Tiberias brought her only son here, so that he might find healing on the grave of Rabbi Shimon Ben Yohai and when he reached here he passed away."

Then the Rabbi said: "God forbid that the Great Rejoicing of Rabbi Shimon Ben Yohai should become a day of weeping and mourning." And he said to the attendants: "Send out all the men from the House of Study and from the cave, and let no man enter the cave until I call you." So they went out, and no man was left there.

Then the Rabbi said to the bearers of the bed: "Bring the sick man into the cave." They brought him in and laid him down on pillows and rugs. He said to them: "Go out"—and they went out. When they had gone out, the Rabbi sealed the cave and made the circuit of the cave, on the inside. And he continued in prayer until the time of the afternoon service.

When the time of the afternoon service came, he opened up the cave and brought in eight wise men, who had been careful all their lives to pray with the congregation, and stood with them by the grave of Rabbi Shimon Ben Yohai, who said: "Ben Yohai, you know that ever since we reached the age of understanding we have never let pass the hour of prayer without worshipping with the congregation. And now we here are nine, and this young man makes ten; if you do not beg mercy for him that he may live, we shall lose the opportunity of praying with the congregation."

So they stood by the grave of Rabbi Shimon Ben Yohai, looking at the dead lad, but they saw no sign of life in him. Then each of them put his hand in the girdle of his neighbor, and said: "Ben Yohai, you know full well that ever since we reached the age of understanding we have not prayed in a congregation of fewer than ten, and today, on the day of your death, shall we stand here, ten men of Israel, and not say the afternoon prayer as a congregation?" Immediately, the old Rabbi began to say the Ashrei prayer, and he read each verse with fear and terror and awe and trembling and all his companions read each verse with him word by word. When they reached the verse, "The Lord is near to all that call

upon Him, to all that call upon Him in truth," they heard a
sound coming from the mouth of the sick youth. They listened
carefully and heard his lips whispering: "He does the will of them
that fear Him," and they knew that their prayer had been accepted
by God, and they knew that he lived.

This story is famous all over Safed, and I heard it from a
certain man who heard it from a certain old woman who was
there, but I do not remember whether the old woman came from
Tiberias or Safed.

Translated by: I. M. Lask

*   *   *

A TAPESTRY OF TRIBES

IN A shut-in valley in the Galilee live the remnants of an ancient Jewish community who claim descent from the local Jews of the days before the Great Destruction and Dispersion. According to their tradition, their synagogue was built from the stones of the Temple in Jerusalem which their saintly leader brought shortly after the Romans had destroyed the building. These Jews belong to neither Sephardim, Ashkanizim, Yemenites, Moroccans, Bokharans, or any of the other communities into which the Jews in Israel are divided.

But the number of such Jews of unbroken local lineage is very small. Moslem invaders and the Crusaders put an end to the Jewish communities remaining in the country after the Bar Kokhba revolt of 132 C. E. The massacre of the Jews of Haifa by the besieging Crusaders in the 11th century is the last we know of any sizable Jewish community before the gradual Return began.

After the Great Expulsion from Spain in 1492, thousands of Jews speaking a Spanish dialect and observing their own ritual settled in the northern part of Palestine, as well as in other parts of the Turkish Empire, which then included the Balkan peninsula. Thus we have the beginning of the large Sephardi community in the Holy Land. Sephardi mystics concentrated in Safed, in the vicinity of the grave of the founder of the Cabbala, Rabbi Shimeon Ben Yochai. Among these Sephardi Cabbalists were Joseph Caro, the great codifier of the Jewish law, whose "Shulhan Aruch" is still the guide for the daily life and observance of every pious Jew throughout the world, Shlomo Alkabetz, the author of the hymn Lecha Dodi, by which Queen Sabbath is welcomed every Friday by Jews all over the world, and many others.

The first Ashkanazi Jewish Cabbalist in Safed was Rabbi Isaac Luria, or the Holy ARI, born of parents who had come from Germany to settle in Jerusalem. Ashkenazi mystics, including the sect of the *hassidim* were drawn to Safed; other pious Ashkenazim settled in Jerusalem or in Hebron.

The Ashkenazi Jews, speaking Yiddish and maintaining their peculiar ritual and Hebrew pronunciation, lived side by side with the Sephardim, whom they influenced, and, who in turn, influenced them, while keeping apart. Members of the lesser communities—Moroccans, Persians, Bokharans—tended to merge into the Sephardi community.

Today there are in Israel two chief rabbinates: one for the Ashkenazi Jews, the other for the Sephardim and the Oriental communities.

But the Yemenite Jews constitute a chapter by themselves.

* * *

In 1882, the year in which the pioneers from Russia and Rumania established the first agricultural colonies, a large number of Yemenite Jews arrived in Jerusalem. Unlike Jews from other countries who immediately upon coming to the Holy City joined their own communities—Sephardi, Ashkenazi, Moroccan, Kurdistani, Persian and others—the Yemenite Jews found no existing congregation of their own Jews. The year 1882 saw the establishment of the first Yemenite congregation in the Holy Land.

Most Jews in the Holy City were recipients of *halukah* (distribution or dole) from funds collected abroad in the countries or districts whose names were borne by their congregations. But no such provision existed for the Yemenites.

Some of the leading Zionists of Jerusalem took hold of the Yemenites and trained them in such crafts as stonecutting and established them in this way. While the *halukah* system persisted in the Holy Land for many years after 1882, the Yemenites never formed part of it.

* * *

Individual Jews continued to come from Yemen to Palestine after 1882, but it was not until 1909 that a large contingent arrived.

Those were the days of the Second Aliyah (1904-1914), when the emphasis was on creating a Jewish farm-laborer class. The Yemenite Jews were known to be industrious, devout, honest and content with as little as the Arab for a living, and thus the Jewish colonists could not offer the same objections to employing Yemenites as they did to employing "Russians."

This second arrival of the Yemenites suggested new possibilities. The result was one of the most remarkable missions in Jewish history.

* * *

Shmuel Yavnieli was sent by the Palestine Office of the World Zionist Organization to bring Jews from Yemen.

Shmuel Yavnieli, the young radical from Russia, put on a traditional praying shawl, let his beard and earlocks grow, and set out from Jaffa to Aden by ship and thence through all of Yemen by camel, donkey and on foot. During the first four months he visited about forty communities throughout Yemen. Following are some excerpts from his own account:

> Wherever I came Jews would come to see me, and I would talk to them about Eretz Israel, about the new agricultural colonies, about the Zionist movement. They would listen with great joy and at times went into ecstasies. They would then ask me: "What of the Wailing Wall? What of Mother Rachel's Tomb? What of the Tomb of Rabbi Shimon Bar-Yohai?" My answer invariably would be: "Why ask about tombs and graves and dead stones? Ask about Zion that is coming back to life again, about the children of Zion returning to her lap from the lands of exile and dispersion . . . "
>
> Yemenite Jews kept putting the same questions to me that they apparently had put to all the emissaries from the Holy Land: "Do you bear any tidings about the Coming of the Messiah? Is the hour of redemption at hand? Have you been given any omens?"
>
> My answer was always: "I am neither a prophet, nor the son of a prophet; neither the Messiah, nor the herald of the King Anointed. Nonetheless, I am a bearer of tidings. I have come to tell you about the approaching liberation of our people, liberation that is to come by their own efforts." . . .
>
> They heard my words as through a haze of reverie. This was not for what their wretched souls had been thirsting. What? No Messiah? No miracles? No great trumpet? No eagles' wings? No sumptuous banquets and resplendent clothes?—Then what?
>
> It required a great deal of effort to get these people out of their imaginary world and to bring them into the world of reality.

Many Yemenite Jews chose to read into Yavnieli's message the very opposite of what he said and left for Palestine expecting a life of ease. Some even went despite his warnings that they were not suited to the country. They came back embittered and disillusioned and carried on propaganda against him. A rumor spread that he was a spy sent by the Sultan to trick Yemenite Jews into that part of the Turkish possessions where universal military service applied (it did not in Yemen which was a dependency of Turkey).

But Yavnieli also found loyal adherents, people who understood the meaning of Zionism. Several hundred migrated to Palestine, many making part of the journey on foot across the Arabian desert. Yavnieli remained in Yemen while his comrades of the *Hapoel Hatzair,* in cooperation with the Palestine Office of Jaffa, took care of the newcomers' needs.

Joseph Sprinzak, now speaker of the Knesset, was elected by *Hapoel Hatzair* as special representative to the Yemenites. Sprinzak was still a young man, a comparatively recent arrival from Russia. He had to deal with Jews from another world, but he succeeded in endearing himself to them.

*   *   *

The dominant element in Israel in modern times has been the Ashkenazi Jewish community. But it was the East European rather than the German-speaking Ashkenazi Jew. The latter type, embracing the Jews of Germany, Austria, Czechoslovakia and Hungary, had drifted away from distinct Jewish folk-life, including the Yiddish speech, and had become assimilated to the culture of the country they lived in. Modern German had become the language of most of these Jews, even in countries in which the native population spoke Czech, Slovak or Magyar. Only a small minority of the Zionist immigrants came to Palestine from the German-culture Jewish communities.

But with the advent of the Nazis, there began a large migration of German-assimilated Jews into Palestine. Most of them had never been Zionists and a great many of them were Jews in little more than in name.

Yehuda Bourla

◆

AT A GLANCE

MERCADO KIMCHE was a herculean type of a man: tall, broad-shouldered and of powerful build. His face had a manly grace with a large full beard flowing down over his chest, as if he were a rabbi or communal leader. His voice, too, in conversation with friends, was strong and resonant. If not for a slight tenderness in his facial expression, his beautiful clear eyes and a charming smile generally flitting on his lips, one would take him to be a manual laborer, a blacksmith, a butcher, or, say, the head of a stevedores' gang.

As a matter of fact, he was engaged in the genteel occupation of making men's silken kaftans for Sabbath and holiday wear. It may well be that some of his fine qualities were the result of his daily contact with silk and other fine cloth; he was a kind, friendly generous man. Those who knew his wife, Linda, attributed much of his virtue to her influence.

Linda was a small, delicate woman with much charm. She had a lovely face, a quiet refined manner, a sweet serene voice, and her eyes were of unusual beauty. People used to say that it was one of God's wonders for two human beings to possess eyes so much alike. Generally speaking, every human being has a pair of eyes altogether unlike anyone else's. Linda's eyes had an added quality all their own; besides their bewitching beauty, they reflected in their limpid light all of her great virtues: her modesty, simplicity and nobility.

These and other attributes of Linda became strengthened with the passing of time in consequence of her hard and bitter fate: she was doomed to sterility. In about twenty years of her married

life with Mercado she bore no children. As she passed her days in
anxiety and desire, and as she walked about in desolation alone in
her house, the quiet sadness of her mood impressed itself upon her
more and more.

It was to her husband's credit, people always used to say, that
her melancholic silence never evoked from him even the slightest
hint of reproach. No stranger's ear, whether a friend or neighbor,
ever heard a sound that would indicate the grief of the couple over
their fate. The most they ever noticed was that, whenever at some
festive occasion friends wished them the fulfillment of their desires,
husband and wife would exchange glances which recalled imprisoned birds fluttering within their cage.

One day, there was a great commotion in Linda's quiet home.
It came as a sudden storm. On the threshold of the house one
morning stood the beadle of the rabbinical tribunal with a request
that she come with him to the court.

Amazed and stupefied by a foreboding of doom, she asked the
messenger: "Are you not mistaken? Are you sure it is I, Linda
Kimche, who is summoned to the tribunal?"

"No, no, sister, I am not mistaken."

"And what is the meaning of it? Don't you know?"

"The learned judges know best how to present the matter properly. Let them tell you."

"And what about my husband? How can I go to the court without him?"

"It is on his behalf that the judges are asking you to come."

"My God, am I dreaming? Is my husband there, at court?"

"No, sister, I heard it said that he had gone to Hebron and
had entrusted the matter to the tribunal."

She followed the beadle in confusion and in speechless resignation, as if she were being led to the scaffold.

The anteroom of the tribunal was filled with noisy quarreling
people. Linda sat down in a corner, shrunken and frightened like
a war captive brought to a slave market. Presently, when litigants
emerged from the judges' chambers, Linda was called in.

The presiding judge addressed her in a calm, fatherly voice,
full of compassion, informing her that her husband was determined

to divorce her because of his yearning for children. True, divorce is a harsh act, compared by our sages to the Destruction of the Temple, but our Sacred Law justified divorce when it is motivated by a man's wish for offspring.

When the rabbi noticed how pale she turned and heard her complaint that her husband had suddenly wielded an axe over her head, he said softly: "It is not a sudden decision. And your husband is not heartless. On the contrary, for some years now he has been consulting the tribunal on the matter. He has even undertaken to pay you twice the sum specified in your marriage contract. But, out of compassion for you, Linda, he has failed to carry out his decision until now. But now he is resolved to let nothing sway him. He therefore appointed a deputy, as the law requires, to hand you the bill of divorce. All arrangements have been completed and the beadle is the deputy. You will receive the document from him."

As one struggling out of a heap of rubble after a house has crumbled, in a tear-choked voice trying to make herself audible, she cried out: "I am your handmaiden, my learned masters, ready to kiss your feet. But do let me speak, I pray. If I am doomed to divorce, I will not accept the bill from anyone else but my own husband. I will not accept it from anyone else. Even if you should kill me, my learned Lords, I will not accept it."

The judges retired for consultation and voted to comply with her request. That same week, on Thursday, when the tribunal would meet again, the husband would hand Linda the bill of divorce.

On the appointed day, the act of handing over the bill of divorce was placed first on the agenda for the day. There was a hushed silence in the chamber. Everyone waited for the husband's arrival. Everyone's eyes were watching the woman who sat, bent, in a corner, dressed in black as in mourning.

When Mercado entered, the Presiding Judge called him to his side and spoke to him in a whisper. It was obvious to everyone in the room that the judge was trying to dissuade the man from implementing his decision. But it was also obvious that the man was not to be deterred.

The judges stood up, and the Presiding Judge called on the husband to face the tribunal. He walked over with firm, measured steps, his head erect. Then the woman was called, and she came up, haltingly, resigned to her fate.

The beadle instructed the woman to raise her arms and fold her hands together at the joints and spread her fingers so as to receive into them the document as prescribed by the Law.

The document was placed in the husband's hands with instructions to drop it from above into the wife's hands. Every man and woman present saw Mercado's eyes wander in all directions, trying to avoid his wife's glance. The woman raised her hands, as directed, and stood with arms outstretched as one offering a prayer before execution.

As the husband held the bill of divorce in his hands above her, a stifled voice was heard, as if issuing from the entrails of the earth.

"May God forgive you, my love, as I do forgive you!" Mercado's eyes automatically turned to his wife for the instant it takes an eyelash to flicker, and he was crushed. His hand weakened and slumped. Presently he rallied and made a gesture as if pushing something away from himself and raised his hand high. But the hand trembled. By some unaccountable force his eyes were riveted to those of his wife. There was an eerie silence in the room—every heart beating with anxious expectation.

His hand weakened a second time.

"I cannot do it," he said. "That is what I feared. Her eyes. . . ."

He hurriedly asked if he might tear up the divorce act.

"You may," replied the Presiding Judge.

The air was pierced with the sound of tearing, as though it were an unfamiliar sound coming from another world, distant and unknown.

*   *   *

Ari Ibn-Zahav

◆

MOROCCANS AT THE WAILING WALL

FROM TIME immemorial Arab Moslems from Morocco lived in the neighborhood of the Wailing Wall in Jerusalem. Many of them stopped over in the Holy Land on their way back from pilgrimages to Mecca and settled in the Holy City.

Moroccan Jews who came to live and die in the land of their fathers found a great deal in common with their Moslem countrymen, with whom they could converse in their dialect, which the Palestine Arabs could hardly understand. In this way it came to pass that the Moroccan Arabs, whose notorious ferocity kept Jews away from the Wailing Wall, made an exception for the Jews from their own native land. Later other Jews joined the Moroccan Jews. But until very recently the number of Moroccans among the Jewish beggars at the Wall was disproportionately large compared to Jews of other communities.

Bulissa Hannah had lived in the Moroccan Jewish hostelry for fifty-five years, occupying the same room, before I met her. She was the only inmate in the establishment who had a room for herself. It was spotlessly clean in a house that was incredibly filthy.

The story of Bulissa Hannah was as follows:

Her husband was the renowned scholar and cabbalist Rabbi Shalom Bahabut of Rabat, who, at the age of twenty, followed his master and teacher, Rabbi David Ben-Shimeon, nicknamed "The Honey" into the Holy Land.

In those days, when the Moroccan Jews began to come in large numbers, they had no community of their own in the Holy City, nor anywhere in the Holy Land. They submitted to the authority of the rabbis and leaders of the Sephardic community and worshipped in the Sephardic synagogue.

But the Sephardi hosts, who were fairly prosperous and well-established in the country, looked down upon the Moroccan new-comers who were poor. And so, when the Moroccans, worshipping in the synagogue which bears the name of Rabbi Johanan ben-Zaccai, tried to cantillate their prayers according to their own custom, intoning the melodies they had learned from their fathers in Morocco, the Sephardim forbade it, and the Moroccans had to sing their prayers in the unfamiliar strains of the Sephardi ritual which evoked no feeling in Moroccan hearts.

Then Rabbi David ben-Shimeon, nicknamed "The Honey," the leading Moroccan scholar, hired a room in an Arab's house, to be used as a meeting place for prayer and study. There the Moroccans could trill and warble while praying to God to their heart's desire and they were happy.

The Moroccans had many other grievances. Finally, when the tribunal of the Sephardi rabbis put some Moroccans in chains and forced them to sweep the streets in punishment for some trivial matter, Rabbi David ben-Shimeon called his disciples together, of which Bulissa Hannah's husband, Rabbi Shalom Bahabut was one, and addressed them in the following words:

"How long are we to entrust the Sephardim with all our communal matters? The Sultan who reigns in Morocco today is friendly to the Jews and they are prospering. Why not collect contributions in Morocco for a Moroccan synagogue and a Moroccan Talmud Torah in Jerusalem? Now you go out on such a mission, each one of you in a different part of Morocco, and, with God's help we shall have a Moroccan community in 'The Holy City.' "

Just as the emissaries of Rabbi David Ben-Shimeon arrived in Morocco, an insurrection broke out in the country and the capital of Morocco was about to be stormed by the rebel forces. Wherever the insurgents came, they looted Jewish homes and stores and beat up the Jews. In one town captured by the rebels, the notables set a sumptuous banquet to honor the conqueror and the coming ruler of Morocco. But this was a ruse, and the brigand was assassinated at the banquet. The Jews of Morocco heaved a sigh of relief and thanked the Lord for their deliverance. They well knew that the deliverance had been sent by God together with the emissaries from the Holy Land. Consequently, they gave generously to the disciples of Rabbi David ben-Shimeon.

It fell to Rabbi Shalom Bahabut to go to the interior of Morocco where many Jews had amassed riches from trading with the peasants. Needless to say, his mission was crowned with success. But on his return, while traveling on an unfrequented road with his attendant following him, he was set upon by Berbers who demanded all his money. He refused. The bandits searched the garments of Rabbi Shalom and his attendant, but could not find the money, which was skillfully hidden in the seams. They tied the two Jews to a tree and were about to slay them, but just then a man appeared on horseback, who looked like a Berber, with drawn sword. He demanded to know why these men were to be killed. The bandits said the Jews had bought soap from them and refused to pay. The two captives denied this under oath, and Rabbi Shalom exclaimed: "Lord of the universe! For the sake of Jerusalem, Thy Holy City, save us now from these wicked men!" The Berber horseman threatened the bandits that he would slay them forthwith and the bandits took flight. The stranger untied the captives and accompanied them to the nearest town. Then he mysteriously disappeared.

In gratitude for this deliverance, Rabbi Shalom vowed that he would donate all the commission due him from the collection to the building of a Moroccan synagogue in Jerusalem. The gift was accepted and, in return, the administrators assigned a room to Rabbi Shalom for the rest of his life.

Rabbi Shalom's room was in the hostelry, which at that time was inhabited only by scholars. In those days Jerusalem was still Jerusalem—as Bulissa Hannah explained to me: it was not Paris or "Londra" (London)—it was the Holy City. The scholars of the Moroccan hostelry lived four men to a square cubit, but the darkness of their rooms were illumined by the refulgence of the higher spheres and gave them contentment. But after the demise of Rabbi David Ben-Shimeon, the administrators became less discriminating and allowed the common beggars who solicited alms at the Wailing Wall to come and live in the hostelry. That is why the whole building was now filthy, but only the room of Bulissa Hannah, who was Rabbi Shalom's widow, was so spotlessly clean.

For forty-two years Rabbi Shalom lived in that room—from the day the building was completed until his death. He never left the building, where the synagogue, too, was situated, for fear that, in walking on the street he might inadvertently commit a sin by looking at a woman, or by touching an unclean animal such as a donkey or a dog. Only on the day of Rosh Hashanah, when it was enjoined upon the Jews to go towards water, where they would throw off their sins—only then did Rabbi Shalom leave the building. He would go to the courtyard of Esther Nahon, which had a deep well, to perform the rite of "tashlich." As he walked, he was accompanied by many disciples, surrounding him on all sides, so as to keep his eyes from beholding a woman or a unclean animal. The Turkish Chief of Police of the Holy City had so much regard for Rabbi Shalom that each year he sent two policemen to escort him to tashlich.

Rabbi Shalom derived his sustenance partly from teaching, partly from support given him anonymously by a wealthy admirer, and to a considerable extent from direct help from Heaven. Thus, on the eve of Purim, when his wife, Bulissa Hannah did not have a penny to prepare the feast, Rabbi Shalom quietly told one of his pupils to go ask Mordecai for help. The pupil went to the Wailing Wall, read the psalms and called "Mordecai the Righteous! My Teacher has no money for Purim!" He did so after each psalm that he recited. A man came over to the boy, gave him a package and continued with the reading of the Book of Esther. The money lasted until the following Purim.

Rabbi Shalom was eighty-four years old when he died, surrounded by his friends and disciples. Before emitting up his last breath he whispered to those around him: "Take care of my Bulissa Hannah! She has been a virtuous and devoted wife to me all these years." Then he beckoned to a famous Cabbalist from Aleppo to approach him, said something to him, and while quietly reciting the "Shma," expired, as if falling asleep after a Sabbath repast.

Mordecai Tabib

◆

1917

DAYS NOW arrived in which great events took place and memorable deeds were performed. When people met in the colony's marketplace, or in the synagogue, or at any gathering, they had much to talk about. Reports of what was happening reached even the Yemenite quarters in Rehovot.

Now there was a certain Ashkenazi Jew whose name was Joseph but whom the Yemenites crowned with the title of Rabbi Joseph because of his scholarship, wisdom and wit. This Rabbi Joseph was in a habit of paying periodic visits to Master Yihyeh, the leader of the Yemenite Jews in Rehovot. To be sure, he was not a local man, for the local Ashkenazi Jews never set foot in Yemenite homes. He was from Jaffa and was one of the Hapoel Hatzair people. Whenever this man came to Rehovot, Master Yihyeh would invite to his home all the elders of the Yemenite community, and there would be a good deal of discussion. The Yemenites would tell Rabbi Joseph their troubles and voice their demands, and Rabbi Joseph would reply with some soothing words to comfort them.

This time when he came, and what with so many rumors in the air, one the very opposite of the other, Master Yihyeh and his friends had been waiting for him impatiently. No sooner had word of his arrival spread than they all hastened to Rabbi Yihyeh's dwelling. After Naama, Master Yihyeh's wife, prepared the refreshments—mostly dried melon seeds and a drink of Arab brandy for a benediction—and having spread out the cushions on the floor they all reclined comfortably. Now Master Afgean, who was the oldest of the guests, spoke up:

"As the Scriptures say, a word in its proper season is good indeed

. . . What is the news you bring us, Rabbi Joseph? We hear many rumors and we do not know what to make of them. Now you tell us what they all signify . . ."

Rabbi Joseph, who had become adept in the Yemenite form of discussion, began by uttering a short sentence which could mean a great deal but whose meaning needed further elucidation:

"Redemption is at hand," he said. And then he added: "It seems that the days of the Messiah are upon us."

Sweet were those words to the ears of the listeners and they remarked on all sides: "Goodly are your tidings, Rabbi Joseph, goodly are your tidings."

They put their hands to their ears the better to hear him.

The guest inclined his head towards them and, speaking in a low voice, with frequent stops, he reported: "The Englishman stands at the gates of Jerusalem . . . The Turkish hosts are fleeing him in panic . . . One of the great men of England wrote an epistle to one of our own great men, which is known in the world as the Balfour Declaration."

As he was preparing to elaborate and explain, Rabbi Joseph was interrupted by Salem Said Al-Zindani: "Who is that Ben-Pur and what are his tribulations?"

The name of Balfour was much too strange to the ears of a Yemenite Jew and become Ben-Pur, the Hebrew word for "declaration" is "hatzhara"—a word of recent coinage not familiar to the students of the Bible and the Talmud. Thus, it sounded to the inquirer like "tzara," that is "trouble" or "tribulation."

Rabbi Joseph smiled and explained: "It is not a tribulation, but a declaration, and it is like "the copy of the writing" spoken of in the Book of Esther, in which the King's decree was inscribed. It is an epistle in which that great man of the Righteous Among the Gentiles wrote that the victorious English people were taking Palestine away from the Turks and giving it to the Jews so that they may gather in it from all their dispersions."

Speaking thus, he sat up on his cushion and looked around at the guests, his eyes sparkling. His listeners, too, sighed deeply to express their agitation and their eyes became moist with the great delight his words had brought to their hearts.

However, it was the same Salem Said al-Zindani who presently disturbed their mood of exultation by an unpleasant remark: "To be sure! To be sure! So they'll take Palestine and they'll give it away to the Ashkenazi Jews. There'll be nothing for the Yemenites anyway."

He was going to speak some more in the same vein, but the host, Master Yihyeh, rebuked him: "Hush! You are indeed like that man Sheba the son of Bichri, who spoke against King David! The main thing is the Redemption, you fool!"

Still, the words of the malcontent, even if they did not diminish their faith, did detract from the solemnity of the hour. From then on the Yemenites pelted Rabbi Joseph with annoying questions. They started with the future of the Jewish Homeland and ended up by present grievances.

Master Yihyeh, as the spiritual leader of his community, summed it up as follows: "When the Bible speaks of a stranger and an inhabitant, we are told that a stranger is one who merely eats what he is fed, but an inhabitant is one who grows his own food—he has a small plot of land, where he plants some squash, some onions or other vegetables and takes from his own garden to feed his household."

What Master Yihyeh meant, of course, was that the Yemenites were treated like "strangers" and did not even own a small plot of land.

Rabbi Joseph spoke to them of marvelous things to come. He began with that man Shmuel Hagalili,* who had grown a beard and earlocks and wandered all through Yemen riding a donkey, going from one Jewish community to another, to arouse the Jews of Yemen from their long slumber in the Exile and to come to settle Palestine.

"You have always craved for Redemption," said Rabbi Joseph, "but your ways are too simple. You thought when you saw his fine face and beard, as he rode a white donkey, that he was the King Anointed himself, of whom it is said in the Talmud that he would arrive as a poor man riding a donkey, and you expected that once

---

* A transparently fictionalized name of Shmuel Yavnieli.

you arrived in the Holy Land you would immediately settle down, every man under his vine and every man under his fig tree . . ."

"It was not because of him that we came to the Land of Israel, Rabbi Joseph!" Salem Zindani interrupted him, "I never heard of this friend of yours called Shmuel Galili, and yet I am here."

Master Yihyeh started from his seat to reprimand the vexatious fellow: "You fool!" he cried to Salem Zindani, "have you made up your mind to confuse this gathering? Can't you see that Rabbi Joseph has not intended to discuss this or that single case, but the whole community? Now I ask you, since you are my guest, don't annoy us any more and hold your tongue and keep your place!"

Just then Naamah, Master Yihyeh's wife, came in and placed a coal-burner in the middle of the room. Then she went out and brought back a long narghilleh, filled it with fresh tobacco and live coals, scattered some sweet-smelling spices on the coal-burner and went out again. The assembled men then pronounced the benediction over spices, the narghilleh passed from hand to hand and from mouth to mouth, and then Rabbi Joseph continued his discourse.

"Also you expected that when you came, fully-built houses would stand ready to receive you and that the Holy One, blessed be He, would lower from under His Throne of Glory all of Jerusalem on High with the Temple completed. It was very very difficult for that man Shmuel Galili," Rabbi Joseph sighed deeply. "It was difficult for him to explain the facts to such great believers like yourselves. Nevertheless, he did not shirk from telling you the whole truth. He told you that the Land of Israel was a desolate land, that its soil was hard to till, that the Jews dwelling in it must sink their nails into that soil and their teeth into its rocks to bring forth their bread. He told you that the trouble with the Holy Land was that it did not have enough Jews and that you must come and settle it. And you Jews of Yemen,—may I be the sacrifice to atone for your sins!— you listened to his words, and a hidden chord stirred within your hearts and you did come."

The listeners were moved to tears to hear such words. Nonetheless, Master Yihyeh said: "You have been saying, Rabbi Joseph, that the Land of Israel has a hard soil, that a Jew who dwells in it must sink his teeth and nails to bring forth bread. But we are here.

We have been here for eight years, ever since we left the Exile
land of Yemen. We are eager to sink our nails and our teeth and to
chew the soil. Now here you are, one of the leaders, nearer to our
hearts than any other, and you know that we live here no better
than if it were another exile. We work for farmers and earn a very
meager sustenance. And those Jewish farmers deal harshly with us
and humiliate us, as if we were menial slaves. Why cannot we, too,
be like them, owning our own land, why cannot we be farmers?
That is what we want!"

Master Yihyeh, by his words, removed the restraint from the
others, who had hitherto hesitated to offend Rabbi Joseph by voicing
complaints.

Rabbi Joseph, to encourage them, took the narghilleh from the
hand of Salem Said Zindani, placed it in his own mouth and reclined comfortably the better to hear.

Master Menashe, a powerfully built man, said: "We are not
only bondsmen to them, but the bondsmen of their slaves. When
we work in their vineyards, they place Arab overseers to lord it
over us. From sunrise to sunset I work with the hoe, and an Ishmaelite stands over me, cracking his whip and shouting *yallah!*
Sometimes he hits me with his cane. For he has learned from his
master that I am a mere Yemenite."

Salem Said Zindani now gave vent to his bitterness: "Not only
that, but their watchmen often beat up our wives. And all for what?
Just for a bundle of dry leaves or twigs they gather for their ovens.
Would you believe it Rabbi Joseph, last month one of our women
had a miscarriage because an Arab watchman hit her so hard . . .
And you say that Palestine will be given to the Jews. I am quite
sure it will be given only to the Ashkenazim!"

This time no one stopped Salem's words, but they all nodded
their heads in assent and all exclaimed: "It is true, everything he
says."

Now Master Yihyeh again felt concern for the feelings of his
guest. He sat up on his cushion and said: "You all talk as if Rabbi
Joseph were to blame, as if he were like one of them. But you know
he condemns them just as much as you do. He has been coming to
us all this time and I know him. When you talk about the Ashke-

nazim, you include him—that is your mistake. I tell you, Rabbi Joseph
knows of no difference between Jews from Europe and Jews from
Yemen. To him all Jews are Jews. But it seems to me, in my humble
judgment, that the one real difference between the farmers and us
is that they have money and we are so poor. But I will tell you,
Rabbi Joseph," and he now turned to the guest, "it is written in
the Book of Samuel that the Lord 'raises the poor out of the dust,
He lifteth the needy from the dung-hill (Samuel, II, 8).' It is common to interpret this passage as meaning that the Almighty has it
in His power to make a poor man rich. But I have my own interpretation: it means that while there are some poor people who are
so low that their faces are ground in the dust, the Lord can, if He
will, put them upright on their feet so that, while poor, they may
still maintain their dignity. And that is just what we desire for
ourselves!"

Rabbi Joseph was so elated to hear these words that he got up
and walked over to Master Yihyeh and kissed him on his lips. "As
the Scriptures say, 'He shall be kissed on his lips' for such words,"
Rabbi Joseph turned to the assembled Yemenites. "You are my
master and my teacher, my master and my teacher!" He used the
phrase from the Talmud, when he addressed Master Yihyeh. "These
are thoughts that are deeper than the seas. This is a great truth!"

He waxed more and more enthusiastic and went on to explain:
"I am one of a family of toilers. I don't mean by family my father
or my mother or my brothers—they are not toilers. I mean my
friends, my comrades who came to Palestine to till its soil and to
work with their hands and to build up the Homeland. We have
great plans. You will soon hear about them. Moreover, you too, will
join that family, as fully equal members. Just as you are—for you
are fully worthy of it and it is worthy of you. We hold the same
views as Master Yihyeh has just expressed. But not one of us has
ever found such a wonderful way of expressing them as Master Yihyeh in the passage from the Book of Samuel and his interpretation."

Now Rabbi Joseph went on to tell them about the labor organizations in the country and the plans to form one large federation
—a Histadruth—and about the collective farm called Daganiah,
where people lived in a commune like the Essenes of old, as related

in the Talmud, and about the marvelous old man with a flowing white beard whose name was Aaron,* who like Aaron of the Bible, always sought peace and who elevated manual labor to a religious principle.

All listened to his talk and, when he concluded that they would some day come to own their own land and work their own plots, they replied as with one voice: "Amen, Amen!"

* * *

As the Yemenite notables sat up all night long in Master Yihyeh's home, listening to Rabbi Joseph and talking to him, Master Yihyeh's young son, whose name was also Yihyeh, sat curled up in a corner, absorbing every syllable.

Little Yihyeh was only six years old, the first-born child of his parents, who had come to the Land of Israel childless. Master Yihyeh was forty years old when his little Yihyeh was born to him, two years after his arrival in the Holy Land.

Little Yihyeh had been a pupil in the Yemenite "ma'alamah" (the equivalent of an East European "heder") for over two years. He was well versed in the Five Books of Moses, which, like all Yemenite Jews, he read in a pronunciation which emphasized every consonant, vowel and half-vowel, and in the Rashi and many other commentaries, all of which he knew how to translate into the Arabic version of the Bible as written by Saadyah Goan a thousand years ago.

During the noon recess at the ma'alamah, as the boys sat under a tree, watching Shalom the shepherd setting traps for birds, Yihyeh stood in the center telling his friends what he had heard the night before at his father's house.

"Hm," he grunted as an opening to his account, "that Ashkenazi they call Rabbi Joseph—you would think he was a pious saintly man! Nonsense! Not only that—but he goes around bareheaded and wearing long forelocks like a heathen—as if he were no other than Samson! And him such a short fellow, too! But facts are facts: he is clever and learned in the Scriptures and he knows how to quote them—like a gushing stream! And he is so simple! No fancy dress, no necktie like some of those other Ashkenazim—they should choke

---

* Aaron David Gordon.

on them! He sits down on the cushion and eats and drinks what we all drink and eat and does not make a face as if he has swallowed an insect . . .

"That Ben-Pur, he is one of the great men of the Anglisi. And the Anglisi, he loves the Jews, because the Anglisi themselves, they are our cousins, the children of Esau, our uncle. And the Anglisi wants to take Palestine from the Turk and give it to us. And this Ben-Pur, he is their king. So he sat down and wrote a "relation" that's like a letter. He wrote to one Ashkenazi man of the great men, of the Organization, the Zionist Executive, you know, that when the English take Palestine they will give it to the Jews as a present . . ."

"Whew!" the boys were impressed.

"And what is his name, of that big Ashkenazi man?" one boy inquired. "Didn't I tell you? Chaim Weissman is his name."

The same boy asked: "And when they give Palestine to the Jews, will the Yemenites have a little of it?"

"Go on, you! Aren't we Jews?" Yihyeh replied.

Yehuda Yaari

◆

THE THREE-FOLD COVENANT

MY NEIGHBOR is an immigrant from Germany who came to Palestine some time ago among the countless other refugees to escape race-hatred and persecution. It was just at that time that we came to live in our new flat in one of Jerusalem's modern suburbs. He lives on the lower floor, and I on the one above.

We have no personal acquaintance with each other. It has always been rather difficult for me to get to know my neighbors. Several times a day I pass the door of his flat, and the name engraved in outstanding Hebrew letters on a brightly polished brass plate gleams at me from the door as though it were alive, proclaiming "Richard Oppenheimer."

Sometimes my neighbor and I meet in the hall in the mornings when I am starting out for work and he, too, is going off about his business. The moment he sees me he raises his hat in my direction and uncovering his flaming red hair smiles at me and says: "Shalom. Guten Morgen."

And the echo of his thick, trumpeting voice fills the entire entrance hall.

"Shalom." I return his greeting, raising my hat as well in politeness.

Apart from these infrequent morning meetings and our polite greetings there is no contact between us. Were it not for the aroma of his pot-bellied cigars ascending to me every now and then through his open window I would not know that he was there at all. He is a peaceful sort with quiet ways and his home is just as quiet. There are no noisy children, or the hoarse voice of a gramophone or wireless to disturb us. If anything, it is he who must be aware of the

presence of his neighbor. Not that I have either a gramophone or
a wireless set or even noisy children in my flat; I live above him
and there can be no scrape of a shifted table or movement of a
chair or even noisy tread in my flat which does not sound in the
flat below like a clap of thunder.

Turning over the paper one morning, I noticed that, as is the
custom here, somebody had sent congratulations to Richard Oppenheimer through the columns of the paper on the birth of a son.
Which Richard Oppenheimer could be meant? My neighbor? Yes,
my neighbor and none other. The person offering congratulations
was H. Levy and I knew H. Levy to be my neighbor's business
partner; for on their big shop selling pharmaceutical products and
cosmetics in the main street the name "Oppenheimer and Levy" was
written up large for all to see. I read through the congratulation
once, twice and yet a third time, and pondered upon the mysterious
ways of our lives. In the very house in which I was living a woman
had lain writhing in birth pangs and I had known nothing of it; a
son had been born to my neighbor; and although no more than a
thickness of a ceiling separated us, I had become aware of the fact
only through the pages of a newspaper. Through my brain passed
a sudden vision of a woman taken with the first pains, of the
bewildered husband taking her to the hospital, and so on.

My thoughts went on to other things, I forgot my neighbor and the
son that had been born to him, and began to consider my daily work.

I forgot my neighbor, but that evening I remembered him again.
I had just sat down to eat supper when there was a knock at the
door. I opened it, and in came my neighbor, Mr. Richard Oppenheimer.

"Shalom. Guten Abend."

I invited him in. He stood silent and nervous for a few moments
and I had a chance of a good look at him. He was red-haired with
a narrow forehead, his bronze eyes squinted slightly, his red lips
looked as though they were swollen, his body was well-set and
soldierly, and the back of his neck, I noticed, was fleshy and scarred.
In my Polish birthplace they used to call such a countenance an
Esau face. I could see that he found it hard to express himself. So
I came to his aid.

"Please sit down, Mr. Oppenheimer, can I do anything for you?"

"Thanks. Yes, yes," he stammered and this time his voice was gentle and restrained, entirely different from the voice that sometimes used to trumpet a greeting at me in the hall below. "Yes, yes, I have a request to make of you. The circumcision will take place tomorrow—I suppose you know that my wife has had a son . . ."

"Yes, I heard about it. Mr. Oppenheimer. Congratulations." I shook his hand, and it immediately became easier for him to speak.

"I'll tell you quite frankly, I don't know what has to be done, I'm in a fix. I don't know how to say the blessing tomorrow at the ceremony . . ." His reddish face grew still more flushed and something childlike and innocent about him touched me to the heart, for nothing is so touching as a strong face suddenly softening.

I took my prayer book from the book-case and opened it at the Circumcision Service.

"Here you are," said I.

"Hm, hm," he cleared his throat and half-smiled in still greater confusion, "But what's to be done? I don't know how to read Hebrew . . . Not so much as a single letter. Maybe you'd be good enough to write down the blessing for me in Latin characters." In his nervousness he began fiddling with his fingers.

I was nonplussed. There was something astonishing and even startling in this confession of helplessness on the part of a man like my neighbor. He always went about with such firmness and self-assurance. His morning greeting said: I know everything, I can achieve everything; and now this confession of helplessness, of inability to read the prayer-book. I suddenly felt sorry for him and strove to overcome my astonishment. Sitting down I wrote him the blessing in Latin characters as he had requested, in block capitals so that he would be able to read it easily. Then I read it out to him three or four times. He in turn repeated it after me with a weird German accent, "Plesset ard Dou . . . to mage our zons ender indo de Govenandt off Abraham our Fader." When he began to grow a little familiar with the blessing I rose, thinking it was finished. I offered him my hand but he did not take it.

"I have yet another request of you. Pardon me, for giving you so much trouble," he stammered in a gentle voice. "Another slight request. The name, sir. We find it hard to choose a name for him. You know that my name's Richard. But for our son we want a nice Hebrew name, something out of the Bible . . . Please, do you think you could find us a nice name from the Bible?"

I took the Bible off my table and opened it at random in Numbers. The first words my eyes struck were "Elizur son of Sheneur."

"Elizur," I read from the book.

"Elizur, Elizur," My neighbor was as happy as though he had found a valuable treasure. "Elizur. Wonderful. Grossartig. A wonderful Biblical name. Thank you, sir, thank you. Elizur!" He gave me his hand to take his leave and simultaneously invited me to come to the Circumcision. It was a social invitation, made to do his duty, it seemed to me. Nonetheless, I decided to be present, for I felt that I had a share in the festivity. I had taught him the blessing and I had found him the name; how could I do other than participate in the celebration?

It was a summer evening, hot, dry and still. I sat on my balcony to breathe a little fresh air. My neighbor sat below me on his balcony. For a long time I heard him murmuring to himself as though he were praying, repeating the blessing, "to mage our zons ender indo do Govenandt off Abraham our Fader." For the first time I was aware that we were neighbors.

The following morning I put on my Sabbath suit, took some time off from work and went to the hospital which my neighbor had mentioned to me the day before, in order to be present at the induction of his son into the Covenant of Abraham. I arrived a bit late, after my neighbor had already said the blessing. There was a considerable number of people present. I made my way through them till I reached the Seat of Elijah. The circumcised mite was yelling at the first pain he had suffered in his life, and Reb Shlomo Jacob the circumciser, who is said to have inducted a full myriad of Israelites into the Covenant of Abraham our Father, stood bandaging the child.

Richard Oppenheimer was swathed in a new silk "tallith" and stood leaning against the godfather's chair. His face was set, strained and pale. I regretted thinking when he entered my flat the evening before that he had an Esau face. No, the face was now no longer that of an Esau; he now seemed to be a man overwhelmed by something fateful which could not be avoided. There was a tremendous difference to be seen in his face, and I observed it with wonder. When they reached the naming of the child his face brightened up a little. "Elizur son of Richard," he proudly told the circumciser. The latter automatically corrected it to "son of Reuben." My neighbor was perplexed for a moment. His glance met mine and he smiled at me.

It did not take long for the entire ceremony to be completed and the yelling baby to be taken to its mother. The assembly sat down at the tables to enjoy the wine and sweetmeats. They were a noisy lot, congratulating and toasting one another, chattering, rattling their glasses and laughing. Most of them were German immigrants, of whom I hardly knew one. I sat myself down by the oldest of them all, the one who had been godfather. Both the expression on his face and the fact of his having been godfather attracted me. His white hair rose like a silver diadem on his head. His trim beard and moustache marked his face as though with a capital T. He had the face of a respected man, a man of standing. Had I begun addressing him as "Herr Hofrat" he would assuredly have responded; his face told me as much. But since I was not certain I contented myself by addressing him as "Herr Doktor"; nor was I wrong.

"How was the father's blessing, Herr Doktor?"

"Very fine, very fine," replied the old man in a measured cultured voice. "Very fine, grossartig."

"I taught it him," I whispered in his ear, for I suddenly felt like vaunting myself. Or maybe I just wanted to justify my presence there.

"Indeed, indeed . . . Very fine," murmured the old man politely and poured himself a glass of wine.

"He can't read Hebrew," I continued to gossip. "I had to write down the blessing for him in Latin characters. He can't even read the prayer-book. Woe to the generation. Eh?"

The old man said nothing but finished his glass.

"I suppose his grandfather was a rabbi in one of the old German communities, and yet he doesn't even know what a Hebrew letter looks like. I'm sorry for the father who brought him up like that."

"His grandfather was not a rabbi, while as for his father, he's sitting next to you. I'm his father."

It was only now I noticed that his eyes also squinted slightly, and that there was some slight resemblance between him and my neighbor. I flamed crimson with shame and cursed myself at heart for this sudden gush of chatter. It was impossible for me so much as to open my mouth and beg his pardon.

He poured himself another glass of wine, drank it slowly to the end, and went on: "Since you taught my son the blessing, you might as well know the whole story. His grandfather was a doctor, and I, his father, am the same. I was converted to Christianity when I was a young man, but I never was a thorough-going non-Jew, for I was circumcised, you know . . . I was always a sort of half-Jew and half-Gentile; a very uncomfortable position. But as for my son Richard, I never had him circumcised, for I didn't want to make his life hard for him. I wanted him to be a complete Gentile, you know. . . And now a son has been born to my son, and I was honored with the godfatherhood . . . Do you understand me properly, my dear sir? I sat there on that chair, holding the baby on my knees, and I felt that I was holding two on my knees, that I was supporting my son as well, that I was inducting him as well into the Covenant of our Father Abraham . . . Do you understand me properly, my dear sir? This was a double Covenant . . . no, no. A treble Covenant . . . I too, old man as I am. I entered the Covenant of our Father Abraham together with them . . . "

The old man laughed in a way that was almost frightening, and wiped a tear from his eyes. At that moment his son Richard came up and pressed his hand.

"Mazel tov, Abba! Good luck, father" said he in Hebrew.

"Mazel tov," answered the old man as he rose and left me to go with his son and bless the third to enter into the Covenant— the baby who now lay in the next room, forgetting his pain at his mother's breast.

10 YOUTH ASCENDANT

THE PATRIARCHS and their descendants in biblical times "went down" or descended from Canaan to Egypt or to Babylon, but "went up"—ascended—to the Promised Land. The distinction was probably the result of pure topography for the Land of Israel is hilly. When Jews made their pilgrimages from anywhere to Jerusalem, they ascended the mountain of the Lord. In time the word for going up and the word for making a pilgrimage became synonymous.

In modern Hebrew, immigration to Palestine or to Israel is called Aliyah—Ascent. An immigrant to Israel is an *"oleh"* (pl. *olim*)—an ascendant.

The terms "First Aliyah" (1882-1900), "Second Aliyah" (1904-1914), and "Third Aliyah" (1917 and after), denoting the three main waves of pioneer immigration, are already known to the reader.

Much better known in the Jewish world is the term "Youth Aliyah," organized by Henrietta Szold to save young Jews from Hitler's Germany and later extended to bring Jewish teenagers to Palestine—and to Israel—from other countries of Jewish distress. At present (1955), Youth Aliyah still functions. It is financed largely by Hadassah of America, the organization Miss Szold helped to found and with which she maintained close contact throughout the years she lived in Palestine.

* * *

Before Youth Aliyah came into being in 1934 the collective settlements in Palestine—the kvutzot and kibbutzim—were already well-established and had a well-defined organization.

Part of that organization had its activity outside of Palestine. From time to time *shlihim* or emissaries were sent to the countries of the Dispersion to recruit *halutzim* (pioneers) and to prepare them for life in a collective settlement in Palestine. Special training farms known as *hachshara* farms or *hachsharot* were set up in those countries where the recruits were instructed in agriculture, in Hebrew, in Jewish history and the history of Zionism and were habituated to communal living.

Youth Aliyah made use of the kibbutzim in which to place the immigrant children to prepare them for life in the Homeland. It also followed —though with some modification—the practice of training youngsters on *hachshara* farms before sending them to Palestine.

Henrietta Szold, one of the most remarkable Jewish women in history, was born in Baltimore in 1860. From 1920 until her death in 1945 she lived in Jerusalem.

Following are some excerpts from Henrietta Szold's letters which give an insight into the genesis and development of Youth Aliyah. The excerpts are taken from the book *Henrietta Szold, Life and Letters,* by Marvin Lowenthal (Viking Press, 1942).

✳   ✳   ✳

Oct. 1933—

During the last few months my mind has been traveling back fifty years. It was in 1883 that, as a young woman, I was drawn into activities that sprang up around the East European immigration into America as a result of the Russian pogroms. I remember well how helpful was American Jewry's action, how despicable was American Jewry's refusal to recognize the Russian fugitives as equal brethren. American Jewry of those days was chiefly "German." The wheel has turned. In Palestine today there is helpfulness in full measure, yet no lack of unkind criticism of the refugees as Jews of inferior rank. Palestinian Mayflower Jewry is East European!

In Palestine at least there is the heart-warming reflection that the Zionist idea has been justified. It is stirring to think that the ardor of a handful of idealists, having faith in the efficacy of the age-long nostalgia of the Jew for the Land of Israel as a regenerative force, prepared the remedy before the ravages of the disease appeared. But in Palestine, nevertheless, a tangle of problems is developing around the German immigration . . .

Jerusalem, December 22, 1933

My new job, the organization of the transfer of the children from Germany to Palestine, is growing under my hands from day to day. It deals with children—it is not child's play. The responsibility is great. If and when I carry it through, I think—I should let my active life come to an end with it. Not that I feel tired to contemplate more. But I should make room for the younger, better-trained forces that are coming into the country.

(To Mrs. Rose Jacobs)   Jerusalem, February 10, 1934

The transfer of the youth from Germany is not only chock-full of time-consuming details, but the undertaking is so overwhelmingly responsible that I sometimes am all but mastered by the impulse to flee from it. Recently I took a trip to the Emek settlements—to as many of them as the heavy roads permitted me to reach—in order to choose the places to which the next group to be organized is to be directed. The discussion on the spot, the visualization of what is involved physically and spiritually in the transplantation, took away the breath, as it were, of my mind and soul. And when I have to deal with the delays and obstacles which the (British) government delights in interposing, I rage and despair. The beginnings are naturally difficult, and naturally weighted with responsibility. On their success hangs the fate of what would be a movement of several years' duration.

(To Mrs. Rose Jacobs)   Jerusalem, February 17, 1934

Day after tomorrow, the first detachment, a group of forty-four of "my" children, arrive from Germany. I go to Haifa to meet them, have them examined medically, and get their possessions out of the customs. Then I accompany them to Ain Harod, to see them installed there. I want to see them tucked away in their beds. I feel weighed down by the responsibility of this children's immigration. It's a terrible experiment. What next?

I had thought in the remote days of my youth that one attained to serenity and wisdom with old age. What do I find in my old age? Vagueness, eternal wonder at the meaning of things, inadequacy to the daily tasks, anything but tranquility.

Jerusalem, March 2, 1934

At this hour a week ago I returned to Jerusalem after four days spent in Haifa, Ain Harod, and Kfar Gileadi. It took me two hours and a half to remove mud from my shoes, my overshoes, my coat, my dress, my unders—for from the moment on Monday morning when the train reached the environs of Haifa until the moment on Friday when I escaped from the environs of Kfar Gileadi, it rained and hailed and blew and stormed and then began all over again. Such depths of mud as I trudged through! Every time I took a step I dug up great clods and by the time I approached any destination I was bound for—dining-room or my bedroom in the kvutzot—I was dragging with me a mountain of earth.

What was it all about? The first group of boys and girls arrived from Germany at Haifa, the detachment of forty-three destined for Ain Harod. I went up to meet them, and then traveled to Ain Harod with them and stayed with them there for two days. It was a great experience for me. The beautiful attitude of the Ain Harod community toward the young people, how solemnly and yet joyously they assumed the responsibility for them. The way they introduce them into the kvutza life is a religious poem. They work out a plan of gradual adjustment that is of the essence of delicacy and tact. The boys and girls felt the forethought instinctively. I wish I might have stayed with them a month.

Jerusalem, June 7, 1934

It has been again a full week. It started with the arrival of another group of German children, this time not a very large group. I went down to Haifa to meet them and accompany them to their destination, a kibbutz near Petah-Tikvah. I had visited this kibbutz several times before. They are in Palestine a unique group, for the most part pre-Hitlerite German Jews, all young, and all deeply religious, not only outwardly, not only observant of the ceremonial law, but religious from the same sort of conviction that dominates the thorough going communist or socialist —by which I mean their human relations are regulated by their religious principles. It is still a struggling group. While they have land and are cultivating it and have begun to develop every branch of agricultural economy possible on that strip of land—a good strip—they are at the same time day-laborers in the adjacent villages.

Jerusalem, July 13, 1934

It was a full week and a hot one. Sunday, a meeting in Tel Aviv; Monday afternoon, off to Haifa to investigate possibilities for apprenticeships; Tuesday afternoon and evening meetings on social service problems; Wednesday and Thursday dashing in an auto from kvutza to kvutza to arrange for groups of boys and girls and visiting the groups already settled.

Jerusalem, November 8, 1934

We have had our first loss by death among the youth groups, and I am not easy in my mind as to the care the boy got in the early stages, when he ailed and the typhoid fever diagnosis had not yet been made. I was informed of his illness exactly twenty-four hours before the end, and even then the information reached me accidentally. I believe that is what worries me most, that I haven't yet got it across to those responsible for the groups that I must be informed of every exceptional state or happening. To be sure, illness in its early stages is not always alarming, and I suppose I'd be furious if I'd get information about every cold and discomfort felt by one of the young people all over the country. Nevertheless, the boy's death discouraged me. I constantly see his parents in Hamburg before me.

Jerusalem, December 14, 1934

I have been northward, to pay a flying visit to a kvutza of the Ha-Shomer Ha-Tzair.* The country abutting on the Sea of Galilee was itself a sea when it wasn't a swamp. The auto couldn't approach the kvutza. We had to leave it on the main road, and trudge on foot through the mud to the houses. Mud! Great clods stuck to my rubbers and very soon I could hardly lift my feet, they were so heavy with mud. However, it was a blessed rainfall.

The reason of my trip was a rumor that the Ha-Shomer Ha-Tzair kvutza had not fulfilled its obligation to prepare houses and all that goes with dwellings for a group of twenty-eight German youths to come in two weeks from that time. I was due at a meeting at Haifa at three o'clock in the afternoon. So it was a race against time. We managed it, and confirmed the rumor. You can imagine my state of mind and conscience. I got the promise that all hands would be put to work and things got half-way ready. They are coming eighty-six strong on Monday, and I shall be posting up to Haifa again to meet them and distribute them among seven different places. The undertaking is getting tremendously big. Naturally not all the boys and girls stay with the groups they come with. There are all sorts of reasons for making changes. Such individual cases cause me no end of correspondence—and wondering thought.

---

* The leftist wing of the labor movement.

Jerusalem, December 28, 1934

Two weeks ago eighty-six children arrived from Germany. I met seventy-five of them at Haifa and escorted them to the Emek Ha-Yarden settlements. I remained with them until the next day, saw them well bestowed, assured myself of the presence of screens, mosquito-nets, and sanitary installation; I celebrated a charming reception with them, at which there was feasting, singing, dancing, and speech-making, and for which the settlers of five neighboring kvutzot had come together at Deganiah Aleph. The kvutzot were naturally not established as educational institutions, but they might have been if one was to judge by the way they make these fugitive youths at home and prepare for their training.

My pessimism regularly vanishes when I spend a few hours in a kvutza—I forget that I am a cynic. It's a life of hardship, but not of strain. And the hardship has its compensation in the form of achievement and the consciousness that both the hardship and the success are a common responsibility and a common advantage.

Jerusalem, May 3, 1935

Next week I again go off on a German children investigating and visiting tour in the Emek. I shall spend a few days at a gathering of the teachers and leaders of all the German youth groups in the country, at which pedagogic and organization questions are to be discussed. At this moment the chief point under discussion is the possibility, from the political and financial point of view, of extending the movement to embrace youth groups in other countries, Poland foremost among them.

It is interesting that a movement started by children—the initiator was the Jüdische Jugendhilfe, a federation of Jewish, chiefly Zionist, youth organizations in Germany—gives promise of developing into a Jewish world movement for youth. It is something to be attached to such a movement when one is seventy-four, isn't it? But one pays for the honor. It demands every scintilla of time and strength and involves one in endless minute details of organization.

*   *   *   *   *

Shimeon Sam Smaragd

◆

THAT'S HOW IT IS

ONE OF the graduates of the Youth Aliyah, Shimeon Sam Smaragd fell in the defense of his Homeland in 1948.

Before he died he left enough autobiographical material in English to make a book. In 1952 the book was published in Jerusalem, edited by Molly Lyons Bar-David.

Shimeon came to Palestine in 1940.

*　　*　　*

My pride as a Jew, fanned into being by the crazy acts of fiends, impelled me to go and see with my own eyes those Jews who have a right to be proud not only of themselves, as Jews, but of the country they are building. I had heard wondrous tales about the "halutzim," the pioneers. They made me long to wipe out the pictures of hunted, wretched refugees that reality had engraved on my mind. I desperately wanted to find a justification for a burgeoning pride which I knew to be only a defense against gnawing doubts.

I joined Youth Aliyah in Switzerland and arrived in Palestine when I had just turned sixteen. I went to live in a settlement.

Soon I found out that if I wanted to understand Palestine and the Palestinians it was absolutely imperative to know Hebrew, Jewish history and the history of the Jewish reconstruction of Palestine. In about a year I had mastered the language moderately well and I began to probe into life around and about me.

First there had been the sea voyage made in the company of dozens of young people from a half score of European countries. It had been good fun aboard the ship, as it ploughed through the inky waves of the Mediterranean. By day they had abandoned themselves to the sun, stretched on the upper deck, and at night had danced the "horrah" under the stars. Row upon row of glowing faces had wreathed the railings of the ship, as it strained to its resting place at the Haifa jetty. They had burst into song. The tunes were sung in a curiously ill-fitting Hebrew, but with lots of fervor, and the Jewish stevedores in port had brought them baskets full of big oranges. At the boat the silver-haired lady Henrietta Szold had met them, and told them she was glad they had come home at last. It was more than a little strange. They kept reminding themselves that, after all, this was a new continent.

There were tents in the transit camp, pitched in the sand; there were the scraggy palm trees and the sea and above all there hung a heavy sweet scented air and the sun was so strangely bright and fiery. Later in the day the four youngsters were called for by Rivkah with a beaming look, who had introduced herself. They had liked the "haverah" (she had told them to call her that) with the merry eyes and the little pert nose, smothered in freckles. She told them they were to stay at her "kvutza" for the two-year training period under the Youth Aliyah scheme, and the four had then pelted her with questions.

Now they were passing through the gates of the "kvutza" behind Rivkah. On either side of the path that wound up the hill towards the houses, they could see rows of young trees, each with a little plate-shaped circular depression in the ground around it. The earth was wet and the little trees looked as though they had been lapping up the water that must have been there.

Now the group approached a wooden hut with a roof of grey shingles. On one side of it, to the right as they were coming up, they could see a square lawn, surrounded by a low hedge. Rivkah turned to them: "I'm going to take you to the other boys and girls of the *hevrat no'ar;* that's the youth group. They're probably in there, in the *hadar haochel,** she added, pronouncing the words slowly. She pushed open the screened doors and they trooped in. Ah! It was cool inside. The rows of wooden tables and benches ran down the length of the dining room. On one side on the

---

* Dining hall.

left, there was a wooden partition with a door and two small shuttered openings on either side of it. All the windows were screened with fly nets and draped with gay curtains. The whole interior of the *hadar haochel* had a most pleasant effect; it was a relief from the glare outside and yet, at the same time, it was easy on the eye and airy.

About twenty boys and girls were in the *hadar haochel* when Rivkah and her small flock entered. They all looked at the newcomers with bland undisguised curiosity. Rivkah took over: "This is the youth group, the *hevrat noar* here," she said to the four. "You'll get to know them by and by." With that she left them.

For the moment there was an awkward silence. The four felt some sort of physical discomfort with twenty pairs of probing eyes on them. Somebody got up from a bench and walked across to the new arrivals. A tall boy with an easy smile stretched out his hand and said pleasantly: "Shalom, 'chevreh,' I'm Yosef. Make yourself at home here." One of the new boys shook his hand eagerly. "Shalom, my name is Shim'on." He was smaller than Yosef by a good five inches, but was wide in the shoulders and thick-necked. His brown hair curled thickly over his round face; his eyes were of a greyish blue, and full of queries. Add to this an upturned, rubbery little nose, small ears, a habit of moistening his lips and another of drawing his eyebrows together and you have Shim'on. The boys and girls were clustering around, hailing each other with "Shaloms" in differently pitched keys, but with eagerness common to all, and running appraising eyes over each. The four newcomers found themselves the center of attraction, because the others had already been together for a couple of weeks.

Now the door opened. In came a man with khaki shirt and baggy slacks, that slumped wearily over his dusty shoes. His long legs met only at the top and bottom, in between they kept as wide apart as possible without breaking. Every time he made a step forward it looked as though his foot had got there by the longest round-about way. "This is Moshe, the *madrich*,"* said Yosef to Shim'on.

---

* Instructor.

Moshe, the youth leader, set a pair of serious eyes on the new-comers, shaking hands with each of them in turn. Long exposure to the sun had saturated his face with a darkish, leathern color. Though he was of slender build, his forearms were massive and his clasp vise-like.

"Now that we've got the whole 'chevrah' together," he said, "we can get down to some serious work next week."

"Booh," howled the old hands and the new ones stared. "Show them the shower, 'chevrah,'" the *madrich* went on, ignoring the "Boohs." "Tomorrow is 'Sabbath'; you'll have time to get settled and look around. The others will show you the place."

"Uuuuaaahhh cinnamon buns for breakfast tomorrow," some-body yelped and the knowing ones rubbed their hands gleefully. Now they had to tell the new ones all about the big feed on "Sabbath" morning.

It was late that night when the four *no'ar* (they knew the term by now) sought their beds. It did not take them long to come to terms.

One by one they filed into the *mo'adon,* the *no'ar* clubhouse. It stood all by itself in the settlement yard, a sort of half-way house between the *meshek** (cowshed, stables, sheep pens, storehouse, etc.) on the one hand and the little squat dwelling-houses on the other. This was no mere accident; the *mo'adon* served as a lecture room and club house at the same time, and by choosing this position the planners had once and for all sealed the destiny of the little wooden hut. In its green painted interior with the tiled floor there was a blackboard, always covered with scrawls—the meaning of which the *no'ar* were being taught to divine in the *shi'urim* (lessons), a number of benches and a smooth-topped table. There was a sort of annex to the hut, serving as a store room. In this cobweb clut-tered limbo the *no'ar* kept, among piles of rubbish, the component parts of a ping-pong table. If they wanted to use it, they had first to put the *mo'adon's* furniture out onto the veranda and even then, retreating strategically to catch a shattering drive, they would crash into the wall, so small was the *mo'adon.*

---

* Farm, husbandry.

Well, even so, they had nothing to gripe about, because by giving them the use of this hut the *kvutza* had made a sacrifice. Moshe, the *madrich*, had explained that at length. Many of the kibbutznikim still lived in crowded quarters in the *tzrifim* (huts), many in tents—for the *kvutza* was only in its fourth year. Having a *mo'adon* was a luxury, but people were beginning to frown less on luxuries than had been their wont a number of years ago; at least that was what Moshe had said. Besides, in this new life, if there was anybody considered entitled to a bit of luxury it was certainly the children and the *no'ar*. And then, to put their awakening consciences back to blissful unconcern—Moshe had told them that Youth Aliyah (The Child and Youth Immigration Bureau of the Jewish Agency) had granted a loan to the settlement as it does to all settlements which assume responsibilities for the training of a youth group—for the express purpose of building a *mo'adon* and later, a *no'ar* house. Winding up the *sihah** then, he had promised to have somebody from Youth Aliyah come down from Jerusalem to see them and tell them all about Youth Aliyah work. That was to be this evening.

Already the benches were taken up and some had to squat on the floor. Yosef was sitting in his favorite corner on the floor, his back wedged into the angle of the walls, his long legs thrust straight out in front of him. Asher was crouching on his right, hugging his lean knees. In the huddle of boys and girls in the middle of the room, you could not at first see Shim'on, as others around him towered over his stock little figure. But, sure enough, you could hear his voice. He had become quite a talker. Somehow, he managed to pick up Hebrew quicker than the others, and, boy, did he love showing off.

Right now he was explaining with great expenditure of breath and show of hands—some Hebrew word that he could magically transform into noun, verb and adjective by the addition or subtraction of suffixes and prefixes. What a wizard—this is what Suzannah thought in her irreverent way, while Hayah and Zippora listened with rapt attention. Those two had developed a tender

---

* Discussion.

sentiment for Hebrew, that, alas, outstripped their ability to get hold of the language by far. But they all did their best, as Hanoch said, wiping his glasses, in one of his profoundly meditative moments, which he always got when the intricacies of the Hebrew language baffled him more than usual.

The *no'ar* had changed much in this last couple of weeks. Their faces, forearms and legs had become deeply tanned. They looked coarser somehow, heavier. Or perhaps it only looked that way now, dressed as they were in very short shorts and blue after-work blouses. There is a good deal to be said on this subject of "shorts," according to the boys, at least of the *no'ar*. They were waging a battle of attrition with the *haverah* in charge, who was, however, hard to wear down. So they had hit upon the simple expedient of further abbreviating their shorts by rolling up the trouser legs a couple of inches or so. It was not just that they wanted to get their thighs sunburnt. No, it was more than that. It was another of those quaint expressions of freedom that you could find in undone shirt buttons, rolled up sleeves to give the rapidly thickening biceps completely unhindered free play, unruly forelocks, and of course—the shorts. With all that, they secretly vied with each other in the "elegance" of their after-work clothes. Elegance here meant a kind of subtle affectedness in precisely those little, but significant points—like the roll of the sleeve, the shortness of the shorts, the cunning twist in the top of a stocking.

Then there was another change, too, in their language. More and more Hebrew words had crept into their native tongues that were rapidly showing signs of corruption. Sometimes they spoke Hebrew only, still a kind of sparsely-worded beginners' language, illuminated occasionally by some "literary term," borrowed from the last lesson. They had invented new idioms, inspired by the cowshed, the oldtimers—and the new life in general.

When they had come to the end of their song, the *madrich* (instructor) opened the proceedings in grand parliamentary style and in Hebrew. "This is Hans from the Youth Aliyah Bureau at Jerusalem. He has come here to meet you and to tell you about the work of the Youth Aliyah, of which you are a—ah—small, but not unimportant part. He knows you all very well, though not in person."

Hans opened up in Hebrew, but soon passed over to German because he did not want the *no'ar* to miss anything from his talk. To invite their attention, he suggested they should ask him some questions. Now this was a piece of bad diplomacy. When the last words of his request had been stubbed out by the stuffy air in the room, a silence, heavy and awkward, crept in. It was always the same. Every single one of the *no'ar* afraid of appearing too "keen" —a 'schwitzer' was the proper term—kept silence in intense concentration. Suzannah kicked Shim'on's ankle; he was the talker, loved showing off, could frame a sentence in Hebrew,—why did he not speak up?

Shim'on enjoyed his triumph, had known from the outset that he would be the one to speak first. Every time this happened—and that meant at every discussion practically—he felt elated in his awareness of the others' dependence on him.

"Could you tell us something about the history of the Youth Aliyah?" His voice was cracked, he had tried hard to make it sound natural, but somehow he had blurted out the question. Oh, damn it, why did he always have to be the first one?

Hans told them about the history of Youth Aliyah. "The organization was founded in Germany in 1932. The idea was to transfer young people to Palestine for training in settlements and to save them from the effects of anti-Semitism and discrimination. Henrietta Szold became the Director of this Organization, and she has saved and mothered young people from thirty-eight different countries ever since. I shall tell you about her later, though. . . .

"Let's talk now about a group like yours. Your education here is not limited to the lecture room and to the five hours of agricultural training. You have before you the *kvutza,* a living example of the kind of cooperative system that we hope you yourselves will later on emulate in a new settlement. For you must remember that the training you get here is devised to equip you for a task, the task of building a new settlement in the country together with other groups, perhaps even graduates from our Youth Aliyah, too. That is not easy and while you have the opportunity here—a rare opportunity that the *halutzim* who came here to pioneer years ago never enjoyed—you've got to make the most of it. In the course of your two years' training you can really get to know this kind of life, still new to you: language, work, culture. Later, when you will have to fend for yourselves you will not have much time for this. You can see in this kvutza how the demands of the meshek, the farm, the settlement fully occupy all the members. Now you work only five hours a day and look how tired it makes you.

"I'll tell you something Miss Szold said, and I want you to remember it. You too owe a lot to her and by remembering her words perhaps you are paying back a little of your debt.

"She said, 'The young people of the Youth Aliyah must be the best guardians of our homeland. There are difficult tasks waiting for them in Eretz Israel. They have to prepare themselves while there is time, so that they may be ready to take their place in the ranks of the halutzim who are building our country.' " *

*   *   *

---

* What Miss Szold did not foresee was that the young people of Youth Aliyah were also among the leading defenders of the Homeland, in the Jewish Brigade, in the Palmach and in the Army of Israel. The author of these sketches died a hero's death in the War of Liberation of 1948.

Moshe Shamir

◆

HE WALKED THROUGH THE FIELDS

DARKNESS LAY over the vineyards. They were barely distinguish-able, except for the long continuing masses row on row, the sweet smell, and the cold, clear dew spilled everywhere. The tractors lunged forward out of the yard, raising a film of dust above the gambolling dew. From the other side of the fence the powerful Caterpillars rumbled away and left a trail of dust after them like someone smoking as he hurries by. The dust was not visible; it had sunk down with all its myriad little particles and stuck to the dew wherever the two chanced to meet. It settled on the vines; it coated the thin shoots with grey; it penetrated to the thin whips; it fell over the thousands of clusters, on the round grapes hanging compact and dew-laden; and wherever it rested it clung to the dampness. It clung to the sweet nectar; it clung to the tranquility. The tractors went their way and the vineyard remained motionless. The night had woven into it all the events of yesterday, so that now, before morning, they had become a part of its being. A basket left hanging on the pole was coated with dew . . . pieces of paper that the evening breeze had plastered against the wires and left hanging soaked in so much moisture that they were near dis-solution; the footprints in the earth were covered with a thin veil of dampness, and it seemed as if they had lain implanted in this earth since Genesis.

Morning in the vineyard.

A man was walking down the road. He carried his hat in his hand, thrusting his step out before him as he walked, in the choppy, ludicrous gait characteristic of people who, though tired, are in a hurry; who, though still in the grip of slumber, are already anxious about their work. The hem of his long trousers beating against him and the earth on the path with every step, forced him to hitch up his belt from time to time, trying to straighten them. He passed the vineyard and the wagon path that cut into it—and continued on to the shed. He puttered around in the shed for a long time. He took out the shears from the box on the packing table and arranged one beside the other the whole length of the table, separating the damaged ones. He rustled a batch of packing-paper sheets and loaded them down with a heavy weight: a hammer and a bundle of nails to hold them against the wind. He burrowed into the picking-baskets.

. . . Finally, he took thin stakes with white paper flapping from their tips and went to mark out the rows for picking.

Everything was fine. Now the time had come for the workers to appear. He raised his eyes and scanned the path leading up to the farm. The road hugged the slope in a wide sweep, running cramped between the vegetable fields, the tree nursery, and the fallow pieces belonging to the green fodder. When it cut across the main road it split into two arms. One, which was broad to accommodate the wagons, continues winding around the hill, while the second, which is crookedly narrow, is a foot path which rushes to the fence, bursts through it at a little swinging gate, and dashes on to the dining room.

The lone worker stretched out his big hand and shaded the cap over his eyes. The sunlight stood barrier between him and the rising road. He forced his eyes open to discern what the little gate was releasing at that moment—a big troupe of boys and girls, hats and kerchiefs, columning dust, and baskets filled with lunch. . .

This is Yusik, in his customary practice of getting everything ready so that when the pickers reach the vineyard, there will be no cause for delay or wasting time on all sorts of nonsense. They just had to take a pair of shears and pull the empty basket along, go to the rows, and no matter how plentiful the questions or how much they dawdled—picking, began at once.

"Today there are no rookies, Yusik!" declared one picking-girl who considered herself responsible for this branch of the farm, and mourned over every additional newcomer who had to be initiated into the mysteries of the craft. Nevertheless, Yusik walked among the pickers and inspected their first baskets. He remarked about a blemished cluster, a crushed grape; he mentioned the dampness, the shriveling. "Remember the packing-girls," he chided. "A bevy of nervous wrecks. What can you do— that's the way they want it. Quality better than quantity."

He stepped out of one row and crossed the patch to enter another, when he saw Mika. Slightly confused, and perhaps somewhat excited, she was snipping off the tip of a stem, her whole being brimful of questions and hesitation.

"You're picking, Mika?"

She nodded her head and raised the shears demurely: "See!"

"So they saw to it that we should have at least one rookie today. Nu—you're sick of the kitchen, eh?"

"Or they're sick of me."

"All of them are sick of you?"

"Oh, what's the difference. Where shall I work?"

Yusik returned to business with a will. His voice receded to a lower, indefinite tone: "So—where to work. . . . Come, you'll begin a new row. You've picked before? Take a few baskets from here."

They stood, the two of them, in the shade of a heavily laden vine at the head of the row; and Yusik began his slow, good-hearted, meticulous explanation.

She looked long at Yusik. He was more interesting than his teachings. His head was big and heavy, really heavy, too heavy for the spare body that it crowned. He was hairy and dark, despite the big patch on his head whose baldness was covered only by a down of stray hairs. His cheeks were black with an aftergrowth that extended up to the orbits of his eyes and down to the opening in his shirt. From his ears sprouted a soft bunch of black hairs, and his eyebrows were huge. His voice was deep and rich. You couldn't distinguish many nuances in it—but what appeared to be a monotonous timber was, in actuality, a goodly supply of simplicity, of self-assurance—that assurance so characteristic of a man who is thoroughly learned in something which is utterly unknown to those about him.

Yusik was in charge of the vineyards, that much she knew, and that's all. For, whom did she ever meet at work? Whom did she have a chance to know in the kibbutz aside from a few of the kitchen experts, the yard-man, the work managers, the madrichim,* and of course, the leaders of the group, and who else? Many of the members of the kibbutz were still strangers to her, strangers beyond the exchange of greetings. They were absorbed in their affairs, in the focal points of their existence, in those most important-things-of-the-world of theirs. And what appears to you so imperative, so vital—your youth group, its boys and girls, its problems and discussions, where-shall-we-go-when-we're-finished-here, studies, self-development, etc., etc.—all these aren't anything to the others except as an episode. Another youth group in Gat Amakim. So what's all the fuss about? Among the kibbutzniks there are many good and warm-hearted people. For instance—this Yusik. First meeting with him, a pleasant man. He's—straight. He understands. He listens to you. . . . And still, would you dare ask him for a pencil in the evening when you need one?

Yusik rose to go. "The collection row is over here. You see? Now, while the air is snappy it's not so terrible, but soon it will be so warm that you absolutely must not leave a full basket in the sun. Remember that—Now, let's see how you'll do."

Mika clipped off a cluster and held it before her eyes to inspect it and correct its blemishes. She was a full-formed, slightly plump girl, as is characteristic of most of the girls from Youth Aliyah, girls who saw great suffering and arrived at peace famished and vengeful. She was dark, not only in her hair which lay in a heavy roll on her neck, but also in the texture of her dusky skin; in her lips whose darkness shadowed their freshness, in the short, thick down on her arms. She was not a pretty girl, she was a fine-looking young woman who still contained all the restlessness of youth within her, alongside the wariness born of bitter experience. She was a member of Willy's youth group, the group that came from Teheran,

---

* Instructors.

and among them she was considered an important and valuable individual, an exacting person, full of life; attractive but cruel. . . .
They pointed her out and judged her as we judge among ourselves
—a hard person.

The kitchen workers didn't like Mika. If the truth must be
told, then the customary explanation—the malice of aging women
towards a new youngster—doesn't hold water here. We surmise
that Mika had something to do with it. From the day she was
allotted a "stretch" in the kitchen, after a noisy, confusing discussion
in the "hevrah" which ended in a vote—she clung to the contention
that an injustice had been done her. She hated domination, she
hated the cries of the diners in the hall: bring me this; give me
that; hey over there. She abhorred the worried rushing about of
the workers among the stoves and pots, this hysterical anxiety for
. . . for what? For . . . this gluttony, for this hurried shovelling in
of food. It was not within her power to divine that beneath all
her petty animosities nestled a dread of constant, daily, overt contact with human beings. She was unable to understand that it was
not the strict work system that she despised—but her own weakness, her past.

Mika put the cluster into the basket, eyeing it appreciatively
for the last time. It was good. She pressed forward, tossing a
heavy branch aside in her search for more bunches. . . . She moved
her head—and dishevelled the branch, pulling off leaves that were
dried. Some of them crumbled up under the collar that lay helter-
skelter on her neck, they tickled her lightly and stirred up apprehension of ants or other bugs. She tried to get after them with her
hand; the shears slipped out of her fingers and at the same moment
the heavy bunch of grapes fell and smashed to the ground. She
seized the cluster—they were damp, and they stuck to her fingers.
With the cluster and the shears in hand, she sought an outlet to
the light; her neck got caught by the shoots and as she pulled away
forcefully, she bumped her forehead on a sunken pole and—it
wasn't at all pleasant!

It was enough for her to get up off the ground and rest
a bit while standing, and swallow deep draughts of everything
about her: the vineyard, the singing of the pickers, the rustle of

the cypress wind-breaks and the dust trampling on a piece of paper, the racket of hammers from the packing-shed, the muffled cries in the distance and the view of the farm on the hill—it was enough for her to embrace this scene for a little moment to decide deep in her heart that she was happy.

*   *   *

THE SOIL OF THE HOMELAND

THE EFFORT to settle city-bred Jews on the land in a difficult unfamiliar country has been accompanied by strong emotional experiences, which found expression in literature.

In the early days of Zionist colonization, attention was centered on the colonies of Judea, where most of the settlements were situated. During the period of the Second Aliyah, the cry was "Who will build the Galilee," where the virgin soil seemed to call the pioneers.

In the 1940's, and, even to a greater degree, since the establishment of the State, the arid Negev, which occupies nearly half of the country's area, has become the target of Zionist colonization, the object of idealism, and inevitably, of inner conflicts within every individual who considered settling in it.

Asher Barash

◆

HAI'S WELL

IN A POOR little colony which lies high up in Lower Galilee there was a little man who had a little wooden hut, a dunam of land, and a wife and three children. The man went by the name of Nathan Hai. He was a farm-worker who had gone through all kinds of transformation in Judah and Samaria and Upper and Lower Galilee. He had fevered a lot and affectionately cursed the ways of the old and new Yishuv alike, besides using a sharp bachelor's tongue to tease the girl workers and mock at marriage. But, when he was thirty-five years old and looked like a dwarfed and wrinkled olive trunk, he took as a wife the "Rosh Pinah seamstress," who was younger than he, and settled down in the little colony. Within five years they brought three healthy sons with good appetites into the world, and the burden of life rested thenceforth on the two of them.

How did he come to the name Hai? After all, he was not one of the Sephardim among whom the name is common, but a fellow from the neighborhood of Dubno. The truth was that the name "Hai" was short for "Hai vekayam" (hale and hearty). This was his regular reply whenever anybody asked him: "How are you, Nathan?"—"Hai vekayam!" And to be even more precise it should be added that even this expanded name of "Hai vekayam" was only a translation made by one of his friends, who was hot for the Hebrew language and translated into it the Yiddish reply that he had been giving for several years namely "Hai-gelebt!" (Hai-alive). Nathan cheerfully accepted the translation, but as time went on and he said less because his troubles grew greater, he would simply answer "Hai!" And so the short name remained and everybody from Dan to Beersheba knew him as Nathan Hai.

Like a dozen other fellows of his own type in the Second Aliyah, he was a kind of monomaniac. And what was his particular mania? Water! The redemption of the land and hence, obviously, the redemption of the nation and the Ingathering of the Exiles depended only on water. If Eretz Israel could only get enough water it would be a paradise. And he had bundles of proof, both by word of mouth and in writing, from hundreds of sources. He would begin with a verse at the very beginning of Genesis, "And a river went forth from Eden to water the garden" (which goes to prove that if there had been no irrigation there would not have been any Garden of Eden), and go right up to the famous phrase of Kaiser Wilhelm to Herzl as he sat on horseback in the heat of the day near Mikveh Israel: "It needs water, plenty of water!" And then he would add his own experience.

Nathan Hai did not rest content with talking about water but was the servant of water everywhere. He investigated the water situation in the country from the salt water in the sea and the exceedingly salt water of the Dead Sea to the waters of the rivers and the brooks and the wadis: spring water and flood water, underground water and rain water, upper water and lower water, water for irrigation and water for power. For months and years he took a hand with the well-borers in various parts of the country. For months and years he toiled in the motor cabins of the orange groves, working at draining and drying swamps and laying irrigation pipes. In brief, wherever there was water, there he was to be found. And they say that the old worker and writer who was the teacher of all the workers slapped him on the shoulder once and, speaking to him, quoted a verse from the Book of Job, "He gives blossom from the scent of water."

And now came something queer. This Nathan Hai, the water man, chose as his dwelling place a desolate colony in Lower Galilee, which was white with dust the greater part of the year. One might have supposed that in this way he wished to symbolize his great longing for water. For, if he had dwelt in one of the Sharon colonies

where there is an ample water supply, the source of his longing
would have dried up. But in the Galilean colony, swooning with
thirst, the staff of his longings put forth blossoms like Aaron's rod
in the Bible; and he never wearied of talking about water.

In the center of this colony there was a well with a wheel over
it, whose water came from the rains in their season. If the winter
was rainy, the well was full and it had enough water (only for man
and beast and the few yards of green round the houses) until the
beginning of August, after which nothing was to be brought up
from the well bottom save mud and mire. If there was little rain
in any year the water lasted until mid-June or, at most, to the
beginning of July. After that there was work for the water carriers
(and naturally Nathan spent no small amount of time on that job).
Morning and evening they had to take the mule and the big barrel
on two wheels and fetch water from the distant fountain on the
Arab land; water that had to be bought for good money. If the
water carrier came home late in the evening there would be a
cloud on the faces of the colony people, as they asked themselves
what they and their beasts would have to drink.

But Nathan was not the fellow to see folk suffering and do
nothing. From the time he became an established citizen among all
the others in the place (by right of his cabin and his dunam, of
course) he would get in touch with every "factor of consequence in
the Yishuv" in order to raise the question of water for the Galilee
settlements in general and, in particular, his own colony which
suffered most from the water shortage. It cannot be said that Nathan
Hai's efforts did not bear fruit. He set all the wheels in the Yishuv
moving about this business of water, from the staff of the Baron
de Rothschild in Palestine and abroad to the Jewish National Fund
and all the departments of the Jewish Agency. He kept them all
busy with letters and memoranda and interviews about the water
without which the colony could not live. No excuses helped. They
came, they investigated, they sent experts, they hewed and they
bored, and they bored and they hewed, inside the colony, down on
the hill-slope on the one side and then down on the other hill-slope;
a mile away from the house that lay farthest north and a mile away
from the house that lay farthest south. They bored and they stopped,

and they went back and they bored again. Drills were broken, workers were injured, and one who fell from the stand broke his spine and was crippled for life. But they did not find any water. In one spot they bored for six weeks and found moist earth; and the pump even brought up a few pails full of fluid mud. Some of the local inhabitants began dancing an Arab "Debke" all round, but after they bored a little more it all stopped and once again the drill brought up only dry cold unfriendly gravel, to the disgust of the inhabitants.

But Nathan never ceased prophesying, "There is plenty of water in our good earth. It has an artery throbbing like the heart's artery in the human body. It is only necessary to find the pulse, to set up the drill at the right spot."

And one day (nobody quite knew how he managed it) Nathan fetched out of the Negev an Englishman with a little yellow beard, wearing a Bedouin "Kefiya" and "agal" round his head. This fellow had spent many years in the Sudan, spoke Arabic with an English accent and a lot of hard gurglings, and he carried a little wand with which he walked about like a lizard, touching the surface of the ground, holding the wand and watching it trembling, and deciding accordingly whether there was water at that spot or not.

The Englishman decided on a new spot for boring a well. However, after all the bitter experience and waste of money there was no longer anybody prepared to invest the first hundred pounds that were needed to begin the work. The local inhabitants fed the Englishman on the best to be found in the house of the "mukhtar," and also presented him with five pounds that they collected in the colony before giving him an honorable send-off. But no boring followed.

Meanwhile Nathan Hai lost his strength. He was already past forty-three. His hair, which had been curly in the old days when the Rosh Pinah seamstress had stroked it with trembling fingers and whispered, "Nathan, you have nice hair"—most of that hair had fallen out, leaving a sunburned scalp that was as smooth and gleaming as silk. The three children, all of them boys, did not make the little hut any quieter, particularly since Eva Leah always had to be sewing with a machine in order to make most of the living.

She used to sew for the Arab women of the surrounding villages too; and he, fully aware though he was of the husband's duties to his wife and those of a father to his children, earned very little. Sometimes Nathan would have to go faraway for weeks on end seeking work, and during his absence his dunam would suffer from jaundice and bareness.

Not that he ever became melancholy. That is, he looked miserable enough, particularly his eyes which had sunk deep and burned with repressed unhappiness. But his mouth still knew its job. He would make brief jokes, and when he came to talk about water it seemed as though his own trunk had been watered and the living water had entered his veins. His eyes would gleam and his tongue would serve his flights of imagination in lively fashion. "Before long any amount of water will come up to irrigate the land of the colony and make it yield. It is pouring along under our feet. Can't you hear it? Just listen carefully and you will!"

The listener would slap him on his shoulder, look him in the eye and ask: "And what's the news with you, Nathan, about making a living?"

"We live, so-so—Hai vekayam. Hai!"

II

When their youngest child was six years old, after an interval of six years that is, it came about that Eva Leah found herself in the family way again; for the fourth time. The whole household became apprehensive. Nathan Hai himself also grew afraid. That was all that was missing! As it was the three they already had were wandering about like starving jackals, in rags and tatters. Eva Leah sewed for everybody, yet for her own children she could not sew shirts or a pair of linen trousers. She simply did not have the time. And if she were to take time off to sew for them, what would she have to put in their mouths? And now this was coming! After they had thought they were finished with any more children!

The local nurse and midwife scolded Eva Leah, abused her thoroughly and demanded and insisted that she should go to town and do what had to be done. "Human beings aren't swine!" she permitted herself to say coarsely. She was an old maid with principles.

(Once upon a time she had been one of those who had "gone to the people" in Russia.) For a moment Eva Leah hesitated, saying to herself, "Maybe she is right and it would be worth doing what she suggests." But when she said as much to Nathan he opened a pair of startled eyes at her, then spat for all he was worth and cried in a voice which was not his own: "Listen to a block of dry wood like that? No, as long as I am Nathan Hai, you won't do anything so abominable!"

And the item was struck off the agenda.

It must be confessed that from that day forward there was a different mood in Nathan. He seemed to be transformed into a kind of tense machine on springs. He was on the move all the time, traveling to Tiberias or Haifa, to Afulah and Nazareth, even to Tel-Aviv and Jerusalem. After spending a few days or weeks there he came home fetching in his rucksack a few things that they required. Maybe some tinned food or some cloth or knitting materials, and so on. And his tired-looking purse would also have a little ready cash.

So there was a little light in the hut. Nathan's face looked worse, to be sure. He grew thinner and seemed to shrink. The silken bald patch turned to a burnished copper, and his eyes flamed as though he had the fever. But he was in a good mood. Often he would answer those who asked how he was with his old phrase of "Hai-gelebt!" but would quickly correct himself: "Hai-vekayam!" The children were dressed in a more orderly fashion, for if he spent a few days or weeks at home he compelled Eva Leah to turn down a few customers in order to sew some clothes for them.

The day of the birth was on the way. They reckoned that the child would be born in the middle of August.

The ninth of Ab passed at the beginning of August and Eva Leah completed her full term. Everything was ready for the birth. They had already spoken to the midwife, whose fury had not quite died down at the "barbarism," but she had no choice save to accept the fact. So she came into the hut from time to time to see that everything was in order.

On the eighteenth of Ab the birth-pangs came. Nathan quickly filled two tubs of water. Although Eva Leah had not cried out, the nurse heard and came running, only to see almost at once that the birth was not normal. After an hour of sweat and toil she realized that the doctor had to be brought in from the neighboring colony because the danger was increasing. She told this to Nathan. He asked no questions but grabbed his stick and dashed off to the colony.

It was the forenoon, in the heat of the day. High up in the heavens sailed distant white wisps of cloud, enjoying a sun bath. The little colony was silent with its poor little houses. The few gardens were grey with the remains of scorched vegetables, looking like stains of rust or zinc. Only the pruned eucalyptuses at the wayside rose green with their young branches. The way down the slope to the wadi was thick with beaten dust. In the skies three vultures were circling in a triangle: one in the north, one in the west and one in the east. Nathan noticed them. It immediately occurred to him that they were coming from the water, one from the Kinnereth, one from the sea and one from the Jordan. This thought gave wings to his feet, so that he did not notice the sweat running down like a fountain of water from his head to his collar. It took an hour through the wadi to reach the big colony, but he ought to get there in half an hour, for he was running. Why had he not taken a horse or donkey? It simply had not occurred to him. Now it was not worth his while going back. He had already passed a quarter of the way.

Nathan passed the cemetery on the little hill. He glanced at the handful of scattered tombstones, two of which stuck out so importantly while the rest lay like stones in the field. He suddenly was frightened at the sight of the cemetery, and the thought of Eva Leah twisting and turning in her birthpangs, all in ever-greater danger. He went even faster down the slope, running with his stick ahead of him. The sweat poured over his face, into his mouth, and down his neck and over the hair of his open chest. When he got to the bottom it was no longer so hot and he felt a little easier. He removed his hat, held it in his other hand and allowed his gleaming bald patch to absorb the sun.

All of a sudden, at the entrance to the wadi, he felt a kind of slight stab in the head. His legs began to quiver. They seemed to grow light, lifted themselves a little from the earth and fluttered in the air. His heart beat as though it was running away with itself.

The light turned dark suddenly. He fell on his stick, quivered a little, turned over at the wayside and slipped down into a shallow ditch.

III

Two hours and more passed but Nathan did not return, neither did the doctor arrive. The midwife came out of the hut with her hair in disarray, and shouted in a way that the little colony had never heard since it was founded. Nathan's three children immediately stopped playing, startled; they sprang up and stood staring as though they were senseless. One by one grownups came from the houses.

The woman shouted at them: "What are you standing like blocks of wood for? Go and fetch the doctor quick! Eva Leah is dying!"

Within half an hour one of the local lads had fetched the doctor on his cart. But the doctor found Eva Leah lifeless. And the child remained within its mother.

A village Arab found the body of Nathan Hai in the ditch five days later. He saw kites busy and gathered round there. He approached and recognized the dead man. So he went and told the "Mukhtar." When they brought him away from there his flesh was already going. His face and eyes had been pecked by the beaks of the birds of heaven.

They buried him as he was without cleansing him, besides Eva Leah's grave. The three orphans were portioned out to three houses, one to each. The youngest one was adopted by the midwife, who had fought like a lioness against death but could not prevail.

The colony mourned grievously. In one day three souls had been cut off and a family had been uprooted in the little community. Who can understand the Cutter-off of life?

IV

Once Nathan Hai had been brought to burial after the fashion of Israel he was eased of the burden of his life, which had been beyond his strength. Eva Leah lay not far from him, her child within her, and rested forever. "There rest the exhausted of strength" and who was so exhausted of strength as to compare with Eva Leah?

Even before her marriage, as long as she had been in Eretz Israel, she had been harnessed to the yoke of hard work; first as a worker, then as a domestic, finally as a seamstress. Even after she had married Nathan and given birth to three sons one after the other, each coming before the other was big enough to look after himself, she had continued to sit bent over the sewing-machine which had sucked up the rest of her blood. But she was a good person of spirit and character, and no matter how she suffered she was never heard to make a complaint. Now she had gained the rest she deserved. The children had been orphaned of their father and mother, but were better off than they had been. Each of them was in a good home, his bread provided at the proper time and his clothes not lacking. Best of all was the little one. For the captious and bitter old maid gave him all her pity and love. He was small and tender in her eyes.

And he, Nathan Hai, had attained full rest. His bones, worn and broken with hard work, now took it easy. His brain, which had grown weary with concern and alarm for the souls depending on him, could also rest and devote itself entirely to the one thought which had filled him from head to foot while he was alive—the thought of water.

For days and days, for months and months, he lay listening, sending forth his will, one might say, like delicate antennae deep into the earth. He forgot everything. He forgot himself and the whole world. Somewhere, in some hidden place a pulse of water was bubbling and throbbing, longing to be revealed. Summer passed, winter vanished, a new summer came, and his will grew as tense as a violin string, while his water sense grew keener than ever.

The following summer, in the heat of the month of August, a year after he had fallen at the wayside, a faint sense of moisture reached him. First he did not know from which side it came. He grew very excited. He had to gather all the strength of his will in order to sense precisely where it came from. At length he realized it exactly. It came to him, a cold and pleasant stream, from one specific point. There it was! The vein of water gathered in his awareness. It was not far off. He had had to labor with his awareness for a whole year until he found the spot. Ha, ha, it was certainly not the spot to which the English water diviner had pointed! No, the fountain was here, below the cemetery. Exactly ninety yards in a straight line. West of his grave! Ninety yards, according to the numerological value of "mayim," the Hebrew word for water!

All his bones rejoiced. Now he knew what he had to do. He knew. A dream. The dream he had dreamed on earth had come about. Now he knew what he had to do. The locked and sealed water must rise up.

V

The following summer, during the hottest days of August, Nathan Hai appeared in a dream to the "Mukhtar" of the colony for three nights running. He appeared with radiant face, and this was what he said: "Wake up and get up! Go out and bore! Exactly ninety yards in a straight line west of my grave! Thirty-three yards down the water is waiting for you. Don't delay! For a whole year I have been bringing the water up to that point. Don't miss the chance. I shan't be able to keep it there very long. Uncover it!"

On the first night the "Mukhtar" woke up and in the darkness told his wife about the strange dream. They both decided it was nonsense. But next day the man went about all day long not knowing what to do. The dream would not leave him alone even for a moment. After the second night, when the dream was repeated again, he told it to several of the local people, and one of them went so far as to remark: "It isn't just nonsense." After the third night the "Mukhtar" summoned a meeting of the committee and they decided to try. Thirty-three yards—the cost was next to nothing.

Now it so happened that not far away the water company was boring a well. They had already gone down more than two hundred meters. They had already been boring for three months. They had already made their way through two strata of rock, and now they had reached a third which was even harder. But there was no sign of water. Work had stopped three days before. The borers had simply grown tired and given up. Their tools lay where they were, like dead corpses.

Two committee members went to the company in Haifa and

deposited thirty-three pounds, according to the number of yards that they wished to have bored. Next day the well-borers came to the spot, which was already marked with an iron spike. They dug a little, put up the stand for the drill and began to drill.

Lots of jokes were heard, as they worked, and the deeper the drill bit, the lower grew the spirits of the people and the smaller their faith in the "Mukhtar's" dream. After the drill had passed the thirty-yard mark they all but gave up, and felt that they wished to ask the workmen to stop; but were ashamed to do so.

And then, all of a sudden—

It was noon, the heat of the day, just the time at which Nathan Hai had run off to summon the doctor and had fallen while running and dropped into the ditch. White clouds were sunning themselves in the sky. Three vultures were circling in a triangle. The final thuds of the drill sounded in the silence of the colony—and the iron rod in the hands of the drillers suddenly beat, while a lapping sounded from the deeps. Before they could see what had happened a sound suddenly rolled and echoed all round. Water! Water! The little pump standing there suddenly emitted a jet of water, pure water from the hole. It gleamed like crystal in the sun, fell to earth and melodiously flooded all the neighborhood. And the pump went on pumping the precious fluid on the ground.

There was not a living soul in the colony who did not come to see the sight. All of them stood over the little pool, gazed through tears and trembled with excitement and joy.

The experts measured the force of the current. There were two hundred cubic meters an hour. A fountain of salvation had been opened to plants and living creatures. Now the colony would begin to grow and flourish. The words of Nathan had come about.

VI

Before long a big reservoir was built. It was big and tall and stood on five tremendous pillars, four at the corners and one in the middle. A proper pumphouse was also built. And the village water festival was held.

Many people came from settlements near and far to rejoice with the people of the colony, whose thirst had been quenched with much water. Each one brought his gifts of all wherewith the Lord had blessed him. Round the well they planted saplings and fresh flowers that were amply watered. The whole of the square intended for the rejoicing crowd had been besprinkled with water. Every white shirt, every white blouse, whether of man, woman or child, was adorned with a green twig. Neighboring Arab horsemen took their place amid the horse-riders of the colonies. Tables on trestles stood ready, loaded with good things to eat and drink.

Three choirs of children from three schools in three colonies stood on the platform, the music teacher keeping them quiet with the conductor's baton. They were waiting to sing the song "And you shall draw water with gladness from the fountains of salvation."

In the front row, like a vanguard, stood the three children of Nathan Hai, each smaller than the next; all dressed in suits that were as white as snow.

In front of the pumphouse, over the iron door, was an inscription in large letters:
HAI'S WELL
"This is the well of Nathan Hai, and as such it shall be known forever."

But one man, the man who writes this, looked sorrowfully at what he had added while nobody noticed, in chalk on the iron door and in small printed characters: "Let Eva Leah also be well remembered."

Alexander and Yonat Sened

◆

BRACHA

BRACHA TRIED to imagine that she was in a broad field, in the center of the great, green expanse of a real farm.

Upon beginning to work, she had tried to hide all that clung to her of the "city." From Hannah, she received a work shirt and a pair of shorts and there was no suspicion of finery about them. She couldn't ask for a kerchief, however, and she bound her hair with her own, the red one with black futuristic designs on it. Her legs, of which she was proud, were now burned a bright scarlet, like a baby's skin after a hot bath, and they were painful to touch.

The "dura" (sorghum) had succeeded very well, even better than had been expected. It had been sown in the spring, on the field that had been flooded by the earth-embanked water reservoirs in the winter. The caked earth had been plowed and sown while the lower levels still had moisture in them; the soil, freed from the choking dryness, had sprouted. It was a helpful and promising discovery.

Sacks of "dura" were piled all about the field, which looked like an accidental puddle in the surrounding desert. And they were counted and recounted with all the excitement of a lover's first kisses.

"Hey, two hundred sacks—that's no joke."

"Just like in the Emek. . . ."

"Now all we need is an asphalt reservoir and some 'Lemans' and we'll be sitting pretty."

"Hey, two hundred and forty sacks already."

With ever greater frequency, one heard these words, "Asphalt Reservoir" and "Leman" repeated in the confines of the tower.

Bracha had by now learned that an asphalt reservoir was one with a tarred floor and sides so that the water could not seep into the ground as in the previous experiment, but could be used for irrigation all the year round. A "Leman," on the other hand was Klatzkin's name for an idea that was all his own. It consisted of giant seed beds, stretching over many dunams, that would prevent soil erosion by having the terraces between them act as blocks to the streams of water. At the same time, moreover, they would be able to absorb great quantities of water at once and distribute it quickly and evenly. In the course of innumerable conversations these speculative "Lemans" became so real they could almost be seen out there in the emptiness.

Bracha discovered her first blister under her thumb where the knife handle pressed, and she was a little ashamed of the patrician delicacy of such hands. What discouraged her most was neither the heat nor the sweat, not even the blister or the backache, but rather the fact that she was unaccustomed to organizing her movements. Which fingers to use; how, and to what distance to move the sack forward; the whole law of muscular efficiency that was so unknown to her—now became a problem. And when she felt finally, that she had swung into the rhythm, that her progress was easy and correct—to cut, place, step,—cut, place, step—to drag the sack—she would suddenly become confused, as though some wheel had slipped from the track, and her system seemed awkward, and once again she didn't know how to begin.

No matter, she would learn, he would no doubt learn a great many things in this vacation from the art school in Jerusalem. Who knows, perhaps these months in Ailata with Shragai might even give her the strength to come back and live here when she'd finish her studies. That would be another two years. Two years! What an enormous stretch of time! The whole world could turn over in two years. It was now two and a half years since Stalingrad to the end of the war. Yes, the war was over.

Here it was hardly felt. How simply one said it. "Here it's hardly felt." What would a soldier returning from the front say? In another two years she would be twenty-four. Could she give up her studies? No, she had already tried once and failed.

She had not noticed that Reuven had already finished his row on her left while she was only half through with hers. Now when she saw his face smiling at her, she had a suspicion he was making fun of her work (she had not yet discovered that Reuven's smile was nothing more than an expression of his good nature).

She quickened her movements. Although she had decided that she would not let herself be carried away into competing with the boys—that she would work quietly and steadily—she became angry with herself when she heard Yoav declare that he had already finished four rows. At the same time, the workers with their remarks and their laughter seemed far away, in another world, parallel to her world, but never touching it. However, when she had completed her row and Yoav exclaimed, "Very good," in a voice full of astonishment, she felt a warm friendliness sweep over her. She thereupon decided that the burning sun and the hard work had made her err in her heart. It would be good to sit at lunch opposite Shragai and to know that his eyes caressed her sunwarmed face, the face of a woman returning from work in the fields.

From the bed near the window in the hut one could see the sky, the endless evening sky of the wilderness. At this time of the year the hut was vacant and Bracha had brought a clean sheet and had shaken the blanket free of the accumulated dust.

"The first day isn't so bad. Even the tiredness after work is something different and idyllic. But months, years of this sun . . . ?" Shragai spoke heavily. The last light of the day shone in his grey eyes.

She smiled, seeing through the meaning behind these words. She herself was inclined to believe the opposite, that the first day was still full of the restlessness and the newness—that only by a long series of days, months, years of work-hours and rest-hours, of a home being built and of Shragai's heavy hands—could the good quietness come. One only had to know how to live this life and perhaps, she too could learn. Yes, all of Shragai's thoughts were concentrated on this single theme—her coming to Ailata. What he had said about working in the sun was only calculated to make her weigh carefully before making a decision. How transparent his irony was!

"You know, Shragai," she started to speak and moved her head along his arm, "there's something I'm almost ashamed to talk about, still. . . . . There are people, and not necessarily people whom I have no use for, who ask, 'And if I'm not in a kibbutz, does that mean I am not a good Jew?' Why this fanaticism of a closed sect? I—and no one else. If someone has inclinations of his own—a special talent, let's say, I'm not talking about myself, of course. . . ."

"You don't have to apologize." He moved his arm from under her head. "A chosen sect? That's nonsense! A chosen sect is closed and isolated—we aren't. And hasn't a man the right to be proud of his accomplishments?" He was silent for a moment as though he was gathering his thoughts and continued, "Let's speak plainly. We are afraid of speaking plainly and to the point because it may sound like propaganda. But tell me, do you see any other force in the country, besides the kibbutz, that will go to settle in the Negev under these conditions."

"Very well. But I wasn't talking about that, I was talking about the special cases, though sometimes I wonder whether we don't all belong to the special cases."

"There is so much talk about 'special cases' in our time—we just can't afford to give in to them any more." Shragai sputtered impatiently. He immediately softened, however, and went on. "In any event, there seems to be even more excusing of oneself than there are special cases. Everywhere in the world it is accepted that even the 'special cases' aren't exempted from the battles. And I think that what we are doing can only be called a long battle. . . ."

"But it's not true that only the kibbutz fights."

"Of course not. As Jews we have many fronts. It just so happens that the most difficult and dangerous is the kibbutz. We are pioneers. What can I do? There is no other name for it, except this puffed-up title. And for that job we need a great, great many people."

His voice released restraint and flowed freely. Bracha no longer saw his eyes. Only the shadow of his head was dark against the night. "You see, Bracha," he was saying, "I don't want just to chat with you. I am talking about things that have cost me a lot of what you might call, 'inner struggle.' We can't ask as yet, whether the kibbutz is the final goal. I see it as a cell, a revolutionary cell preparing a new system, a new way of life. I see the kibbutz as a framework in which, today, one can do the maximum. And, incidently, I think that in our time, especially, each and every human being is obligated to do the maximum."

Bracha closed her eyes. Sentences like these required lots of pondering and mulling over. . . .

"As for me, Bracha, I need these 'special cases' here—at the front. Even the talented ones have their place here. Otherwise I will find it terribly boring. . . ." He tried to slip a touch of softness into their conversation.

"For you, yes. But what about the others?" Bracha fastened on to his last words.

"The others too. Except that not all of them know it."

"You are always justifying them—the kibbutzniks—as though there weren't any fools and hypocrites or evil-minded ones amongst them." Her voice was a little tired now. Shragai knew that the hard day's work was taking its toll.

"There are, naturally so. Perhaps I did think once that there weren't. But I don't want to be one of those who, after their eyes have been opened up to the evils of the world, can only grow up by losing faith in everything. Of course there are such types. So what of it? We're not an ideal generation. We're a generation that's learning to work, fight, defend—that's a lot. The kibbutz framework is a guarantee that you have placed yourself in the correct position for battle."

"But it's in the nature of framework that they also bind! You understand?"

"Yes. It's not so easy for me either. Sometimes it's very hard. But look. There's a picture in a frame hanging on the wall. That's an opening to a world, an opening from your room to a whole world. I don't think it's possible to get out on the high-road to freedom without a framework."

"Oh, you're just trying to convince me with illustrations. . . ."

"Why, you—you little—even if you were convinced you wouldn't admit it." And he ruffled her hair. She sighed and lay back.

"Tell me, Shragai." And her voice was low and subdued,

primarily from the strain of thought. "Tell me, do you believe that there will ever be an ideal generation—a generation without fools and hypocrites!"

Once again she was the girl complaining about life—about the heavy time she was born to live in, and she was asking for an answer for all the sorrows of the world.

"I think, I believe, Brach'ka. Just as I believe that there will come a generation without tuberculosis or cancer."

"But why not in our time? Why is it always, that everything is not in our time?"

Now there was nothing else for him to do but embrace her and tell her about all the things that could still come about in our time.

12 THE INFERNO

THE SECOND World War brought about the destruction of six million Jews in Europe. Shortly afterwards, following a bitter political struggle between the Jews and the British, which at times took on the aspects of a war, the Jewish State emerged, and a war between the Jews and the Arabs resulted.

The Jewish population of Palestine, which had grown from about 60,000 in 1917 to over more than 600,000 in 1947, was consolidated during the war from an autonomous community into a nation ready to assume full sovereignty.

Much of what took place outside of Palestine exerted a powerful influence on developments in Palestine. The Hitler atrocities in Europe increased the demand for keeping the doors of the Homeland wide open for Jewish immigration and engendered within the minds of Palestinian Jews a readiness to fight. The war with Hitler evoked a desire among the Jews to take part in the war on the side of the Allies. Throughout the thirty years that Britain administered Palestine, American Jewry, led by American Zionists, supplied the largest part of the funds for the building up of the Homeland and, as time went on and friction with England increased, American Jewry further used its influence to induce the United States government to support the Jewish side in the conflict.

When the war broke out, a movement demanding the creation of a Jewish army to fight for Palestine, arose in the United States. As the war drew to an end, the political agitation for the creation of a Jewish State in Palestine grew to unprecedented proportions.

British rule in Palestine lasted from 1917 to May, 1948. During those years the attitude of the British officials from the High Commissioner to the lowest ranking policeman varied greatly. There was a more narrow margin of variation in the official policy, but the general trend was towards a steady restriction of the influx of Jews into the country and of their acquisition of land for further agricultural colonization.

In 1939, during the general atmosphere of appeasement of that period, the tendency to constrict the growth of the Jewish Homeland culminated in the White Paper issued by the British.

There was never, however, any serious attempt to interfere with the internal cultural autonomy of the Jewish community in Palestine. The Jewish community was organized into a local National Assembly with an Executive called Vaad Leumi (National Council). Of more significance was the affiliation of the most active and most articulate section of the Jewish population with the World Zionist Organization. The relation between the local autonomous institutions of the Jewish community, which administered schools and health work, with the World Zionist Organization was not unlike that of a State Government to the Federal.

As the Yishuv, or Jewish community in Palestine grew, developed and matured, Palestine Zionists began to exert more and more influence in the councils of the World Zionist Organization. In 1935 the seat of the Executive was moved from London to Jerusalem. Men and women who had attained leadership in local organizations entered the Zionist Executive in Jerusalem. Ben-Gurion became the Chairman; Kaplan the Treasurer; Shertok (Sharett) the Political Secretary; etc.

Throughout these years Chaim Weizmann remained the leader of the Zionist movement, and, except for a brief interlude, the President of the World Zionist Organization. He lived in London, but also established residence in Palestine, in the colony of Rehovot, where he founded and directed the famous Institute of Science bearing his name.

Relations between the official Jewish authorities (the Jewish Agency or Zionist Executive; the Vaad Leumi) with the British were roughly equivalent to those between a dependency and a suzerain power. The degree to which Jewish organizations should or should not co-operate with the British was always a matter of vehement internal dispute in the Zionist movement. As British policy became more hostile, the tendency to resist and refuse co-operation increased. On two matters, however, policy was uniform: on the matter of self-protection against Arab attacks, the Jews preferred to rely on their own, unofficial and secret organization; and during the Second World War the Jews insisted on taking part in the struggle against Hitler as a full-fledged ally.

The British were as reluctant to grant the desire of the Jews for armed participation in the Second World War as they had been in the First World War, but finally yielded. At first they allowed Jewish units in the British forces; later they consented to form a Jewish Brigade.

The number of Jews in the Jewish units and the Jewish Brigade in the 1940's was much greater than in the Jewish Legion of 1917. Unlike the First World War, this time the Jewish units consisted almost exclusively of Palestinian Jews, most of them native-born Palestinians or those who had grown up in the country since childhood. The fighting was done outside of Palestine—in North Africa, in Italy and other parts of Europe. While fighting on the British side, Jewish soldiers also defied British restrictions on Jewish immigration and helped rescue Jews from concentration camps and bring them to Palestine.

As the Jews attempted to circumvent British restrictions, penalties and suppression became more and more severe. The Jews in Palestine grew restive and indignant. In time dissident groups, refusing to abide by the authority of the Jewish Agency and the Vaad Leumi, organized terrorist acts to drive the British out of the country. After 1945, during the incumbency of Ernest Bevin as Foreign Secretary, the struggle between the British and the Jews assumed warlike proportions—a war fought mostly at sea and in Palestine ports.

Weizmann, who always believed in the ultimate justice of the British, was opposed to belligerent action and found himself at odds with the majority of the Yishuv and American Zionists led by Abba Hillel Silver. At the Zionist Congress in Basle, in 1946, when fateful decisions had to be taken, Weizmann disapproving of the temper of the majority, refused to stand for re-election as President. He held no official position of leadership when the State was declared in May, 1948.

Nevertheless, in February, 1949, when the first President was elected, Weizmann was the unanimous choice of all but those who had seceded from the World Zionist Organization in the 1930's and organized the dissident groups of terrorist action in the 1940's.

Shortly after his election, Weizmann published his autobiography (Trial and Error, Harper & Brothers, New York, 1949).

SELECTIONS FROM WEIZMANN'S BOOK "TRIAL AND ERROR"

Some time before the issuance of the White Paper, when immigration restrictions were already in force, the desperation of the Jews fleeing from the coming destruction began to rise to its climax; the efforts to reach the safety of Palestine led to the tragic phenomenon of the coffin boats, as they were called, crowded and unseaworthy vessels which roamed the Mediterranean in the hope of being able ultimately to discharge their unhappy cargoes of men, women and children in Palestine. Some sank in the Mediterranean and Black Sea. Some reached Palestine either to be turned back or to have their passengers taken off and interned or transhipped to Mauritius.

One of the worst cases—that of the *Patria*—occurred during the war under the Colonial Secretaryship of Lord Lloyd; and on hearing of it I went to him, in despair rather than in hope, to try and persuade him to give permission for the passengers to be landed. I was met with the usual arguments about the law being the law, to which I retorted: "A law is something which must have a moral basis, so that there is an inner compelling force for every citizen to obey. But if the majority of citizens is convinced that the law is merely an infliction, it can only be enforced at the point of the bayonet against the consent of the community."

An Arab State of Palestine in five years; a limited Jewish immigration during these five years, and none thereafter without Arab consent. I could scarcely believe my eyes. We had, indeed, begun to feel that the discussions had become meaningless for us; and after what had happened to Austria and Czechoslovakia nothing should have surprised us.

The disclosure to us of the Government document which was to become the White Paper coincided roughly with Hitler's unopposed and unprotested invasion of Czechoslovakia and the occupation of Prague. I remember that day well, because Jan Masaryk came to dinner with us. Between Masaryk and us there was, until the end, a deep friendship, both on personal and general grounds. There has always been a great affinity between the Masaryks and Zionism—Jan's father, the founder and first President of the Czechoslovak Republic had been a strong supporter of the Balfour Declaration—and now, in the days of the White Paper, the representatives of the Czechoslovak Republic were beginning to be treated by the Great Powers as if they were Jews.

An atmosphere of unreality and irrelevance hung over the twenty-first Zionist Congress which sat in Geneva from August 16 to August 25, 1939. We met under the shadow of the White Paper, which threatened the destruction of the National Home, and under the shadow of a war which threatened the destruction of all human liberties, perhaps of humanity itself. The difference between the two threats was that the first was already in action, while the second only pended; so that most of our attention was given to the first, and we strove to assume, at least until the fateful August 22, when the treaty was signed between Germany and Russia, that the second might yet be averted, or might be delayed. But on that day, when Hitler was relieved of the nightmare of having to wage war on two fronts, even the most optimistic of us gave up hope. The Jewish calamity merged with, was engulfed by, the world calamity.

The paradox which was revealed with the opening of the war deepened with the passing of the months. In the fight against the Nazi monster no one could have had a deeper stake, no one could have been more fanatically eager to contribute to the common cause, than the Jews. At the same time England, then the leader of the anti-Nazi coalition, was keeping the gates of Palestine closed against the unhappy thousands of men, women and children who were making the last desperate effort to reach the safety of the National Home. . . .

And yet we were determined to place all our manpower, all our facilities in Palestine, at the disposal of England and her Allies. What else was there for us to do?

Moshe Mosenson

◆

LETTERS FROM THE DESERT

October 23, 1942

THIS IS THE eve of the attack at El Alamein. These have been days
of wandering and I feel as though I have been swallowed up by
them. Only in the evening, when you curl up in your two army
blankets and the wind whistles and the cold penetrates into your
bones do you begin to think about the wonderful things that exist
for you somewhere so far away. You begin to think of your room,
of your wife and children and of the winter winds that howl and
break against thick walls. All this seems so far away, almost like
a fairy-tale. But during the day all one can think of is the noise
of trucks, the anxieties of work, etc. You are absorbed in them and
forget everything else.

It is two years now since I left home for the first time. Two
long years! And now again like two years ago, we are going out to
the front; this time with no illusions. This time everything is clear
to me in advance.

November 10, 1942

All about us, on the battlefields are the dead bodies of Germans
and Italians that are still unburied. The fields are sown with crosses
everywhere. Do you know what is in our hearts as we wander about
on what used to be enemy territory? Our hearts are full of joy
all the time. We exult like children at the sight of German tanks
that have been burned and smashed. But this is not enough. We are
still advancing. Enemy soldiers seem to turn up on every side,
making for the roads, hungry, depressed and asking to be captured.

Yesterday we camped on a battlefield. On every side we saw
cars, cannons and machine-gun posts that had been burned. I set
up my little tent alongside my car, put my blanket inside and afterwards I took out my radio, connected it to the battery in the car

and listened to the "Voice of Jerusalem." Hurrah! The Americans have invaded North Africa! From now on they will be advancing toward us. Great days have come. We shall cleanse all of Africa of this filth! The dread of destruction will no longer hover over our country. If you could look at the sky and see the hundreds of planes flying forward, our planes, you, too, would be fortified and encouraged. Our strength has grown and increased. The days of Tobruk are gone forever, when tens and hundreds of planes used to bomb us and not one of ours dared to come out against them.

I want to keep my promise. I promised that the next time I would come home on leave it would be from Tripoli. The Americans may get there before us. But, in any case, our fears for our homes are lifted and we have blazed the way to victory. . . .

Yesterday I listened to the radio and heard the news from London. It is strange to listen to the radio from a battlefield. Near my car is a grave and the mound over it is still moist. On the board that is stuck into the mound is a cross and a German helmet. A Nazi went to his rest here—and near his grave sits a Jewish boy and listens to the radio from London without fear of the Gestapo . . . isn't it weird?

You write about the scarcity of working hands and you ask, by the way, if it would be possible to let some soldiers go, and me among them for the sowing, for the season is "urgent." . . . Don't you know that here, too, the "season" is "urgent?" For we are busy with sowing today, too. If only there were ten thousand of our boys in the western desert today! It will no longer be easy for them to conceal our share in this. The Jewish motor units have gained praise of all kinds and on the day of reckoning it will be impossible for them to wipe it out.

There were casualties in two motor units. In a third, a Jewish captain rode over a mine in his machine and his fate is not yet known. One of our drivers also rode over a mine, but he managed to jump off his truck loaded with inflammable stuff which went up in flames immediately. Some of our boys were attacked by enemy planes but managed to get through their initial ordeal by fire safely. Some of them had nervous upsets. But most of them came through all right. We have a young boy of eighteen with us who comes from Turkey. Suddenly he announced that he wanted to go home. As this was not granted he started a hunger-strike. He did not eat for three days. Today I took care of him, talked to him and won his confidence. I gave him a clean pair of socks and he washed his feet and changed his socks; I brought him a can of pears and he ate with me and was soothed for the time being. I hope that he will be better.

The membership of the unit is quite new now. In the evenings, or at difficult moments, you sometimes long for good friends with whom you shared difficult times. They are all scattered now. Eventually I shall probably make new ties with these comrades, only now, in the meantime, there is no one with whom I can really talk.

December 6, 1942

Yesterday we had a Hanukah party. It took place in a large machine shed that was built by the Italians with a tarpaulin over it. There were a thousand of us from five of the motor units in the neighborhood. It was a very impressive gathering. At the end, as usual, a feuilleton was read and gusts of laughter swept the hall until quite late. It is good to see one's comrades laughing and it is good to know that we were able to bring this about and to give them some pleasure so that they could relax a little from the heavy strain that weighs upon them in army life. The rabbi, or military chaplain, was also present and he brought us some dreadful news of the Jews in Libya. He saw a sign near a road that said in Italian: "Jewish Group No. 1," and learned that the Nazis and the Fascists took all the Jewish males in Libya to the front as civilian roadbuilders. No more than a few of them survived. He met the remaining few that had belonged to this unit and heard tales of horror from them. Most of the Jews of Berci, Derna, and Benghazi were hanged, shot or slaughtered. The remaining ones were dragged off. The aged man who had blessed me at Berci died shortly after our retreat; the young daughter of the Ben-Dusa family, whose guest I was, was carried off by the Italian army; the mother was raped by drunken Italians and was then stabbed to death and the rest of the family were taken to labor battalions and no one knows how they met their death.

That is how it is, and we, in Palestine, what have we to complain about?

You write that you have learned how to hate. Yes, we must hate with our whole being. But to cultivate hatred, to live off nothing but hatred—nothing can be more terrible than this. The heart must be taught how to hate uncompromisingly, to hate profoundly, but to love at the same time. To love the good, to love man, to love our people. But there is no question of abstract hatred or abstract love. We must learn how to give everything we have, everything that is dear to you, the best of your life and your future in order to defeat the enemy and to save our people. This is how it must be. True hatred is nourished by love. One must be ready to go to one's death for the sake of life itself.

January 3, 1945

Let me tell you about a recent visit of ours to a nearby town. This was another sad encounter with Jews. On that Saturday the local rabbi arranged prayers and 250 of us attended. The town is very beautiful, but most of its houses are shattered and destroyed. There was a Jewish community of thousands here before the occupation but now there are only 250 left. They stood at all the windows and balconies in the Jewish quarter and welcomed us joyously with "Shabat Shalom." Their faces were radiantly happy. The children clung to us with love. Formerly the community maintained a Hebrew school. Now we met the children, pale, with large sad, intelligent eyes. I hugged a little boy of about the age of Ron and tears choked me as he said: "Take me and my mother and father to Palestine." There was so much knowledge of life in his eyes, such bitter knowledge. This is a child who saw his uncle hanging in the street for five days. These children have seen a great many terrible things. For months they did not see the sunlight. At that moment I realized how happy our children are.

We went to visit some Jewish families. There was such sadness in their faces, such fear. All the Jewish shops have been plundered. One group of soldiers was accompanied by the rabbi's little boy. He ran ahead of us and called: "Father, Jewish soldiers! Father, look, he has 'Eretz Israel' written on his shoulder." (And he was right. The wife of R. had embroidered "Eretz Israel" instead of "Palestine" on his shoulder.) The rabbi looked at the words and kissed the shoulder the way one kisses a Mezuza. While they were praying I got up and went out into the corridor. I searched for the family with whom I had eaten one Sabbath Eve in another city, but I couldn't find them. However, I met one of their relatives who recognized me. He told me that multitudes of the Jews in that city had been murdered and that this family was among them. More terrible than anything else is the knowledge that it is impossible for us to bring them to Palestine: this thought drives one mad. So, in the joy of these encounters there is also much bitterness. How can we comfort them? Can we be satisfied with praying together at the synagogue? And where will they get the immigration certificates and the clothes and a loaf of bread?

February 19, 1943

Finally let me tell you about my most precious experiences on this trip, my encounter with the Jews here. As we passed through a little town in our cars marked with the Star of David both in front and on back, we suddenly saw people dressed in European clothes shouting to us in excitement, "Shalom!" I stopped and two boys jumped on to my running-board. "Shalom, Yehudim!" they said and we shook hands. Their first question was "Do you have any newspapers from Palestine?" I searched around in confusion and finally found a copy of *Hegeh* (I use it to teach one of the refugees Hebrew) under the car-seat, and gave it to them. One of them took it with his eyes shining, looked at the Hebrew letters, kissed the paper and said with moving sincerity, "We shall read this aloud in the synagogue." I think this must have been the first time that a secular newspaper was kissed in distant North Africa. Behind me the trucks were blowing their horns and I was unable to hold up the convoy any longer. All along the streets of this little town stood Jews cheering us with, "Shalom, Yehudim!" waving their hands in excitement. The eyes of many of the older people were wet with tears, and the children shouted with joy. Our hearts were warmed by all this. But all this was only an introduction to what was to happen to us in the big city, from which I am writing you.

There are 20,000 Jews in this city. The streets that we drove through were loud with cries of joy, cries of "Shalom." Ecstatic greetings were pouring upon us from all sides. We felt as if we were dreaming all this excitement. We drove straight through the city to the outskirts, let the Negroes out, and camped there. I immediately went back to the city, in search of Jews. At the gate to the city I met a man wearing spectacles and I spoke to him in Arabic, "Where do the Jews live here?" Answering in Arabic, he said most of them lived in the Jewish quarter, and he looked rather startled. I suspected that he was a Jew. However, I hesitated to ask him about this and went on in Arabic, "Where is the nearest synagogue? Could I go to worship there?" At this he smiled and asked, "Are you a Jew?" Then he looked at my epaulettes and saw "Palestine" and shook my hands with a warm "Shalom Aleichem." From then on he did not leave me alone. Simon L. is his name. I went along with him and he told me in fluent Arabic about the Jews of the city. He explained that wealthy Jews had built the suburb we were in and the poor Jews used to rent rooms there to escape the bombings. In the days of the German occupation there was a joke circulating to the effect that the Allies would have to save them from the Germans, the Italians and the British Air Force. . . . I went with him to his house. There we found his wife, his sister, two younger brothers and a little daughter of five called Eliza. All of them, except for the mother, speak Hebrew fluently. Little Eliza didn't leave me alone for a moment, singing Hebrew songs and laughing with joy. In the meantime two neighbors came in and I was amazed at their fluent Hebrew. It seems that most of the Jews of Tripoli know the language.

When we entered the house the table was set and the family was sitting and waiting for me. I saw some of the neighbors coming in with pots and realized that they were helping the mother to prepare a fitting meal for the occasion. I knew that this was not to be one of their ordinary meals and that they were not in the habit of eating their fill. There were all kinds of delicacies at this meal. After dinner many of the neighbors came in. I talked to them about Palestine and I gathered that they had heard nothing about the fate of our people in Europe. I told them about the atrocities the Nazis committed upon the Jews in occupied countries. How intently they listened! After that they opened their hearts and

told of what they had been through. Simon L. asked that all the
Jewish soldiers come to the Jewish quarter the next day to have
their Sabbath meal there. I told him that there were sixty of us.
He replied, "We'll divide you among us. Every family will take
a soldier." Thus I sat with them until it grew late.

From their tales I gathered that the Jews of Tripoli were also
due to be carried off to the concentration camps in Tunis. And
probably these 20,000 Jews would be dead today if Montgomery
had not attacked before the Germans were able to complete their
plans for the liquidation of the Jews. It was from them that I first
heard of the concentration camp for the Jews of Cyrenaica in Jiddo.
This camp was erected 200 miles deep in the desert. There the last
remainder of the lovable Jews whom we met a year and a half
ago in Bardia Tobruk, Derna, Berci, Benghazi and other places were
gathered. They also told me that there were at present about 200
refugees from this concentration camp in the city. During the retreat
some of the inmates tried to escape into the desert. The Italian
guards shot them while they were escaping, but 200 succeeded in
reaching Tripoli.

Yigal Mossinson

ASHES

THE EVENING was starless. Hanan was sitting upon a rock between the sea and mountain, his cigarette tracing circles of light as if it were a firefly. I heard the waves lapping the yellow sands of my childhood and a saxophone wailing from the hazily blue piazza of a beach cafe.

"I hate them!" said Hanan.

"Whom?" I asked as I sifted the moist sands through my fingers.

"Those dancing up there," Hanan answered, thrusting the crumpled pack of cigarettes down the pocket of his military shirt.

The evening was starless. Two shadows passed. They whispered to each other and gazed far away into the sea. The woman giggled. She leaned upon the man's shoulders. He drew her close and for a moment they stood there embraced. Then they continued walking along the shore with fingers entwined. Again the woman giggled.

"A man builds a tower of dreams," said Hanan, "plasters and whitewashes it, removes the remnants of secularity that may have been clinging to his house. He climbs up a hill to fetch some cyclamens for his tent, returns and sees that the wooden floor has been scrubbed clean, that his books have been dusted on the shelf, that a sort of poor man's holiday has meekly and modestly taken up its abode with him. His hands hold a fresh garland of cyclamen, his eyes are good and calm; she has been here. Sonya has returned from her day's work in the garden. She has tidied the tent. She has spread the white sheets over the beds.

"But here comes Hayim, Hayim Spiegel! Quietly, tip-toe, he enters the tent, lowers his head with his silvering hairs, slouches down with his dirty workclothes on to the carefully spread couch and is mum.

"Outside, a crowd has gathered. Through the lifted flaps comes a glimpse of dusty shoes, a bit of hairy leg in sandals, the blue edge of an apron. The hoarse voice of Motek, the yardman, rasps in the stillness: 'What has happened!'

"Sh-sh, excited voices hush him.

"The doctor enters. His spectacles have slipped down to the edge of his nose, and you see that his eyes are crossed. For some reason or other he takes hold of the case, twisting it and stroking it with his long white fingers.

"Stubbornly, Hayim gazes at the top of his shoes with blank staring eyes and sees nothing. The doctor presses the clay jar so earnestly, it is almost shattered by his nervous fingers.

" 'Where is Sonya?' I finally get the words out of my dry throat.

"Neither answers. Each is silent. Outside, feet are still shuffling. I sink on the stool of woven straw. 'The towel is not in its place . . . she . . . went . . . to. . . . There were two towels on the hook.'

"One thought swiftly gives place to another. The heart tries to guess. You are silent, afraid to ask.

" 'I want my mother! I want my mother!'

"I recognize the voice. It's Sonya weeping bitterly: 'I want my mother!' Then a peal of horrid laughter, muffled blows and the sound of a smashed pane.

" 'She is in the dispensary.' Hayim says, 'she is being watched.'

"I know. She is in the dispensary. . . .

" 'She was in the showers. She was showering and lathering her body. Suddenly she began to imagine the most incredible things,' Hayim says to the tip of his shoe. Why does he speak of 'she' and not of Sonya! I thought. 'What did she say?' Hayim's knees tremble. 'Just silly things. . . . Everything will turn out for the best, Hanan.'

" 'What did Sonya say?' I ask again.

" 'That . . . the soap was made of human grease. That the green soap was made of the fat of rotted human flesh. That she wanted her mother. That mother was waiting at the Warsaw Railroad Station, and she must not be late. That she had left her mother

alone at the station when she herself had gone to Palestine, and
that mother was still waiting. That she oughtn't to have done it,
to have left her waiting so long: there was no air in the station,
and mother had a woolen scarf wound about her neck, that was
liable to choke her!' That's what Hayim Spiegel told me.

"I left the tent. The yard lay scorching in the sunshine, and
small clusters of people stood scattered in the shade of the cottages,
staring silently in the direction of the dispensary. I had to cross
the open yard, and I did. Step after step, stride following stride,
late September and a yard blazing with light. I saw how the ward
was covered with a belt of greenery. I saw the first wagtails hopping
along the ground, and heard the mournful note of the lark from
a cypress. I thought of graveyards and saw stone walls topped with
fragments of colored glass."

Hanan stopped. The cigarette went dead. He struck a match
and I saw his face aglow and his deep dark eyes.

"Up on a hill near the settlement was a ruined well, the remains
of a water-wheel, and a domed chamber of stone alongside. Sonya
and myself were removed there. The doctor thought that the shock
would pass, and that there was no need of fetching her to town."

Hanan was not crying. He only moved his palm across his brow,
and shutting his eyes, continued, "Yes, a man builds dream-castles,
and then one day all is in ruins. All's collapsed. And the mind,
the clear mind of a companion becomes broken soap. All the death-
trains moving eastward rattle in it. You feel it in the twitching of
the fingers, in the grating teeth and the wail. God Almighty! . . .
that wail rising from the white bed: M-o-t-h-e-r!

"There were moments when her clarity of mind returned. She
would be affectionate as a child with a bashful, conciliating smile.
She knew that I was awake nights watching her. She knew why
the doctor would stay at her side now and then saying in his deep
voice, 'It will be all right! It's going to turn out all right! Just
patience!' Yes doctor. He had also known the taste of what's called
'Europe' . . . a shambles from sea to sea!

" 'Hanan, did they hear my screams down below?'

"I would stroke her cheek and caress her. 'No, Sonya No one
heard.'

" 'And this will pass?'

" 'No doubt about it. You must believe so.'

" 'Yes. Everything passes in life . . . and life too,' she said with her mocking, sad smile.

"And once again, Sonya was as I had known her. I never loved her with a sorrow so lucid. I had never gazed at her as much as I did in those hours.

" 'Do you hear, Hanan!' she suddenly rose in horror. 'Do you hear—a train!'

"Remotely, wheels were chugging along. A freight train was moving in the distant hills.

" 'Only a freight train, Sonya,' I tried to calm her, 'iron, gravel, cattle, a long train with just a single man driving, just one lonely man.'

" 'And mother?'

" 'Sleep, Sonya, sleep. It's a freight train with a coal-grimy driver in the cab.'

" 'You lie! And mother?' Then afterwards: 'Hanan! Hanan! They are coming!'

"She stepped off the bed. I didn't oppose her. She wore a white cotton night-gown, her feet bare, uncovered, her back turned toward me, and then she began to dance. What fingers! What arms like serpents! And the shadow, that shadow accompanying her on the white walls!

"And when she was tired, she came up to me asking, 'Hanan, are you afraid? And why did you lie?'

" 'I have never lied to you, Sonya.'

"It was midnight. I sat motionless with Sonya crouched in my lap. I tried to imagine that she was asleep. I heard the rustling of the bats in the old well, a shutter creaking in the wind, the cry of a child from one of the houses down the slope. It must have been a long time that we were clutched thus in the white room. I heard the ticking of the clock which stood on the table shifting its unseen hands.

" 'They are r-i-n-g-i-n-g!' she muttered as from sleep.

" 'Sleep. Nobody rings at midnight. Everyone's asleep. Only the guardsmen are about at this hour. . . .'

"But Sonya was right. I too heard the ringing. Slow. Still. Ding-dong and stillness. It was thus the bell would be tolled when there was a funeral, or in case of alarm, an attack or fire. What had happened? I opened the door wide; the entire village was illuminated by fire. The hay-loft was burning!

"Sonya awoke and stood at my side. She wound her arm about my shoulders and watched the blaze.

" 'Burning?' she asked in a sleepy voice.

" 'The hay-shed next to the cow-barn!' I thought: 'The cows must be gotten out of danger! Whatever can, must be saved!'

" 'Everything is burning. That's nice,' said Sonya with an insipid smile.

"I left the room. I shut the door from the outside and hurried to the site of the fire. The settlement was immersed in a thick pall, tongues of flame were scattering sparks everywhere. Hayim Spiegel dragging wet sacks ran as if butting the air with his brow. A woman in a bathrobe stood near a barrel and screamed: 'Wet sacks! Here are the wet sacks!' Yet nobody paid attention. Everyone was turning pell-mell, still half lost in webs of sleep, and looking wild and dishevelled. The cows snorted and beat their hoofs as they bellowed away. Several people were struggling to get the bull up and moving. And the beast, fleshy, heavy-limbed, strode ponderously in his fatness with his steel nose-ring reflecting the flames. On the roof of the barn stood someone half-naked spraying streams of water from a hose along his knees towards the burning wall.

"Motek, the yardman, moved from one crowd to another: 'Back! Back! Don't get in the way!'

"The people stand silently. A wall collapses. Sparks fade skyward. The fire licks on with a thousand tongues.

" 'Back! Back!' cries Motek pushing the crowded circles of women and old folk with his chest and elbows."

Hanan is looking toward the sea. The wind scatters his hair, and he blows rings of smoke into its course.

"The cow-barn was saved. Smoking embers lay among the puddles. Now and again a flame rekindled and died. A few men remained behind looking for some tools that had been stored in the shed. And I? I returned to Sonya. No, to put it exactly, I returned to the stone room. Absorbed in the thoughts of the labor of many months which had vanished in smoke, I did not notice the nurse coming toward me.

"'Hanan, where is Sonya?'

"'In the stone room. She is in the room. I bolted the door.'

"'She isn't there.'

"I saw the questioning look and the anxiety in the wrinkled face of the old nurse.

"'Not in the room?' I murmured confusedly. 'Why I bolted the door from the outside!'

"'The lock is broken,' said the nurse. 'There's no one in the room. The lamp's burning, but no one's there.'

"'Perhaps she's gone out to look at the fire! Just wait in the room while I go out searching. Wait, for she may come back in the meantime.' And, without stopping for her answer, I turned running down the slope into the village.

"'Did you see Sonya?'

"'No!'

"Hayim Spiegel was still among the ruins of the shed. Sweating, his hair singed, he stood pouring a bucket-full of water over a smoking rafter.

"'Hayim, did you see Sonya?'

"He did not look to see who was speaking.

"'Sonya?' he repeated the question. Then he lifted his grimy, mournful face. 'Did you speak to me, Hanan?'

"'I asked, whether you had seen Sonya.'

"'No. No. I haven't seen her,' he said absent-mindedly still gazing at the embers. 'Ashes. Ashes. The labor of an entire year gone up in flames! Look, Hanan: Ashes!'

"He did not look toward me. He took the bucket and turned with heavy steps toward the barn, eyes still fixed on the puddles of slush.

"I returned to the stone chamber. The nurse stood at the door waiting.

"'Not there?' she asked in apprehension.

" 'No!' I answered, leaning upon the stone wall to keep myself from falling.

" 'We must arouse the village,' said the nurse, 'they'll look for her.' "

Hanan scribbled in the sands with his finger. The croon of the saxophone was heard from the hill and the echoes of the dancing steps trotted above the noise of the waves. Hanan listened to the music.

"There's a song that comes from the heart of a man who's happy and there's a song that comes from sadness. Yet what's the song of joy in the mouth of one whose soul's been consumed?"

Hanan shrugged his shoulders and did not wait for an answer.

"Then, while we were standing near the stone room, there came the sound of a song rising from a cliff in the upper part of the ravine. It was a great slab of rock, its straight walls facing the village, and there was Sonya singing in a strange sad melody, a happy song she herself had composed in Yiddish, the language of her childhood. It was about a bridegroom, how he would delight the heart of the bride on the wedding night, and how a choir would sing at her window while the spring flowers bloomed in the dark fields.

" 'She's going to fall!' cried the nurse, 'She'll be smashed to pieces!'

" 'Hurry and call the doctor. I'll climb up to her.'

" 'Go carefully. Don't frighten her.'

" 'Call the doctor!' I hurried up the ravine. The overhanging cliff was immense, and in the night looked tenfold more precipitous. A little woman in a white gown was seated there on the brink of ruin. I would have made my way toward her, and come from behind by a skirting trail, but I was afraid. Perhaps it would be too late. Step by step I climbed up the crag, hurt by each projecting tooth of rock, torn by the brambles, but my eyes fixed upon her figure in the pale moonlight.

" 'Return, my son, return once more
    Unto thy father's house of yore
    For there thy cradle once did rest;
    A mother nursed thee at her breast.'

"That was Sonya's song: Suddenly she arose and stood with her full stature at the cliff's ledge, . . . a wild looking woman with dishevelled black hair, standing in a white gown on a high cliff bathed in a sea of pale, grey moonlight. I stopped, I was afraid to move, lest I frighten her.

" 'Return, my son, return once more . . .'

"She began to descend. Grasping the protruding rock and the roots of bushes, she slid down into the ravine. I went to meet her. She trod lightly, unaware of the threatening chasm below. When she was close, I whispered to her, 'Sonya!'

"She turned her head toward me. 'Are you waiting for me?' she asked numbly.

" 'It is I, Sonya: Hanan!'

"She came up to me, sat on the ground.

" 'I am tired.'

" 'Come, let's go back to the village.'

" 'It's all burned. Everything's burned,' she said picking pebbles and tossing them into the ravine.

" 'They saved the cow-barn from the fire,' I said.

" 'It's all burned.'

"Then she lay down and began to crawl. She clutched my legs and cried, 'It's all burned. Only ashes are left. Ashes. Even you are no more than ashes. We are all remnants of a great fire, and Mamma was burned too. She was burned. You were not burned because you have no heart!'

Hanan rose. He buttoned his uniform and asked, "Got a fag?"

As he lit the match, I again caught a glimpse of his face by the little yellow flame.

"I must go," he said. "Tomorrow I leave with my battalion for Africa. Sorry that I've got to guard those supply dumps and not be with our drivers up on the Italian Front. Some say that guarding sardines and jam is a 'war effort.' They may be right, but I'm sorry anyway. I'd like to beat those bloody devils for all they did to me, and for Sonya who's shut like a wild beast in a cage, my Sonya who turned into ashes."

Hanan looked out toward the sea. "Well, good-bye," he said without turning, and I knew that his heart was choked with tears.

"Shalom, Hanan, bon voyage, my friend."

He moved off, his slouched back fading along the strand.

It was a starless evening. I heard the wash of the waves licking the yellow sand of my childhood, and a crooning saxophone from the piazza of a beach cafe aglow in a blue mist. And I saw a man about to sail on the morrow with his battalion for somewhere in Africa, and his figure was being swallowed among the shadows of the houses facing the sea. I wanted to repeat that song of Sonya:

"Return, my son, return once more
Unto thy father's house of yore."

but the saxophone crooned above and lots of people were dancing there, and then I thought that the sea was rolling in waves of black ashes.

Moshe Carmel

◆

THE CITADEL

IN THE DIM LIGHT of early morning on May 18th, 1948, just two hours after the surrender of the enemy in the city of Acre, I made my way to the Citadel. The ramparts, still captive to the all-pervading gloom, reared massive, sullen, against the steadily-brightening skies. From time to time, a long rifle shot rang out. From the Old City came a burst of machine-gun fire, like the yelp of a hurt dog. Then a dull silence reigned absolute.

The gates of the Citadel, for years the Central Gaol of the country, stood breached, deserted. A group of Arab warders, bewildered and fearful, stood in the outer prisonyard, surrendering their arms and begging for their lives. Nine years before we had passed through this gate, my comrades and I, our hands manacled, and our fate determined for ten years or for life imprisonment. Then all had seemed so solid, immutable, definite. The wardens, the walls, authority, had seemed so permanent, even everlasting. Now, how strange it was, everything was broken, confused, with the vestiges of that administration, once the outward symbols of its power were cast off, dispersed, unwanted.

I passed through the outer yard and mounted the bridge, leading to the inner citadel. Here it was, lined with empty, deserted cells, their doors gaping as if dumb-struck. This was our cell, here the patch of floor my mattress had covered, here had I lain for many long months in prison. How desolate it all was, how strange. The lives of hundreds of human beings had throbbed here, bitter constricted lives; lives of despair, of decay, of utter hopelessness in which, in spite of all, some dim prospect has gleamed, died and flickered again. Here hundreds of men, made in the image of God and in the image of the hangman, had lived out their stormy inner lives, for years and years, often for decades. (One prisoner I knew had been incarcerated for twenty-nine years.) How much desire, yearning, aspiration, had pulsated here, burning to ashes the souls in which they abode, crumbling their bodies to dust. Where were they now, my fellow-prisoners, of my own people and of theirs? Who among them had been delivered and who had died?

This was the execution cell. Unlike the others it was still secured with a heavy padlock, and its two doors, one grilled, the other solid, barred our way. The soldier at my side took his rifle, fired into the lock and forced it. The doors swung open wide. There was the hangman's hook, the trapdoor, the execution handle. It was all so appallingly simple. Where were those who had been hanged here, where were the hangmen? A new, horrible light was suddenly cast upon this deprivation of life by man. Why had one hanged the other? By what right, for what principle, under what license? Where was that authority that had had men hanged? Why had it desisted? Why only now and not before? In this plain, gloomy cell installed with such simple devices for the deprivation of human life, the extent to which Man's domination and Man's destruction both lay in the hand of Man, the degree to which only might was right, stood out in grim relief.

I clambered to the roof of the prison, where once the warders had stood, their weapons always cocked for fear of some attempt at escape. I entered the well-appointed, decorated rooms, where the Governor of the Prison, his Deputy and their corps of guards had resided. Everything was neat, in its appointed place, still pulsating, alive. Here, in this room, we had been told of our fate— a long imprisonment. Here our human likeness had been effaced, here we had been clad in convict garb. The Governor in his uniform; his writing desk, the massive volumes of regulations, the seals of the gaol, the portraits of the king and queen, adorning the walls, all had expressed a regime that was permanent, that could never fail.

I went down to the lower yard. In a corner, surrounded by a grill, huddled some dozens of prisoners, lunatics, contorted, stupefied at the sight of their new visitors. In tatters, fearful, yet not comprehending what had taken place, they stared with horror starting out of their eyes, gibbering horribly. The sole living remnant of the prison was this clump of maniacs, forgotten of God and of men, whom a merciful Arab officer, one I had known long before, was endeavoring to pacify. Some of them I could remember but their aspect had changed; they had decayed, become distorted, and the horror that stared out of them was even more intense. ·

I walked down the long, dingy, high-ceilinged corridors, like one dreaming of a time now distant and faint, and my soul within me quivered at those sufferings, now gone. Once again I saw myself in prison garb, robbed of my liberty, filled with the longing that tortured me, still bearing in my heart the love of the good and the beautiful that seemed so far off.

I remembered the comrades, together with whom I had borne my sufferings, the Forty-Three, the men of Ginossar, of Ben Shemen, of Mishmar Hashlosha, all members of the Hagana, who had forged its strength underground, and for that crime had been cast into gaol. Now they were free, they and all the hundreds of others, incarcerated on other occasions for that same offense. Was there in the hearts of those who had suffered imprisonment, for the right to self-defense, a feeling of reparation, that by their merit we had seen this day, were carrying arms proudly, openly, fighting for life and liberty? For us gaol had been no more than a station on our road to freedom.

*   *   *

THE BEVIN BLOCKADE

Slowly we drew nearer and nearer to the land of Israel. We were sailing along the Syrian coast, and then turned south. We hoped to make the shore without being seen. Suddenly, a plane appeared and started circling overhead. The pilot had obviously guessed the sort of craft we were. Eventually he made off, but returned after a while, accompanied by another plane. From then on they stayed with us throughout the remainder of our voyage. After a few hours, a destroyer attached itself to us as well. We had company.

There was no longer any sense in hiding. Some 2,000 people climbed on to the deck. Signals flashed, bright beams of light played on us and all around us, but our ship continued sailing, our escort faithfully following in our wake.

The following conversation—our leaders informed us—took place by signal:

"Where are you making for?"

"Home—Palestine."

They continued: "Listen to us and come with us to Cyprus. We say it for your own good. We want to help you. Perhaps you need medical aid, perhaps there's a shortage of something or other on board. How many are you?"

We answered, "We are going on to Tel-Aviv. We thank you for your offer of medical aid, but we don't need it. We number about 2,000 including women, children, and elderly people." They spoke gently, as if considering the issue: "You won't reach the shore. Why add to your troubles, it would be better for you to turn the ship towards Cyprus; there things will be made easy for you."

We knew the kind of Garden of Eden that awaited us in the camps there, and answered: "We have come from Hitler's camps. We have had enough of concentration camps, even if they are under British care. Why do you hunt us like animals? What is our crime?"

At seven in the morning, the captain of the destroyer announced that he would like to speak to the people without an intermediary. He suspected that his words were not being passed on, and he thought he would carry influence with us. His request was granted. The destroyer approached us. Through the loudspeaker he addressed the packed mass of 2,000 people. How the thousands squeezed in I do not know. You could see clusters of men literally hanging on to the ropes, the masts and the cranes, linked and pressed together, holding their breath, listening to what was being said to them. The words were translated into languages which the immigrants understood.

The answer burst forth as though from one man:

"Palestine!"

It seemed as though the ships trembled at the strength of the cry. The singing of the anthem, "Hatikva," struck the air, then

came the songs of the Exile, and the songs of the fighting partisans.
For hours the people sung unwearyingly.

There were now four destroyers accompanying us. Again and
again they questioned us. "Where is your captain? Who is in the
crew?" Again and again we gave answer: 'We have no captain and
there are no hands on board but us. We are sailing the ship ourselves."

We were by this time only a day's journey from Palestine. None
of us could sleep. All attention was concentrated on the coming
event. The solemn feeling of a holy festival grew as the fateful
hour approached.

Everyone dug into his bag, and brought out his best belongings.
Mothers combed their sons' hair and plaited their daughters' tresses.
The children's eyes sparkled with unaccustomed fire. The flag was
raised.

Suddenly a report went round. A few hours ago one of the
boys had jumped into the sea. As soon as he had become aware
that the shore could be seen in the distance, he had taken a life
belt, a tin of food and water, and making his friend promise not
to give him away, had dived into the sea. He thought he would
reach Palestine this way, but all of us were afraid for him. The
shore was miles away, and there was no hope of reaching it safely.
He would perish. Our ship turned round and went back in search
for him. At once, without comment, all four destroyers turned
with us, and sailed alongside.

They found it strange indeed. What was the meaning of this
change of course so near to Palestine? They asked us, and we
answered, "Someone has jumped into the sea, and we are trying to
save him."

They immediately wanted to help. After two hours they informed us that they had hauled him from the water. They gave
a detailed description. Later they reported on his condition from
time to time. He was on their ship, and they were nursing him. We
thanked them for this demonstration of humanity and our ship again
turned towards Palestine—our company clinging like leeches.

For an hour we made headway. Our companions did not touch
us. Our people's spirit rose and at the same time their nerves

grew taut. We were preparing for a battle of despair. Wooden planks were moved into position, bottles and rubber tires gathered into heaps. Excited children played, "Hunting the Immigrant," and emerged from the battle black and sooty. You felt it was not really a game. They, too, had passed through Europe's school and world war. We drew near the coastline.

The Captain made a distinct promise that no harm would befall us. He asked us to stay on board. No force would be used against us, and before anything was done, the people would be informed. Near the shore, twenty-five British sailors climbed on deck. We received them with suppressed anger. But they kept silent and did not touch us, so we, too, held our peace and watched.

The harbor—the noise of a large army standing to, the terror rose from all sides. Still no one was scared. The three deportation ships came up closer, and we could see the barbed wire all round them. Our hearts divined that they were meant for us. We began to sing, but this time it was a weak, pale singing, without enthusiasm. No brother's hand was extended to us here in our homeland, not even a blessing for the "children returning to their own borders." The strange silence sowed a terrible loneliness in the heart. We were alone here, and surrounded by bayonets and soldiers with their weapons ready. They were pale and tense, all human expression gone from their faces.

The troops took up positions on the deck, weapons in their hands. The order was given for us to move to the other ships. Restrained silence. No one moved. The order was repeated, and again repeated. No one obeyed. The soldiers approached a child of eight, and told him, "Come down." He answered, in Yiddish, "I don't want to." They began to pull at him.

We saw that the worst would happen. They had decided to drag us off by force. Despair demanded that we stand up for ourselves. We would not let them! A hail of tins and bottles poured down on the heads of the soldiers.

But look, they take to their heels and run for their lives.

In the excitement of the flight, one soldier took hold of his gun and shot straight at the mass of immigrants, without discrimination. It was difficult to miss. One boy fell in a pool of blood. They

carried him to the dispensary, but he died. Several people were
wounded. One man, who had two bullets in his shoulder, sat
silently on the deck. He sat there quietly, and only when the battle
was over did he allow himself to be taken to hospital. One man
struggled with a soldier and was fatally wounded.

Wrath flared up at the sight of the man falling, and soldiers
shooting indiscriminately at defenseless people. The British soldiers
on the deck above were surrounded and surrendered at once. They
backed off the ship. Some of them were thrown into the sea. Below,
new groups of soldiers began to climb on board, but they were
repelled time after time. They struck against us like the waves of
the sea against a rock. We had bottles and tins in abundance, and
they rained down on the heads of the soldiers, and even cracked a
few skulls. We had not come here to smash skulls, but we saw
what they wanted to do to us, to people who longed for a few
years of peaceful and honorable life, after the years of fear. It was
as though every heart had made a silent promise—They shall not
pass!

Later they turned hoses of sea-water against us—these, too,
were of no avail. Presently we saw them put on their gas-masks.
The last stage had come.

They dropped the bombs, gas bombs. A white fog rolled up
and enveloped us all. Our skins were scorched, our eyes singed and
our breath came in gasps. To more than one of us came the memory
of the gas chambers. Unfortunately, most of the bombs fell into the
large hold, where more than 2,000 people were crowded together.
Terrible cries burst forth. People twisted with pain, they stormed
upwards, a seething mass, unable to see each other. Many were
almost trampled underfoot and children were nearly trodden on.
Mothers lost their children, children searched for their parents.
This continued for twenty-five minutes. Babes were carried on high,
people who didn't know the first elements of swimming jumped into
the sea. The attackers knew that there were women there, many of
them pregnant, they knew there were babies there, and old people,
but that did not stop them throwing bombs. The deck filled with
women, children, and the aged. Boys and girls tore their shirts
into shreds, and gave them away so that people could dip them in

water and put them over their eyes. A child of eight ran to fetch a bucket of water from the kitchen. I saw him returning with the bucket, one hand over his eyes, the other handing out water. When he had done his job he fainted.

When the first clouds began to thin out, more bombs were thrown. Sometimes we caught the bombs and threw them back. We managed to return dozens of bombs this way. One was hurled into a bunch of soldiers, and put them to flight. They had weapons enough, but not spirit to match ours. Many times I heard the soldiers' shouts from the harbor. They shouted for joy when we were captured.

For the sake of truth, I must record that I saw some signs of humanity, of pity, of disgust at their own deeds, but they were very few. There were sailors who stood with tears in their eyes, some who cursed their being here. Once when a rifle was fired at us, we saw the officer running to the soldier who shot, and knocking the rifle out of his hand.

Then three bombs fell into the wing where the mothers and babies were. We were sure the eleven babies would choke. Our hearts trembled—they were children, the children of this ship, they were our dearest possessions. Our hearts trembled more for them than for anything else. In those minutes the opposition was broken.

The battle lasted an hour and a half. Still it was only half an hour after everything was over that the troops dared to board the ship. They did not conduct themselves with excessive courtesy. They began to take us below to send us across to the deportation ships. Even now, people did not go of their own free will, but had to be dragged. It was hard to continue the struggle when choking, and especially with the fate of our children, our babies and our pregnant women weighing on our conscience. Many of us inwardly asked, "Where are our brothers in Palestine—where is the roar of the wounded lion of the people of our country?"

On the gangway we were searched minutely. Many of us were robbed by the soldiers. Watches, rings, cameras, fountain pens, anything which had survived our wanderings all over Europe, passed now into the possession of the troops. Ornaments and Magen David trinkets were torn from the necks of women. A scroll of the Law was thrown on a heap of bags, and when some boys went to lift it up, they were beaten. Thus we were despatched to a new exile.

The ships sailed, we did not know where. They skimmed over the sea, and only afterwards did we find out that they were not yet sailing for Cyprus, because a case questioning the legality of our deportation was being fought in court. The ships were floating prisons. We were locked behind barbed wire walls. We felt frustrated, eternal prisoners, but with it the strong sense of unity among us increased sevenfold, as did our confidence that in spite of all, we would reach our homeland. But it is difficult to convey the terrible feeling of being alone in the world. There were moments when I thought, "Whose fate was worse, that of those who were carried off from this land to Exile 2,000 years ago, or our fate, we who were on the threshold of our land, and diverted from it before we saw it."

Suddenly we saw land again. The ship seemingly sailed backwards and forwards, awaiting the decision of the court. The sight of the shore—Athlit, someone suggested—stirred our souls. We were 1,200 men together in the lowest hold of one ship. We began to sing. Our little songsters opened with the song of Kinneret—

"Oh my Kinneret,

Were you really there, or did I dream a dream?"

All that was locked in our hearts burst forth. Everyone, from babes to old men, wept. One of the old men sang "Kol Nidre." Our cheeks were wet and salty with our tears. For a moment I imagined that in our weeping I heard the weeping of generations, the weeping for our Temple destroyed, which would not be silent in our blood.

13   IN BLOOD AND FIRE

ON THE night of November 29, 1947, when the news was flashed from Lake Success that the General Assembly of the United Nations had voted to set up a Jewish State in a part of Palestine, the Jewish community joined in frenzied celebration. But the celebrants knew that many of them would not live to see the birth of the new State.

Immediately, irregular Arab bands, supported by several neighboring Arab states, and with the tacit connivance of many British officials, took to attacking, murdering, pillaging and burning. The siege of Jerusalem began. The Jewish defense now entered a new stage, one which was immediately named The War of Liberation.

The British soon withdrew from Tel-Aviv and its surrounding Jewish settlements, and from the most thickly populated Jewish areas. The Jews proceeded to organize a government and an army. The Haganah and its shock brigade, known as the Palmach, formed the nucleus. The volunteer Haganah was gradually transformed into a regular army. After the State was officially proclaimed on May 14, 1948, the army became known as the Zva Haganah le-Israel, the Israel Army of Defense.

On May 15, 1948, several Arab armies invaded Israel.

The spectacular victories of the Israel armies over the Arabs became known throughout the world and for the first time brought to the world's attention the military prowess and patriotism of the Jewish community in Palestine and Israel. The roots, of course, go deeper into the past.

A voluminous literature has grown up in Israel on the history of Jewish defense, and dealing especially with the War of Liberation. Much of it has been translated into English. There is, perhaps, need for a separate collection in English on modern Jewish wars.

In this book only a few selections in one chapter can be offered.

Shlomo Nitzam

◆

ARMED CIVILIANS

WE WERE digging ourselves in, in the small wood whose trees pushed up through the bank of the river. The darkness gave rise to illusions, and at every rustle of the leaves we cocked our rifles . . .

It was a scene still unlinked to cordite and fire.

When the Palmach mobile unit arrived, they had hardly stepped inside the entrance of the station before they announced that "it was different" in other places. Of course! There, it was hotter, the hours were shorter and passed more quickly, the pulse was stronger —in other words, there "it was all so different."

We at our station guarded the bridge, our job being to see that no one crossed it, and that no one crossed the waters which flowed quietly and so securely. And no one crossed the wide expanse of field which spread out calmly as in the days of peace. We kept watch on the Arab village opposite, whose simple peaceful appearance led you to believe that its quietness was—despite everything —not a bogus quiet.

The field units kept on speaking about the other places, districts riddled with bullets, mountains mobilized for battle. We looked at our district, with its river, bridge and fields. It hit its face, ashamed.

Then the first shots were heard.

For days before we had seen them on the hill of the village opposite, just a little way from the green house. We had seen them training. . . . You don't see because you are not looking straight: look right ahead, not there—there, where I'm pointing! See? They are splitting into units. They are raising their rifles. They have disappeared; now they have reappeared. Obviously, the command: "On the ground—fall!" What is the Arabic for that? Is that all you are interested in? How calm the village is! Give me the field-

glasses; its inhabitants have taken up positions. Shall we load . . .
in case? No! Wait for the command! We number them at about
sixty. If they come—they shall not cross the bridge.

Perhaps they will rush the river—over there, near the grass
—that is possible. No, at all events let them come. Who said sixty?
Do you see—hundreds! You are right, by God you are, but they
are only training.

It was lucky that it was dusk. We felt the district smoothing
out its wrinkles, masking its valley with darkness, on the alert. We
loaded our guns, the sten-gunners fetched extra magazines.

For all that, night passed quietly. Morning drove night from
the fields to the wood, where it held out for a while, but morning
broke through it. However, it would not flee, and hung in low
wisps of magic grey the whole day until evening arrived, its shadows
joining the wisps together, and night recovered its position. Meanwhile, the river sent up misty clouds and our landscape surveyed
itself—and its face grew sullen with shame. Another fruitless night.
The whole region lay under a peace of compulsion. There was the
feeling of a soldier who has deserted or a volunteer who has been
turned down.

We waited for the new guard to relieve us. We were bored
and sleepy in our sector, which stretched from the bridge, facing
the Arab village, eastward to the third electric pylon. The sector
after that belonged to another unit.

The guard was slow in coming, as usual, and we showered
curses on their heads.

"The devil take them!"

"Whom?"

"Whom!"

"Really, whom?"

Only the commander was weighed down with responsibility.

"What is this nonsense? I hope they take their time. It doesn't
matter if they don't come at all."

And, suddenly: "Who goes there?"

Crack-crack-crack! Here they are! The first long-awaited shot—
you had hardly experienced the first shots and already you knew
what was happening and where, and had your own weapon at the

ready and were all alert—and it seemed hours ago! Where was weariness? Where? We were awake, ready! The shots were many and close.

Minutes grew smaller, time contracted. There they are—all at the end of the bridge.

But they shall not pass the bridge, that is clear! The man assigned to it crawled to his grenade-post.

If they approach . . .

. . . Fire!

And we fired.

And the wood! A moment before it had been basking in the shadows, breathing peace and quiet and the sweet scent of flowers. They were all memories now. The men lay flat, handling their weapons in an orderly way.

They did not cross the bridge: we crossed it and put them to flight.

Afterwards we went to different stations, and the stations led us on to history.

The defenders of Tel Aviv.

Just that. And the simple meaning is—a city went forth to defend itself. Citizens and not an army. Citizens the whole year round—teachers, road-sweepers, shop assistants, bank clerks, businessmen and factory workers, actors, and synagogue beadles, dressed in mufti, with ammunition belts slung over.

Obviously there were the field units which had been well trained before us—they were already an organized army, swift, mobile. They had uniforms and boots and leggings. They were half the army. But the other half—just us . . .

The day-watch crawled through the trench to us—they, too, armed civilians.

THE BATTLE OF MISHMAR HAEMEK

After units of the Hagana had struck heavy blows at Kaoun and Sandala, bases of the Arab "Army of Liberation," Fawzi Kawkji began his offensive against Mishmar Haemek on April 5 by shelling it. This was followed by an attempt to overrun the settlement, and when the assault was thrown back a joint Arab-British proposal for a truce was made.

The following are the facts about the battle as told by an eye-witness:

The battle for Mishmar Haemek began in the early hours of Friday morning. For many days past we had concentrated large forces there of the Palmach and the Hish (field forces). Units of the Hagana from all over the country congregated in this area with the object of defeating Kawkji's avowed plan of "wiping Mishmar Haemek off the map." The settlement had been a thorn in Kawkji's side, affecting his whole military operation.

During the noon hours we watched from various observation posts, while a number of Hagana units occupied positions in the woods, on the plateau, and to the west of the settlement, preparing for general assault. The wireless center unceasingly recorded messages from Headquarters to the General Mobile Field Headquarters. The Commander in charge of the operation was broadcasting information to his officers regarding the enemy's movements, the direction in which Hagana reinforcements were moving, and details for withdrawal and covering fire.

In the direction of Abu-Shusha we could see from time to time the red headgear of Iraqi soldiers as they peeped through their lookout slits. The village looked sleepy. No doubt its men had observed the large force which was approaching from the west, and was not prepared to engage it.

There is also no doubt that the British knew about the great assault about to begin and, in fact, armored columns of the army appeared on the scene. The Commander applied to enter Mishmar Haemek, and a British Colonel with a marked Eton accent and a monocle, carrying a thin cane in his right hand, alighted from the vehicle.

"Can I speak to the local Hagana commander?"

"What about?"

"I wish to prolong the cease-fire for an indefinite period or for at least another twenty-four hours."

"As we informed you, sir, we are not authorized to consider

such a proposal, but we shall pass on your request and reply to you immediately."

"It seems to me that you are not well placed to refuse such a generous proposal."

The Hagana Commander looked at him, smiled at his friend, and said, "We shall see."

The Colonel stared back at him, shrugged his shoulders, returned to his vehicle, and drove off. Five minutes later the first large explosion shook the air. The Operational Commander ordered his officers to take over the combat units of the Hagana who had been waiting impatiently for the moment of assault. Our men streamed from the hills, appearing here and there between the dark forests and the wide-open fields. The red skies and the setting sun reflected large shadows on our units as they advanced towards their objections.

South of Mishmar Haemek is the extinct volcano where the Iraqi soldiers had dug in their light field guns at the beginning of the week and had shelled Mishmar Haemek. The volcano was our first objective. From the opposite hillock a heavy mortar kept sending up its shells on to the volcano, and soon we saw the first assault group storming the slopes. The hill was enveloped by smoke. A rain of bullets from heavy machine-guns kept streaming at it. Ten minutes after our men had got to the foot, the peak was taken by storm in a synchronized attack made from two directions. We could hear the conversations of the officers on our wireless set as they consulted each other in the midst of battle on the best method of advancing and where to meet again. Our reinforcements and the paths of the enemy's retreat were clearly seen through binoculars.

When our first troops were established on the big volcano, and the little volcano on its right had been captured in a similar manner, it seemed that some pause would follow, and that our men would rest for a few minutes from their vigorous assault. But that was not so. As soon as the first wave had taken the summit of the volcano, we brought up our mortars, and the bombardment of the main enemy base and its headquarters began. We were now shelling the village of Rubayah Fuka, which lies on a ridge a mile to the south-east of Mishmar Haemek.

It was evident that the storming of this plateau, defended by posts equipped with excellent automatic weapons, would be difficult and costly. The people who were watching the course of battle had anticipated a long and tiring struggle. They were surprised when they heard over the wireless an order from one of the Unit Commanders to another, who had reached the rear of the village and was engaged in sabotaging the enemy's lines of communication from the direction of Menassi, to join him and attack the village from the rear.

Thirty minutes later we heard the first results. Our men were established at the approaches to the village. At its center we could see a light flashing repeatedly—a heavy mortar, which the enemy was employing to bombard the attacking troops and their bases on the volcano.

"Hello, Mishmar Haemek, Hello, Mishmar Haemek," bellowed the voice from our loudspeaker. "I have a message from Hagai, I have a message from Hagai. If you can, direct your mortar on the center of the village, where the enemy mortar is in position. Be careful not to aim to the right, as our men are there. Hello Mishmar Haemek, Hello, Mishmar Haemek."

The pencil of the wireless orderly glided swiftly across the note-book. He hurriedly tore off a page, and gave it to the runner, who quickly took the message to headquarters. The Commander immediately picked up the telephone, "Hello, No. 6 post, mortar, shell center Rubayah Fuka. Range 1,400 meters, area of target not above 100 meters. Careful. Don't hit the ground to the right, where our men are established."

"O.K." answered a young voice from No. 6 post, after repeating his orders.

We stood at our observation posts with our binoculars. One of the young officers was holding a map, and pointed out the boundaries of the areas already held by our troops. "We are establishing a new kibbutz up there," he said, "Upper Mishmar Haemek." But the rest of us were not in a mood for such jokes. The battery's observation post was only a few yards away from us, and transmitted the order to the mortar section. There was a loud detonation —the first shell had gone, and then another, and another! Now we must count up to twenty-three before the sound of the first explosion reaches us.

"Hello, Mishmar Haemek, Hello, Mishmar Haemek, you're great. You did exactly what was required. The enemy post has been silenced, and they are retreating in confusion."

The time was 10:45, the enemy had retreated from Rubayah Fuka, leaving a great deal of arms and military equipment. Men of the Palmach stormed the positions in the village, broke into the houses, and fifteen minutes later were in complete possession of the village. When this information reached Mishmar Haemek, the tension which had gripped all who had been waiting the night long for news, eased. The workers who had suffered that week from the ceaseless enemy attacks, who had faced unsupported the Arab guns and heavy mortars breathed freely once more, and their hearts felt grateful to those young and courageous men who had come to rescue them from a situation not at all cheerful.

It is almost impossible to describe the elated state of the men who had taken the village. They occupied and fortified positions with great speed, some of which the Arabs had built, and some of which they had built themselves rapidly, on the spot. So there was not much time for them to give vent to their joy. The Arabs who had retreated towards Menassi were heavily attacked by a Hagana ambush, and their reinforcement route was cut by the blowing up of a bridge which joined Menassi and Jenin. At last they were forced to turn back, and began organizing for a desperate counter-attack on the captured village. All through the night our men stood their ground in the village, and other commanding posts which they had captured in the area, against continuous enemy attacks, which mounted to a supreme effort to recapture the lost area. The mortars and machine-guns barked all through the night. Only after three a.m. did silence set in. Both sides had grown weary of the battle, which had raged for over nine hours.

After Kawkji's Iraqis had rested a little and began to recover from their defeat, they renewed their attacks early in the morning. At nine, the hillocks began to thunder. Enemy reinforcements had managed to reach the spot by mountain paths. Our forces had, in the meantime, been relieved, and the newcomers were ready for this new counter-attack. And by now new plans for fresh attacks had been prepared at the Hagana headquarters. To the north of Mishmar Haemek, hundreds of Iraqi soldiers were stationed in Abu-Shusha, and until they were eliminated victory could not be complete. At 9:30 we observed the first units creeping out of Mishmar Haemek's forests in the direction of that village. Ten minutes later the first few houses in which the enemy troops had fortified themselves were in our hands. I was so close to the battlefield that I could see the men storming the houses, hurling grenades. Through the windows and gaps in the houses the Arabs could be seen running in great disorder towards the houses further inside the village, leaving behind them great quantities of arms. Men of the Hagana pursued them, causing many casualties, and taking a number of prisoners. At 10:30, an hour after the beginning of the assault, the village was completely in the hands of the Hagana. Only a few of the enemy's chickens remained in the burning and ruined remains of the village, the eyes of our field cooks surveying them greedily.

All this time Kawkji himself was on the scene in one of the nearby villages, and kept sending British messengers (neutrals, of course) to the Hagana, with the request to cease fire and make a truce. He invited men of the Hagana to come and meet him in his village, but the reply was that the Hagana preferred to meet him on the battlefield.

His motives were quite clear. His plans to capture Mishmar Haemek by the brute power of his guns had failed. And now he wanted to extricate himself with "honor" from the mess which had involved 2,000 of his men without any results. But even in this he failed.

Menahem Talmi

◆

THE BURMA ROAD

LATRUN. It is the 25th of May, 1948, early in the morning. Down
from the mountains of Jerusalem swoops an unbearable desert wind
hamsin. Thick vapors rise from the forest, while the heights round
about flame and throw up their heat in every direction.

"Some *hamsin* this, eh! I can't remember the like!" somebody
growls to his mate in the courtyard. The latter is running round,
trying to find a momentary patch of shade, and answers while in
full flight: "Nor can I. Dreadful! And by the way, what are they
banging away at so hard over there?"

"Latrun," nods the other decidedly and with a certain dignity
as he turns on the tap, from which cheerfully gushes a jet of cool
splintery water.

"Really?" His comrade stares at him. In such a heat as this . . .
"Poor devils." "Cold water," the first one squirts the balance of
the water out of his mouth, and wipes his lips on his sleeve. "There
are lots of new immigrants there, not much good for a place like
Latrun; and apart from that—the heat! No . . ."

The other takes refuge under a shadow falling from the
triangular roof of a store house. Such a *hamsin*. . . . To have to
fight and run without water, and what's more—when you are new
in this country, and the climate has not yet got into your blood—
the *hamsins* are enough to exhaust anybody and stretch him out.
How can it be possible to fight under such conditions? And Latrun
is no joke. . . . Cold shivers ran up and down his spine as he tried
to imagine for himself that horrible feeling of parched throat,
sweat, heat, weariness and shaky knees. "Dreadful!" he murmured

and went back to the yellow tap, while his ears picked up the echoing explosions reverberating from the Vale of Ayalon.

He drank and continued on his way. And then there was nobody left in the big farmyard except perhaps a shimmering lizard, the only creature in the neighborhood to enjoy that awful *hamsin*. But as the explosions grew louder the lizard felt itself uncomfortable, picked up its feet and cleared off.

At Latrun the fighting was raging in all its savagery. Latrun had to be taken at all costs in order to cut once and for all through the forces encircling Jerusalem. Food and arms had to be brought to the citizens and defenders of Jerusalem, and the city linked organically to Israel—not left suspended in mid air, as if in a vacuum.

On that black, stifling day there still was a certain amount of food supplies in the warehouses and on the shop shelves. There was some water left over from the good days. But both were running out, and there was no place from which to replenish the supply. Weapons were next to non-existent, and those the town had were not adjusted to the needs of this fierce war, the like of which no one had imagined. The heavier types of arms were also very limited. Where were they to come from when the road was cut through the wall-like siege? And, at the same time the Jerusalem fighting was growing more intense and required more and more food, equipment and particularly fresh weapons, in order to fight back and strengthen the defense.

The Arab Legion holding Latrun was well aware of the importance of this spot. They had concentrated powerful forces there, including armor and artillery. They had heavy artillery, numerous and powerful pieces. The foreign officers, English, German, and others kept on reiterating to the Arabs that this spot had to be held whatever might happen. This was the heart of the country, the only hope the Jews had for a stand in Jerusalem, and also the gateway to Ramallah and the Arab triangle. If they could manage to hold out against the attacks of the Yahud, then they would see the fall of the shelled, ruinous, hungry, thirsty and weaponless Jerusalem. For the soldiers of the Israeli Brigade that was now going up against Latrun,—they did not need many explanations.

They went off, prepared for anything and everything.

The *hamsin* sucked like an obstinate leech. They thirsted for a drop of water, for the tiniest patch of shade, for a grain of quiet. Unbelievably vast swarms of sandflies and midges, the infamous *barhash* of the countryside, swarmed in the air and viciously attached themselves to ears, lips and necks.

There was the sound of the shells and the clips and belts of machine-gun bullets. The Brigade was very young. It had been born only a day or two earlier, created amid confusion and in great haste. Real war had been forced on the nation overnight, and there was still a shortage of equipment, arms, training, and the tradition of a regular army. The young Brigade lacked a great deal, and had no water bottles—those simple receptacles containing so many cubic centimeters of fluid, without which it is impossible to fight for long, and in the absence of which the body refuses to make an effort.

The thirst had its effect before long. The midges and sand flies, enemy number Two, allowed no respite. They were worse than the whining bullets. The enemy had astoundingly accurate ordnance and firing tables, with the aid of which he controlled every peak, cranny and hollow. No strength or intelligence was required to train the shell-spitters upon the heart and the hidden places of the assailants. And it was already a hot day and fully light. It was much too late. The advance was far more slow than had been provided for in the operational plan. The enemy's strength was greater and his weapons more numerous than had been estimated. It would be impossible to deal him a severe blow under these circumstances.

In the distance rose the Police Station, while the black asphalt road gleamed—the artery communicating with besieged Jerusalem, the one link needed for the liberation of the city. But the wounded, the exhausted and the faint were too many. There was no sense in going on.

The withdrawal began. Fire was unexpectedly opened on the retreating men from the Beit Susin flank. There was reason to apprehend outflanking, and a tiny panic began to filter through the whole withdrawal operation. The rear-guard, whose job it was to cover the withdrawal, stood firm and held up the enemy, literally with their bodies, in order that their comrades might reach a safe spot. No small number of them were obliterated, but it was thanks to their devotion that the rest managed to get back to the base by the skin of their teeth.

The Jerusalem highway shimmered indifferently in the light of the dying rays of the sun. It was not ours and nothing went hastening along it to bring salvation to besieged Jerusalem. The two camps rested quietly licking their wounds, wounds gained in a battle which had ended in a draw. Yet the effort and suffering had not been in vain. The enemy's broadcasting instruments at Latrun were working at full strength, crying aloud for "reinforcements!" They reported great numbers of Jews endeavoring to take Latrun, and the vast amount of arms in their possession. Send help and reinforcements quickly, they demanded again and again.

That same night reinforcements began to stream down to Latrun from Ramallah and Jerusalem. The latter city breathed rather more freely for a little while.

Darkness was already descending on the besieged city. There was no light to turn on, because fuel reserves had been used up. Occasional, isolated shells burst in the streets. Brilliant rockets flew on high. The soldiers stood at their posts, morosely silent. There were no shells with which to return the heavy fire. The flour was giving out. A cigarette was something in a rosy dream, and the food rations had become astonishingly poor.

"What will the end be?" wondered the inhabitants concealed in their shelters. In the south Egyptians invaded, in the north were the Syrians, while in the center the other Arab armies were busy. It was beyond the power of the youthful army, which had only just come into being, to allocate manpower and fire-power sufficient for those going up against Latrun for the sake of Jerusalem.

The Dale of Ayalon seethed and fumed, gleaming with lights and flames. Machine-gun bullets by the tens of thousands were dashing about, thrusting at the earth on the hills and the rocks; some phosphorescent and gleaming, some invisible and whistling. And the enemy fought back. Once more their summons for aid went speeding across space on the waves of the ether, cries of fear exaggerating the number and strength of the Jews coming up against them.

This time they fought at very close range. The armored cars proceeded to the police fort, stopped facing it and belched forth their fire. Brave lads with bottles humped on their backs also crouched near the building and spat fire through nozzles at the fortress and its windows. It seemed as though Latrun were about to fall into our hands. It seemed that the moment was not far distant when the siege of Jerusalem would be lifted! But the new, weary infantry was only a glimmer of strength against the enemy, and had to retreat.

One armored car was still untouched; it continued firing furiously in order to provide cover for those withdrawing. Within it was a quiet, brave girl wireless operator, communicating with the rear, with her headquarters. Until the very last moment her mouth was at the transmitter, while she reported on the gradually declining fight, on the fire and position of the enemy, as far as she could see through the narrow slot of the loophole. Her voice was clear and calm, and it was impossible to realize from it that her moments must be numbered. All round her flamed the armored cars, while the dance of death was in full swing. And now a tongue of fire leapt and seized the car.

"Hallo, hallo, there," she said in her clear voice. "My car is on fire. . . . Direct your shells more to the right, more to the right. . . . Is that clear? Over."

"Hallo Leah."

All of a sudden a pillar of smoke mounted upwards as the car blew up to bits. A twenty-five pound shell had descended plump upon it destroying every trace of the vehicle.

The voice of the girl ceased to come over the wireless at headquarters.

Latrun was not taken. The siege was not lifted. In Jerusalem the fight went on under unbearably difficult conditions.

The road to Jerusalem was closed. Nobody could enter the city or leave it. Bab el Wad, the pass into the Mountains of Judea, was still No Man's Land. The lofty eucalyptuses on the road nearby did not know as yet before whom they had to bow—whether to us or to our foe.

One Palmach lad, stout and tousle-haired, had to get to his home down in the Lowland, the Shefela. He simply had to get there. Even his Commanding Officer recognized the urgent necessity, in spite of the difficult situation on the Jerusalem fronts, and although every fighter was worth his weight in gold; certainly a chap like this one, gifted, brave, active and experienced, would be missed. But he had to go. It really was absolutely necessary. "Well," said the commander. "You have a week at your disposal. Let's hope that a convoy arrives and you're able to leave. That's all. Good luck, lad."

Days passed and no convoy arrived. Where could it come from? His mood became sour, and the Palmach resourcefulness began to create something out of nothing. He had to get there, and that was all there was to it!

He was properly versed in the tracks and trails that lay to the south of Latrun. Long before, during the long survey hikes, he and his companions used to follow them regularly, and by day and night alike. Yes, he could well remember every trail, every tuft of weed, the wells and the terraces. That was an idea! To follow those paths, to move along them in the dark and to arrive!

Next day he reported to his commander.

"I'm off."

"What!"

"I'm going, I say."

"How?"

"On foot, towards Hulda."

"Wha—at!"

"On foot, and by night."

"Have you gone crazy?"

"Maybe."

"Listen. You know, it's not such a bad idea. . . ."

The dialogue continued for about ten minutes, and ended like this:

"Well, good. Depart in peace. But remember! You never asked

me! All the responsibility falls on you. So be careful, and good luck!"

When he went out, the officer scratched his back and moaned in admiration from his very heart. "Oh those Palmachniks!" The thought indicated his powerful affection for those dear and courageous boys, whom nothing could stop.

This particular lad was both courageous and shrewd. He found two others who were prepared to set out with him on that unprecedented adventure.

When the dark fell they left Kiriat Anavim, accompanied by some private arms in the shape of a German rifle, a sten, a pistol and a number of grenades. They got a lift as far as the pumping station closest to Bab el Wad. Comrades there shook their heads at them and did their best to dissuade them from this "ill-considered and irresponsible step"; but when they saw that there was no changing the minds of the three, they gave them some more ammunition grenades and good sound Palmach wishes.

That night the moon chose to ride on high at the very peak of the heavens, and it shed its pale whitish-blue light everywhere. Casual shots went whining through the air, thoughtfully tracing their course. It was hard going through the woods on the southern slopes, but that did not tire these lads, who were long used to such difficult jobs. The only annoying thing was the moon—what shameless, impudent brightness!

After ten minutes' careful walking through the thick woods, they were chased by shots from Arab Legion patrols wandering about. They spent three hours crouching behind a huge rock.

The Arabs began to get tired of simply shooting off their rounds into empty space. So they stopped and went their way.

The three lads got up and went on, very carefully slipping through Hartuv. From time to time they hurriedly concealed themselves, lit the tiny flashlamp they had with them, and worked out the road on the map. Then, onwards once again.

The moon gradually sank and a dew-filled gloom settled. Suddenly dogs began barking. The three fellows saw houses rising before them, and heard people talking at the top of their voices. Talking Arabic.

One last rapid and energetic piece of crawling, and they were swallowed up in a sea of tall grain-plants, all three of them. The plants were moist and silent. In a little while the sun would be coming up. The very first before-dawn gusts of breeze were beginning to stir in surprise. It was already possible to see Hulda, with its forest on the height. They crouched down again in the standing corn and waited till it was broad daylight, for fear of our own minefields and snipers. Day quickly dawned. Through the gate of Hulda entered the three; tousled, weary and drenched with dust-covered dew.

They passed between the huts and cow-sheds. Nobody paid them any attention. They were just another three dirty lads who had turned up. They went and got hold of the local commander, a silent taciturn fellow, and he hurried them along to the wireless room.

"Hallo Korah one, hallo Korah one, here's a spark to Pessel two. Pessel two—over."

The wireless girl at the Jerusalem Mountains Headquarters crouched over the table, and without any great pleasure took up the earphones which had begun buzzing and thundering in her ears. With the stub end of a yellow pencil she began scribbling letters on the piece of squared graph-paper before her. She flicked the pencil to one side, spoke into the loud-speaker, and took off her earphones again.

"Listen, send the spark on to R. It's urgent. Somebody has got through to Hulda. Where from? I don't know, but that's what they call urgent." She shrugged her shoulders: "Let them have it their way. . . ."

* * *

Evening descended. The gloomy shadows lurked and spread from the distant mountains of Jerusalem, while the last sparkles of pale silences still quivered below in the plain. There were ten jeeps lined up in the open space, waiting with their drivers whose dusty goggles clung firmly to their hair. In the jeeps were dismantled guns, with sealed boxes in which were worn and rusty shells.

Lukash spat out the glowing stub of his cigarette and felt the slender length of the sleeping cannon.

"Guns, shells," he said to nobody in particular, gazing proudly at the four cases strapped and chained to the car. "Eh, the blighters! d'y' know w't 'sload means, what a trip it'll be and the tears in the eyes of the Jerusalemites when they see what the Palmach toughs are bringing 'em? A barber up in Jerusalem, says to me, 'Just take a look, Lukash, they're giving us a hundred and fifty grams of bread a day. Is that a ration? For all our enemies. . . . That's a joke, eh? But give less, give us a hundred, I say, as long as you fetch cannons and shells!' And just imagine! We're bringing them the goods. It's tremendous!"

The bell began ringing hoarsely.

"Let's go and eat, eh?"

"And how. I'll tackle three pounds of salad and stow it away. Up in Jerusalem we'll be eating rocks and shrapnel."

"And the dust on the way—that's a bitch!"

After that it was absolutely dark, in which the ten-jeep columns grumbled as though they knew what was in store for them that night. The drivers sat impatiently at the wheels, vibrating slightly to the throbbing of the stationary engines. The three officers walked round talking together in whispers, or from time to time inspecting the loads as they had already done a dozen times or more during the past hour.

Finally, they started out with all the bustle of a first trip, leaving behind them a pillar of dust in the courtyard. The track led to Beit Jiz. Behind the rounded humps of the eroded hills concealing the Latrun area thudded and echoed the sound of choked explosions, while distant sprays of machine-gun bullets dashed by like chariots.

From time to time the skies were rent by the sudden light of rockets, that dallied and then melted to nothing.

"Oho, what's that?" shouted somebody above the noise of the engines.

"A brigade . . . going up to Latrun."

"Whaddya say? That's a grand cover for us."

On the rise to the right, crouched Beit Jiz, silent and tense. Hoarse-voiced dogs barked desperately, but were not heard because of the thrumming of the angry engines going down from a real track to a very doubtful one.

"Space out between the jeeps! Put in your specials! Everything O. K.? Forward!"

One turn of the wheel forward and back brought the jeeps onto a donkey-track in the thick darkness. At first the eyes strained wide-open in effort, seeing only darkness and vague shadows which were nothing at all. Each moment brought the night column closer to No Man's Land, with all that was concealed within its midst.

The shakings were violent. The boxes of shells and cannon parts moaned behind them, grumbling softly, steadily, over the sudden lurchings and deep blacknesses.

In the race that followed between the dawn and the jeeps, it was the jeeps that won. Before daylight emerged, they had been swallowed up in the courtyard of the settlement, dusty, weary and prepared for the next day. The shells and cannon they were transporting were covered over with tarpaulins and all awaited the coming night. They waited for Jerusalem, and Jerusalem waited for them.

Another day passed and the world was deep in silence. The jeeps, the cannon and the shells waited in the corners of the courtyard while the weary drivers snored and sweated in broiling huts from which the heat had not yet departed. Here the cannon and the shells waited idly. Jerusalem hungered for them, ceaselessly shelled as she was and without the wherewithal to strike a single blow at the positions of the enemy.

Commander E. and his friend renounced their afternoon rest. From noon on they went surveying and inspecting the tracks and trails below Beit Jiz, all the way to Beit Susin and onwards. They were dog-tired after the previous night, and scratched and bruised all over. But the route became more and more clear to them as they went. They now knew where it was possible to pass with jeeps, and the places from which they had to steer clear.

*   *   *

Jerusalem still slept its nightmarish, restless sleep. Enemy guns were pouring their vast weight of shells, noise and destruction. The streets, frozen under the wing of fear, shook every time a shell hit, to be followed by the howling of shattered window-panes, falling plaster and dust in the gloomy alleys.

A child in a shelter woke up as a shell landed in the next street.

"Daddy!" he howled, "I'm afraid!"

The weary father, whose face was covered with beard-bristles, groped in the dark and hugged the child.

"Hush. . . . Don't be afraid," he said, shivering in the chilly dawn.

"Why haven't we any cannon, daddy?" asked the child, breathing his father's smell deep into himself.

"We'll have them, sonny, we'll have them tomorrow. Now go to sleep."

"And who is going to bring them?"

"Who? Why, the Palmach, sonny, the Palmach."

"Who are the Palmach, daddy? Are they the ones with the hats like the special police, and with beards round their faces?"

"Yes," smiled the weary father.

"And they will really and truly bring us cannons?"

"They'll bring them," he said. "They'll bring them tomorrow. Now just turn over and go to sleep."

And that tired Jerusalem father who longed to sleep did not have the least idea that he was telling the truth, and that his words were in the nature of a prophecy that had already been fulfilled. The child fell tranquilly asleep. Beyond the emplacements of the enemy guns the dawn broke, red and hesitant, as though ashamed of having left the world to the night and its horrors. Two shells fell and burst; a dreadful pillar of smoke leaped straight aloft and the cries of women and children mounted on high. Two seconds later a couple of armored ambulances passed at top speed.

"It's here! To the right!" a shaken man with bewildered soul and tousled hair wearing pajamas shouted to them, pointing with a trembling and hopeless finger.

At that very moment they were unloading the cannon and cases of shells from the dust-covered jeeps. The first cannon for Jewish Jerusalem.

People watching from the pavements found their eyes brimming

with tears; in their expression was compressed all the pain, suffering and fury of the hard months that had passed.

"Cannon, cannon . . ." they said quietly and affectionately to the
others, the brave and daring fellows who had brought them.

"Tomorrow night we shall bring more," the lads answered
smiling, and went on undoing the chains and straps.

A division which had not yet rested after Latrun went up and
took Beit Jiz. A day later it took Beit Susin. Fresh strongholds were
put up for the Army of Israel, points which promised security on the
flank, and also a frontal advance.

The men looked glumly at the hills concealing Latrun, the spot
where blood had been shed and strength expended. They looked
longingly and yearningly towards the more distant Bab el Wad,
of which the treetops could be seen on the hillsides. Several times
a day a half-tractor, colored brown, made its way with difficulty to
these parts. But not to Beit Susin, a spot to be reached only on all
fours—a difficult and inconvenient method.

Up from the coastal plain came a yellow bulldozer, a huge-
bodied thing which had a healthy contempt for hillocks and rocks
and slopes. And pretty soon it had managed to level out and effect
some kind of improvement in the path leading from the Latrun-
Masmieh road to Beit Jiz.

Nobody could have told you exactly who the fellow was who
had thought out the wonderful and daring idea which they immediately began executing—namely, to leave the highroad alone
for the moment, and to break the siege from this spot, from Beit
Susin, across the neglected No Man's Land to Bab el Wad, which
was already ours by that time.

A beginning was made with thorough-going surveys. On the
Beit Susin slope lay a green garden, a quiet spot. And since it
had been planted on the slope it consisted of terraces above
terraces, all covered with green. A forsaken spot it was, that garden,
and nobody ever as much as looked at it. The Brigadier came down
to take a look while his staff waited for him up above. He spent
a long time down there, while his brain worked out the plan. When
he came back, puffing and blowing, he said: "This is where the
road will run."

"How can it? And how about those accursed terraces?"

"This is where the road will run," he repeated. "And we shall be in Jerusalem before a week has passed. We shall be there, I tell you! Send us the bulldozer. I'll show you how."

Then the tractor-drivers slapped the huge machine on its shanks and said: "To work, baby. There's going to be a road here. We've said it!"

With them were about a dozen hard workers, and within a week they had reached the top of the height which runs steeply down to Bab el Wad, towards the Hartuv road. In less than a week!

From this point forward, at the section which is now called the "Fork" or the "Castel" (after the other steep patch on the old road to Jerusalem further along) and which is about three hundred-odd yards long, the real difficulty began; the problem was as high as a great wall. No car could climb up or climb down here. The stretch was too steep and rocky, and there were too many deep crevasses in it.

The Brigadier, dead weary after sleepless nights, needed a few hours of rest. Before going off he ordered the chief engineer of the brigade to survey the road and prepare the plan. And off he went.

It seemed to him that he had barely fallen asleep when a hand shook him by the shoulder.

He opened his eyes in annoyance. Over him leaned the chief engineer with knitted brows, shaking his head.

"What's the matter?"

"No. Can't be done. In any case, not there."

"That's the only place," growled the Brigadier, controlling his anger.

The engineer shrugged his shoulders.

"That is where the road will pass, I said!" he trembled with anger, while the sleep left his eyes, "Yes, there."

He jumped up from the mattress and dashed to a jeep: "Come along and I'll show you!" he growled drily to all concerned.

Reaching the fork, he took them along and began to descend the hillside. He placed stones at certain distances, marked certain curves and said: "Here, like this. A curve here and another strip here." And he bent down again and put a stone in place.

One of the group thought to himself: "Gone moonstruck."

"The road will run here!" That was the slogan, that was the order. "Here and nowhere else!" That stopped all argument, and it was the signal to start at once. And so it was. Thenceforth everything went at top speed. Strong-points covering the planned road were taken, another giant tractor was brought up from the coastal plain, and experienced rock-hewers and road-makers were brought down from Jerusalem. They worked at fever pitch. Far more difficulties than had been foreseen suddenly appeared. Sometimes the workers would lose heart and they would slacken for a moment; however, the Brigadier did not leave the section for a single instant.

The enemy encamped nearby sensed the activity, saw the pillars of dust rising after blowing up the obstinate rocks. They did not guess anything, but still they began to concentate forces at this spot. The first shells dropped in the area, hesitantly and speculatively. The road-layers and rock-hewers grew really frightened. They were afraid to work under this hail of death-dealing metal. They tried to get away, to slip off elsewhere. But the very presence of the Brigadier forbade it.

One of the great hours arrived. The huge caterpillar tractor was to tamp the road down as far as the hill. The hill was in full view of the enemy, who could easily train their artillery on it. The tractor drivers, who had already spent several days on the spot, were well aware of the danger. The order was given to them somewhat doubtfully and hesitantly. They silently mounted their seats without a sign of hesitancy or doubt. They pressed down the throttle to the last notch, their lips set firmly, and the machine started moving ahead. The shovel in front went cutting into the hard rocky soil. Behind the tractor the road slipped away. The first bed had been laid down. Shells fell soon enough. The tractor continued to forge ahead. It reached the hill, moved there a few moments for all to see, clear within the range of the Arab artillery —yet nobody was hit! Then it came down into the slope once again with a dust mantle over it.

The enemy, who had become thoroughly alarmed at what must be happening out of his sight in this area, sent out patrols to find out what was going on. While the workers were toiling night and day, bitter pitched battles were fought, with heavy losses on both sides; but the attacks were broken. The work of opening up the new relief artery to Jerusalem was not interrupted for a single instant.

As yet they did not trust this new road. They could not wait until it had been properly laid and completed. Jerusalem was on the verge of starvation. It cried for food and weapons.

Work went on feverishly along the Palmach road which lay below the future "Burma Road." Jeeps brought their precious loads by night to the point where the track was no longer suitable for wheels. Then the men loaded it on their backs and humped it across the stretch to the cars that were waiting on the other side.

And that night they had to transport flour, food, weapons and herds of cattle. Hundreds of men, mules and their drivers, camels and jeeps transferred about fifty tons that night! And all this was done secretly.

*   *   *

The spearhead platoon descended to the valley and patrolled it; it was quiet and in order. The commandant got into his jeep and slipped down—the first jeep whose tires licked that new road, though as yet it was impossible to climb up. The bulldozers went on. The second to come down was a taxi.

"I said that the road would pass here!" said the Brigadier gleefully. "And here it is!"

And at the same time they were feverishly laying water-pipes, one end of which was open aloft while the other pointed open below. Tanks loaded with fuel came from the plain and poured the fluid into the opening, while the Jerusalem tankers waiting below swallowed up the precious liquid and dashed away with it to Jerusalem.

In another day the "Burma Road" was open. People stopped carrying loads on their shoulders, but passed up and down that steep and dangerous stretch where nobody had believed anything could be done. The siege had been broken.

Jerusalem was linked to the rest of Israel through the "Burma Road."

14 SCROLLS OF FIRE

NOAM GROSSMAN, son of Reuven Avinoam, was born in Brooklyn on April 8, 1927 and was brought to Palestine when he was two and a half years old. As a student at the Hebrew University, Noam excelled in historical criticism. He was killed while leading a sortie in the Judean hills on March 4, 1948. His will stated:

"To be opened after my death.

"LAST WILL AND TESTAMENT

"This will is written in haste without time to say goodbye.

1. Bury me in the Nahlath Itzhak cemetery in Tel-Aviv.

2. Do not print any tributes to me in the newspapers.

3. My salary and the money due me is to be turned over to my family to establish a fund with which to buy rifles for the Haganah.

4. My personal effects are to be forwarded to my family.

5. Do not mourn for me. I did only that which I was called upon to do."

In memory of his son, the father changed the family name from Grossman to Avinoam (Father of Noam). Soon the father published a small volume commemorating his son. It included a few poems by Mr. Avinoam, who is an outstanding Hebrew poet. The first of these poems opens with the words: "For all these, we thank Thee, God!" (For the years the parents had the joy of their son, for his heroic end, and for the mourning.)

Most of the volume consists of the writings left by Noam; essays, letters, and diaries.

Many such volumes were published in Israel after the War of Liberation—by parents, brothers, comrades and persons on the collective farms to which the deceased had belonged.

In time Mr. Ben-Gurion, as Minister of Defense, charged Mr. Avinoam to collect all available documents and to publish a series of volumes. Mr. Avinoam was then taken from the Ministry of Education, where he served as school inspector and put in charge of a special department created at the Ministry of Defense for the Commemoration of the Fallen Soldier.

The first volume of the Scrolls of Fire was published in 1952.

SKETCHES OF SOME FALLEN HEROES

HANNAH WAS born to Menashe and Naomi Avrech on April 7, 1929, in Givton, a *moshav* (smallholders' co-operative village) on the coastal plain. Brought up in a home of hardworking pioneers of the soil whose atmosphere was to determine the course of her life, she completed the local labor school and went on to study agriculture in the Girl's Agriculture School at Ayanot. While there, Hannah was active in the immigrant camps and among her fellow-students who were recent immigrants. She was among the founders of a students' pioneer group at Ayanot with a view of establishing a new kibbutz.

In a letter to her sister, dated May 5, 1944, Hannah wrote:

"What are the foundations of society? Mutual help, solidarity, equality, comradeship. We came here to carry on the pioneer tradition. We want to start a large project of our own."

The kibbutz nucleus which Hannah helped to found received its preliminary training at Ma'oz, after which it joined the new kibbutz at Bet Ha'arava, near the Dead Sea, where Hannah distinguished herself. The kibbutz is a constituent of Kibbutz Hameuhad, a federation of Mapam settlements. There she met Yehuda Solomon and the two fell in love.

Yehuda, son of Zeev and Shalomit Solomon, of a family of old Zionists and Hebraists, was born in Berlin on February 20, 1928. In 1933 the family migrated to Palestine where Yehuda received his education at the Balfour elementary and secondary school in Tel Aviv. Despite the progress he made at school, he cut short his academic career and took up manual labor to meet the needs of the country's upbuilding. He apprenticed himself to a plumber, continued his academic education through evening courses, and became a member of the Trade Section of the Working Youth Organization and of the Hagana in Tel Aviv.

At seventeen, he enlisted in the Palmach, the shock brigade of the Hagana, where he gained distinction as an instructor and later as the commander of a unit. He was completely dedicated to the twin ideals of agricultural work and defense which animated the Palmach. His group was assigned to the kibbutzim of Tel-Joseph, Ma'oz Hayim and Bet Hashitta for training on the farm and for military exercises, and later, at Bet Ha'aravah, he joined the kibbutz nucleus to which Hannah Avrech belonged, but his military duties kept him from active participation in the farm life of the kibbutz, and away from the settlement much of the time.

In 1947 Hannah wrote to him from the kibbutz:

"I am well, but I miss you very much. Some evenings here are so lovely and the scenery is so glorious that my heart simply breaks. I am so happy that both of us decided to join the kibbutz. I am now at peace with myself for having told you all about my fears and misgivings in connection with this undertaking. I am sure that together we shall be able to overcome many obstacles. . . . You know, I had planned for the two of us to read many books together and to exchange impressions. But, since this is now impossible, I shall have to do it alone. . . . I love so much to work in the tree nursery. I love every kind of agricultural work. . . . What a pity I did not study music! I am going to have my children take up music no matter what!"

On April 3, 1948, Yehuda took time from battle to write to Hannah:

"Every letter from you makes me so very happy that I cannot find words to express my feelings. . . . Here, on the one hand, a letter arrives from your sweetheart far away. . . . Do you know, my darling, what this means these days? We have been visited again by tragic bloody days. We all move around here like shadows, waiting impatiently for the day when we can leave this place and begin carrying out the difficult responsibility placed on our shoulders. We just haven't any more patience to wait. Last week we lost many dear comrades and even now our men are engaged in a life-and-death struggle for the Jewish communications with Jerusalem.

"Yesterday I received a letter from home. How much strength our parents need to encourage their children in the front lines! Sometimes, my dear, I think they have more courage than we have. Not a trace of worry or concern in that letter! I can well imagine the tears they shed quietly! I can see them biting their lips to hold back their loud and bitter wail of parents who at any moment are likely to lose a son or a daughter. . . ."

When the exposed settlement of Bet Ha'aravah, besieged by the Arab Legion, had to be abandoned, Hannah was among those who moved to Sdom, there to continue the struggle for a Jewish hold on the Dead Sea. It was during that period that her fiance fell in battle, but her stout spirit enabled her to withstand the deep shock. From Sdom, in a letter dated May 31, 1948, she wrote home to her parents: "It is so hard to write, for the pain in my heart is still great and my soul still weeps over the misfortune that has befallen us.

"Did you hear? Our dear Yehuda fell. It happened on May 15, in the battle for Malkiyeh in the Galilee. There were many casualties in that battle, and fate has stricken us, too. I still don't know the details, but of one thing I am certain—that Yehuda died like a hero, and that he knew what he went for and to what he had dedicated his strength and his energy. He was always ready for what was to befall him, and I am sure that his last request was for us to be of good strength and to be able to bear up.

"Oh, my dear parents, the loss falls heavy upon all of us, but doubly so upon me—and I have one request to make of you: Be strong and don't weep much. He was one of the many and the part he performed imposes the duty upon us to continue in his steps. Be of good strength! This is what your daughter is asking of you, whose fiance it was that has fallen. If I know that you bear up, I shall find it much easier to go on living."

Yehuda Solomon had gone through an officers' training course at Nathanya and had been commissioned to command a unit in the Galilee which was to capture the former British military camp near Malkiyeh, as part of a larger action to safeguard the northern gateway of the country. After gaining control of the camp, he was distributing his men to defend the various sections when he was hit in the head by a bullet. He barely managed to appoint another commander to take his place before he died. This was on May 15, 1948.

Hannah, after a long period under siege in Sdom, was granted a month's vacation. On July 18, 1948, when the airplane in which she left Sdom was attacked by the enemy, five passengers were killed in the forced landing, and Hannah was among them.

*   *   *

Raphael Oren (Orenstein) was born in Haifa on November 21, 1928, to Moshe and Blanch Orenstein and received his education at the local public school, in the Children's Village, Ben-Shemen, and at the TITZ Trade School at Yagur. A member of Hashomer Hatzair, he joined the pioneering youth group of Hassela (The Rock), which underwent preparatory training for kibbutz life at Yehiam. Raphael participated there in agricultural and cultural activities. During the War of Liberation, he took part in the defense of Yehiam and fell in the famous convoy of the forty-seven soldiers. He tried to make his escape after he was wounded, but died as he reached his car.

Early in the summer of 1944, at the age of fifteen, he wrote in his diary:

"The test of one's love for the Land of Israel and of one's devotion to the Zionist idea is the readiness to give one's life without turning back.

"Why am I going to a kibbutz? There are several motives:

"The Zionist idea: preparing places of refuge for our brethren in the Diaspora, reversing our abnormal economic pyramid and building an intensive agricultural economy for the large masses of our people; the idea that the more land, the more settlements and the largest possible number of Jewish farmers who will never be detached from their soil—the greater our strength and our weight, and there is no other way!

"The socialist ideal: that the kibbutz is the only place in which a human being can live according to socialist principles—being neither master nor slave and not living at the expense of others and not allowing parasites to suck his blood."

Entry in the diary on November 11, 1944, describing a pilgrimage to Massada, the fortress on the Dead Sea where the last garrison of the rebels against Rome entrenched itself after the crushing of the rebellion:

"A long winding convoy went out over those narrow paths that Friday morning in December, as from the west, Jerusalem in its whiteness looked down upon us from its perch in the midst of the Judean hills enclosing it, and behind us, from the north, lay the green oasis of Jericho in the sandy desert, and Mount Nebo lay to the east crowned by the greying mists of the morning, the smoke of the furnaces of the potash works curling up in thin spirals, and the Dead Sea lying silent in its smooth blue waters cut in twain by the golden path formed by the rays of the burning sun. We marched in the middle, as if imprisoned among the giant mountain chains which closed in on us on all sides—the serene Dead Sea and the salty barren soil, so characteristic of this area, so peculiar to it.

"All around me my eyes beheld the places which were trodden many times by the feet of my ancestors. . . . It is only on such occasions that your heart is flooded with a beautiful and sublime feeling of love for this land, which for countless generations has absorbed the blood and the sweat of our ancient people in the days of antiquity, their joys and sorrows, their lives and their deaths . . . and then you know that for that very reason this land is sacred to you, precious and near. . . . A similar feeling seizes me all over again and fills my being with even greater strength when my feet stand on the top of Massada and I gaze on the yawning abysses below which surround the fortress on all four sides, and I see the squares of the Roman camps and the large battery which they mounted on the western side, and the ruins of the warehouses and granaries and palaces which survived here on high, the silent witnesses to the banner of revolt which was raised here when the whole country was trodden under foot by the Roman centurions. Then you feel that to us Massada is more than just a fortress, that it serves as a monument and a symbol of self-sacrifice, without scruples, without reservations, to the very end. . . . "

March 3, 1945, at the age of seventeen:

"It seems to be my preordained fate to listen to the same refrain from my mother: 'I hope and pray that you will continue with your studies as seriously as you have until now. My heart tells me you will grow up to be a great man that any mother can be proud of. . . . You are under the influence of some of your friends who lack the ability or the desire for studying. Don't ever let strangers influence you. You are old enough and your family will show you the right way in life, for it is only we who are loyal and devoted to you. Your friends, as they call themselves, are likely to be your most dangerous enemies.'

"Now, what can I say? My feelings are a mixture of amazement, anger and pain. Amazement and anger because of the ignorance and the indifference shown on the subject of our pioneering Zionist effort; pain because it is my lot to be an open bleeding wound in my mother's bleeding heart.

"This denial of our national ideals comes from alien notions fostered in the cafes and in the fashionable drawing rooms of our growing homeland."

August 17, 1947:

"Again we missed the bus. We always miss it. Ten years ago we could have bought plenty of land, but had no money for it. There still existed then a rich Jewish community in Europe, but its immense wealth computed in astronomical figures has now been taken over by the Nazis. There was a time, not so long ago, when the gates of our land were open, but no one came except a handful of pioneers. Now, only now, after having escaped the hell-fire, many hundreds are knocking at our gates, but the gates are locked. Still, all is not lost yet. Whatever has been created in this country is a healthy nucleus with a good promise for the future, if only it is allowed to develop. . . .

"We have a large and wealthy Jewish Diaspora such as we have never had in our history—the Jewry of America! If only it had the inspiration, if only it understood the seriousness of the moment, if it only realized how great is the historic responsibility that destiny has placed upon it! . . . The Jews of America are the foundation, they are the bricks of the walls. Without them the seed will wither

SKETCHES OF SOME FALLEN HEROES

and die, and the foundation stone will remain nothing but a monument to heroism and the grave of a people that has dragged its way through three thousand years of history, suffered all the tortures of hell, drenched every land with its blood, but when given its last chance to build its home, it betrayed itself. Someone said, 'A people that does not seek liberation does not deserve it.'

". . . If this people of whom you are supposed to be the vanguard does not want to be liberated, if it is not ready to do any more than salve its Jewish conscience by throwing to that vanguard a few crumbs from its rich table—why should you be a fool and throw away your life, your comforts—all for the sake of those who do not want it, who find it more convenient to applaud you from a distance, at least to praise you and to admire your pioneering spirit—and at the same time to make a mockery of your efforts by leaving you as an isolated vanguard without an army in its rear?

"Fine, you philanthropic gentlemen, your resentment is aroused; fine, you good Jews of the United States and England and South Africa and of the other rich communities. Sure, you are smarter then I am! You have granted me the privilege of playing Don Quixote, while you have chosen the solid ground like Sancho Panza. You are practical people, you prefer the fleshpots, even when it comes with hatred of Jews and insults; you prefer them to the uncertain prospects somewhere on the rim of the desert, where wild Bedouins and murderous terrorists swarm. . . .

"Then what am I doing here? . . . Let me, at least, save what can still be saved of my own life and go where I can enjoy the pleasures of life while they last. . . .

"So Massada is just a fairy tale. Why should I allow myself to be ensnared by it? . . .

"But no, I cannot. Again and again I pass through the crucible of trials, through the consuming fire of despair, and, in the end, I come out strengthened in my faith. More than ever I cling to the Brenner motto of *Nonetheless,* despite the gloomy reality and just because of it, we cannot permit treason to dominate us. We cannot flee from the battlefield. . . . "

Dorothy Bar-Adon

◆

THE CACTUS PEAR

ONE OF OUR close neighbors is a doctor from Poland, not long in Israel. Recently he visited us to tell us this story about our nine-year-old son. The child was chasing a donkey and, spying the doctor in a strategic position shouted to him in a hurried and imperative tone: "Naphtali, catch that donkey!" While the doctor stood rooted to the spot, the child flew past him shouting over his shoulder, "Naphtali, ata shav? What good are you?"

Naphtali is more the point of this story than the child. He came to report the incident with a twinkle in his eye and obvious relish. He is just beginning not to be shocked when a child addresses him as "Naphtali" and informally tells him to chase a donkey. He considers this a definite progress in his adjustment to Israel. He is beginning to take the Sabra as he is—and is pleased with himself. He's still convinced (nor are most of us) that a little more expressed respect to their elders and betters might be in place. But he's decided to take them as they are and enjoy them. And that's a sensible approach. For whatever circumstances or accumulation of circumstances have created the "sabra," he's here as a positive type—and he's definitely not of the "Yes sir; thank you ma'am" variety.

It is well-known that the Sabra is a cactus with a prickly surface and soft inside. Arthur Koestler in his "Thieves in the Night" pigeon-holed him as "Tarzan" and illustrated him with the story of the boy who returned his Bar Mitzvah fountain pen to his father when he finished school because he would not need it anymore. This "Tarzan" was a good catch-phrase but an over-simplification. While the prickly exterior of the Sabra is now es-

tablished, he still has surprises for his parents and even for his
sweetheart. As an example of this: how many times have we
heard in this last year, "You should read the letters that that
'Laitzan' (clown) left. We just never believed he had it in him."
They referred to teen-age Sabras who died in service, leaving behind letters, diaries, poems, which will, in time, doubtless prove
to be the literature of this Israel war. At the moment they are still
going the rounds, in scribbled form, among relatives and close
friends who, as well as they might have known Haim or Moshka
as lovable "laitzan" are shaken by a depth of perception they had
scarely imagined.

Aside from these unknown Sabras who used their fountain pens
after they finished school, there are the known ones who are now
beginning to be heard. Two of the most talked-of plays last season
and this season, both with a local background, were the work of
Sabras—"He Walked Through the Fields," adapted from the book
by Shamir and the present Habimah production on the Negev by
a member of Kibbutz Naan, Yigal Mossinsohn. A most refreshing
upshoot in our theatre world is the Chamber Theatre which is
practically an all-Sabra project. In their short existence, they have
a knack for choosing good things, even if they're dated, such as
"You Can't Take It With You," which in Hebrew retained much
of its sparkle.

When you consider that, since that shot was fired in Jaffa on
a Saturday morning in April, 1936, disturbances and war have just
folded into each other here—no Sabra in his teens can remember
very much about normal, peaceful times. Yet, there was never a
depressed "pogrom" atmosphere here, but always the exhilarating
march toward ultimate freedom. So it is not all paradoxical that
joy and zest for living should be the keynote of the Sabra. He likes
sports and when things were at their worst here, we were always
amused to hear the radio reports of swimming matches and basket-
ball games. He likes folk dancing (ballroom dancing is reserved
for the towns and still not characteristic of the Sabra). He does the
round dances in costume at festivals and has no inhibitions (not yet,
anyhow) about being thought a "sissy." On the other hand to "hit-
gander" (preen yourself) is a mortal crime. You may be a "gandran"

in your language, if you use too many high-brow words. That is
very bad. But it may be added that in their own quiet way, even
in the rural settlements, the girls are "gandranuth"—they don't
paint, powder or lacquer their finger nails (except in town and
then not at all in their teens) but even a kerchief and a blouse are
worn often with that certain something.

The Sabra likes anything on wheels—he likes to thumb his
way—he likes "patentim" (little inventions) of all kinds—and he
has a resounding sense of humor and sense of fun. A friend of
ours is still chuckling over this one—although he was the butt.
One dark night, he was participating in an unloading action—unloading refugees from a ship anchored near the shore, and carrying
them to shore. In the pitch dark, a hefty refugee climbed on his
back and Haim began to plow shoreward through the cold water.
Then, addressing the refugee in Yiddish, he told him comfortingly
"not to worry" and how "everything will be all right when you
reach Israel"—in fact, they say that it was almost a Zionist speech.
When they reached shore, the "refugee" hopped off, said the
Hebrew equivalent of "Thanks for the buggy ride" and a howl of
Sabra laughter and a howl of Sabra laughter broke over beach.

Sabras talk a language which (to describe it in their fashion)
has midoth (Goodly proportions). Everything has these proportions
from a generous slice of roast beef to a too-plump thigh. Their
slang made its debut in finished, concentrated form in the new
Negev play and people enjoyed it—even the words they couldn't
understand. They're as agile with the language as the daring young
man on the flying trapeze. They can do anything with Hebrew
roots—and when that doesn't suffice they fill it in with Arabic.

In contrast to their parents who are partial to making long
speeches—the Sabra can't stand too much eloquence and expresses
himself in one phrase sentences. And above all, he loathes any
demonstrative reference to "Zionism" or "patriotism." As one Sabra
was heard to say, "I hate the word 'patriotism.'" Then he added
in an undertone, "But I'm so patriotic that it's disgusting."

This is only a meager outline of the Sabra. You can't sum him
up in a word "Tarzan;" nor can you sum him up in an article—
he's a long story—a new expression of Israel after a 2,000 year

break. And sometimes the Sabra isn't sure he knows himself. For instance, I remember Ezra, aged sixteen; a pupil in the Mishmar Haemek high school; an exceptional artist with a promising future Ezra fell during the Iraqi attack on the settlement. He was milking goats, wouldn't leave his post; and a bullet got him. Afterwards, one of his teachers told me: "Only a few weeks ago I had a discussion with Ezra. He claimed that the Sabra in the kibbutzim had been too well cared for—pampered. He wondered if they would be able to take it in a crisis." Ezra gave the answer to this himself.

15

FROM THE FOUR CORNERS
OF THE EARTH

I

STILL DAZED after its ordeal of the siege, Jerusalem was in a festive mood. It was nine months since the State of Israel had been proclaimed; less than two months since the cessation of hostilities and not quite three weeks after the national elections.

Blue-and-white flags fluttered in the breeze from hills outside the city and on public buildings. White streamers with large blue inscriptions in Hebrew hung over poles, across streets and on specially erected arcs on the roads. A spirit of gaiety was in the air.

It was February 14, 1949. In the morning Premier Ben-Gurion planted the Forest of the Defenders in Bab-el-Wad, or the Gate of the Valley, where many recent battles had been fought. In the afternoon 120 men and women gathered in the hall of the Jewish Agency Building to be sworn in as members of the Constituent Assembly. Chaim Weizmann, for many years the leader of the world Zionist movement, read the opening address. His halting voice was at variance with the towering magnificence of his figure. He was obviously tired and nervous. Now and then he would interrupt his Hebrew reading to whisper in English that he did not have the strength to go on. Back home, in his family circle at Rehovot, he sighed: "If only I were ten years younger!"

Early in the morning on February 17, a delegation of twelve members of the Knesset, or Assembly, appeared in Weizmann's mansion at Rehovot. Dr. and Mrs. Weizmann hurriedly dressed and came downstairs into the library. They sat down in armchairs, waiting. The guests stood around. It was a tense moment. Joseph Sprinzak, Speaker of the Knesset, solemnly began in a voice full of emotion:

"Chaim, son of Ozer! We, the nation's emissaries, have come to you. . . . "

Thus was Weizmann officially apprised by his life-long friend and admirer of his election as President.

II

The assumption by Weizmann of the office of Head of State, represented the final step in the implementation of the United Nations decision of November 29, 1947 to set up in a part of Palestine a Jewish State. A century of historic events was crowded in these fourteen months.

Since the United Nations failed to secure the peaceful execution of its resolution or to protect its own creation, the forces of the State of Israel did so by a war of defense. They succeeded in carving out a larger territory than had originally been assigned to the Jewish State and held the largest portion of Jerusalem, originally intended to be an international enclave under the control of the United Nations.

When the fighting broke out, the Arab population, at the behest of their leaders, or, advised and assisted by British officials, or in fear of Jewish maltreatment, fled en masse from the sections in Jewish hands. The flight of the Arabs began about December, 1947 and steadily gained in momentum, until it became a stampede, so that by February of 1949, hardly more than one-tenth of the original Arab population remained in the Jewish State.

At that time Jewish leaders were still undecided about their policy on re-admitting the Arab refugees and the handing over to the United Nations the city of Jerusalem for international control. But the pressure of events and of popular sentiment already turned their minds away from their original intentions to hold the Arab property for their return and to recognize the authority of the United Nations over the Holy City. The Jews felt bitterly disappointed with the United Nations for failing to respect its own resolutions and as the war progressed and the Arabs, even after the armistice was signed, refused to talk peace, readiness to consider the re-admission of Arab refugees faded away.

At any rate, the return of the Arabs to their homes became increasingly difficult with the rise of another cataclysmic event—the mass influx of the Jews from all over the world. They had been coming, even in the midst of hostilities, at the rate of a thousand a day, in larger numbers than had been expected, and in much larger numbers than the country was ready to accommodate. The squeamishness of the Custodians of Abandoned (Arab) Property had to give way to the onrush of this deluge and the early comers and some of the old-timers helped themselves to whatever was left of the former Arab houses.

Jews came from the displaced persons camps in Europe—the survivors of the gas chambers and massacres and hunger; Jews came from the backward regions of North Africa—suddenly rising from their century-old torpor to a new life at the sound of what they took to be the footsteps of the Messiah, heralded throughout the world by the spectacular victories of the Israel Army of Defense. Jews came from Rumania, where many had barely escaped mass-extermination in the camps of Transnistria by the early conclusion of the war. They came from Yugoslavia and Poland by special government arrangement. The entire Jewish community of Bulgaria had been brought to Israel, including a whole shipload of octagenarians from an Old Folks' Home, shortly before Weizmann's investiture in office. Plans were already being completed for the wholesale transfer of the Jewish community in Yemen—the famous Magic Carpet Operation.

They were all welcomed with enthusiasm. Huge white streamers with Hebrew inscriptions in the Port of Haifa bid the newcomers welcome and quoted appropriate passages from Isaiah and Jeremiah and other prophets who predicted the gathering of Israel's exiles from the four corners of the earth. The most jubilant reception was given to the Prisoners of Cyprus —the would-be immigrants who had risked life and limb to run the British blockade only to be intercepted at sea and placed in special camps on the island of Cyprus. The last boatload of the Cyprus prisoners released by the British arrived in Haifa on the *Atzmaut* (Independence), amid banners, flowers and bunting and with music. Special launches went out to sea that Friday morning on February 11, 1949, to meet the arrivals. A committee of leading citizens stood on the shore to receive them. The band struck up "Hativkah," the soldiers stood at attention and the officers saluted. A huge streamer over the main building in the port bore the in scription from Isaiah (LIV, 7): "For a little moment did I forsake you, but with great pity will I bring you back to me."

III

This, then, was the great moment in Jewish history, when 2,000 years were rolled back and the course was to be resumed where it had been left off in 70 C. E. But beneath the surface of exultation many strains were to be noted: religious, communal, emotional, administrative, cultural, but, most of all, economic.

On the day before the new President took his oath of office, a remarkable scene took place in the Knesset. The Assembly was meeting for its third day and was debating the rights and prerogatives of the Head of the State who was to be elected that night. Suddenly a tall black-bearded man in a long frock, such as are worn by the orthodox East European Jews, quickly strode over from the visitors' section to the wall alongside the dais on which sat the Speaker and members of the Government. With his face to the wall and his back turned on the deputies and visitors, he began swaying to and fro, reciting the afternoon service:

> Blessed be Thou, O Lord, our God, King of the Universe, God of Abraham, God of Isaac, God of Jacob, great mighty and awe-inspiring God. . . .
>
> Restore us, O our Father, to Thy Law, inspire us to Thy worship, and cause us to have full repentance before Thee. . . .
>
> Sound a great trumpet for our liberation, raise a banner for the in-gathering of our exiles and assemble us together speedily from all the four corners of the earth into our own land. . . .
>
> Restore our law-makers as in olden times, and our state-counsellors as in the days of yore. . . .
>
> Mayest Thou mercifully re-establish Thy presence in Thy city of Jerusalem and dwell therein again, as Thou hast promised, and rebuild it speedily within our lifetime as an enduring edifice. . . .

The lawmakers and state counsellors of Israel, now restored, paid no attention to the worshiper at the wall, and went ahead with the agenda. Some were perhaps a bit annoyed. There is nothing wrong in an observant Jew reciting the Minha in public. It is done even in the lands of the Gentiles—but he might have retired to an adjoining room where he would not disturb the session.

The man who recited the afternoon prayer probably intended it as a symbolic gesture, one of quiet defiance or a reminder that the fulfillment of God's prophecy of the Restoration is greater than its erring human agents and that the fulfillment of the Prophecy would some day be more complete. It is an attitude characteristic of the majority of religious Jews both in Israel and abroad, though there are many variations of the amount of patience and aggressiveness they show toward the present regime. A tiny minority is downright hostile and considers the creation of the State as a calamity, a black crime against the Almighty.

For the present, the nonreligious are in control, the products of an age that revolted against the tyranny of an extremely exacting religion and embraced the Russian variety of radicalism of the late 19th and early 20th century.

The Meah Shearim quarter in Jerusalem and sections of Safed and Tiberias are Jewish communities which long antedate Zionist colonization. They carry on in the same old mode of life, as if the whole dynamic history of the country since 1880 had passed them by. They seem to be un-affected by Zionism and the State of Israel. Although most of them can speak a fluent Hebrew with the Sephardi pronunciation which is the standard in Israel, they will employ it only reluctantly with outsiders. Among themselves they speak only Yiddish. Any newly arrived child in an immigrant camp will try to pick up Hebrew as fast as he can and use it wherever possible, anxious to feel that he belongs to the country. But not a child in Meah Shearim.

These communities, both in Palestine and in Europe, have lost many people through defections. They represent pathetic, apparently petrified, remnants of a past age. But what they may hold for the future is hard to tell.

The large immigration, most of it from the backward countries of Asia and Africa, where the modern ideas of the separation of Jewish religion and Jewish nationality are unknown, may affect the whole scene. For the attachments of these new immigrants a fierce struggle has been going on since the State came into being. The danger that Israeli Jews may be divided into two nations—that of the secular-minded majority and that of the orthodox minority—has occupied the minds of national leaders like Ben-Gurion.

Before the State came into being, the Jews of Palestine had four private armies—the Haganah, which accepted the jurisdiction of the Zionist Executive in Jerusalem; the Palmach, which was organized as the shock army of the Haganah and began to show signs of independence after its heroic victories over the Arabs; the Irgun Zvai Leumi and the Fighters for the Freedom of Israel—two dissident groups practicing terroristic acts against the enemy. The conversion of the Haganah into a regular army, and, especially the disbanding of the Palmach, was achieved at the cost of a great deal of partisan bitterness. The destruction of the Irgun after a battle which claimed a score of lives left more lasting acrimony. In February, 1949, there was already one national army, which was to play an even larger part in the task of welding together the various communities in Israel, but the wounds were still fresh.

Another three years were to pass before the first attempt was made to abolish the several separate school systems—one for each of the main ideological groupings in the nation.

Another three years were also to pass before the hastily improvised administrative machinery was to begin functioning with reasonable efficiency, the large sums raised in the Diaspora were to be diverted in increasing measure to constructive channels and prospects of greater productivity and economic progress were to appear on the horizon. But our present work does not take us quite that far.

Amos Eilon in Haaretz

◆

THE OTHER ISRAEL

ABOUT 300 ARRIVALS from the lands of exile are here, sitting on mud-covered bundles of clothes, on straw boxes, on trunks. Overhead is a tin roof, clattering under a lashing rain. This is where they wait for the trucks. Three hundred of them—men who haven't shaved, women from Arab countries in summer dress and wooden sandals, European women in dark colored winter coats, Young Hungary in a yellow raincoat, children with legs as thin as broomsticks.

The heavy diesel motor throws hot smoke into the eyes of the waiting immigrants. Sixty percent of these eyes, according to official statistics, are stricken with trachoma.

"Tiberias — Halssa — Migdal — Beersheba — Jerusalem — Afuleh — Beisan — " a dozen different voices of officials of the Absorption Department of the Jewish Agency for Palestine call out in unison.

"Does anybody still have to gather his things?"

"Everybody got his money?" "Money," the word is repeated accompanied by the rubbing of fingers, the universal sign for coins.

"What are you standing there for? Throw your mattress on the truck!"

"Hurry up there, you! There are still another 300 today who must leave!"

"What's that? The truck isn't covered? Nothing else wrong? Are you well? Then get on there!"

"Don't push!"

On the large platform in front of the space protected by the tin roof, among trucks and cars, practically among the legs of the

immigrants, about a dozen porters are milling around, with ropes
over their shoulders. Two of them are children of about fourteen.

"Work, any work," they cry, "we'll carry anything for fifteen
piasters, beds, mattresses, blankets, clothes, handbags, trunks—anything for fifteen piasters!"

But fifteen piasters buy a person's food in the *maabarah* for a
day. The immigrants carry their own belongings.

The men perspire. They have just finished dragging all their
wordly possessions on their backs. It is not much, to be sure, but
now there is the added burden of a folding bed, obtained from
United States Army surplus material, a pink or a blue austerity
mattress, new brown blankets wrapped in an original fashion, and
there is four days' food. The ritual in the Distribution Camp has
been completed. Now comes the future—the *maabarah,* the general
setting for the life of The Other Israel, the Accelerated Pressure
Cooker of Mr. Israel, 1951.

Countries represented are: Iraq, Iran, India, Tunis, Morrocco,
Poland, Rumania, Hungary.

A sign in French—the second official language in the camp—
at the end of the covered space, reads "Departe"—Leaving, This
is the *Shaar Haaliyah*—the Gateway of Ascension—at the tip of
the street called *Kibbutz Galuyot,* meaning The Ingathering of the
Exiles. These immigrants have experienced the two weeks' preliminary ritual of a quarantine and various administrative ceremonies:
they have been washed, given medical examination, haircuts; they
have been classified, mobilized into military service, exempted from
the army, lectured on Israel, given performances by Shoshana
Damari, questioned as to whether they wanted to join a kibbutz, or
a moshav or an immigrants' village. The preponderant majority
are here now, going to the maabarot: tailors and cabinet makers
and butchers and traders and storekeepers and then some more
storekeepers and still more storekeepers.

During the last lap of the ritual I stand with them in the administrative building—really a shack. A dozen officials sit behind
crude wooden tables, getting the immigrants to sign promissory
notes. Two pounds for a mattress, and 2.80 for two blankets, and
1.20 for a bed. It all comes to six Israel pounds. These people

have never had to sign so many receipts, obligations, documents, confirmations, declarations. On the other hand, these people have never been given so much—all for nothing.

In the second room is the medical file. This is "the sieve," as the officials call it.

"Hey, you! The doctor found you have a venereal disease. You can't leave now. You've got to stay!"

"You're all right. . . . But your child there. . . . Go see the doctor again."

"All right now, move on."

"Move on, move on," cries are heard. Some two dozen children with their mothers crowd in front of the white-aproned nurse. The last injection is given.

The immigrant finally gets his ticket of departure. It is addressed to the Director of Camp X and reads: "This is to certify that So-and-So has been assigned to maabarah X."

We left on two trucks. In the first one was the baggage— miserable clothes-bundles, wrapped in other rags which even in Persia would have lost title to the classification of clothes, some wooden boxes with Arabic inscriptions and multicolored designs in oil paint, and some more baskets full of rags, and two trunks full of household articles.

There is the kerosene lamp, for instance, which has come a long way from some village in the hills of Kurdistan. The glass has been broken on the trip, but the lamp is still the jewel of the possessions of Mr. Hadad Clement, who, with four of his children, a bundle of clothes weighing two and a half kilograms and one kerosene lamp, arrived in Israel two weeks ago.

Or this burner with the two pots; Mrs. Sharge was stubbornly opposed to having the burner with the pots make the journey in the first truck, intended for baggage. Now she is sitting on a bench in the second truck, with the burner and the pots at her feet. In addition to these three articles, she has two sons, aged sixteen and fourteen. Her husband is dead.

As the immigrants ascend the truck by the steep iron ladder, all types of legs are revealed to the eye. Some legs are so thin that they look like dry bones covered with a film of human skin; those powerful fat legs belong to the wife of the Rumanian butcher. They are going to Tiberias, with their two sons. One leg hung rigid in grey woolen trousers. A slight knock was heard when it touched the side of the truck. It is a wooden leg; its owner is going to a *maabarah* with his wife and his younger brother. The two will provide for him. But perhaps he will get a grocery store.

Meantime everybody is leafing through his new passport. It is the Immigrant Passport, the Passport of a Citizen of The Other Israel. Among other uses, the document serves as a short biography. Aralian Anouar is twenty years old, born in Teheran, Persia, ten days in the country, accompanied by his mother, thirty-five years of age. This means she was fifteen years old when she gave birth to him. His ten year old sister has trachoma. Value of baggage—nil. He did not bring anything.

Or, for example, Barda Felix, thirty-one from Tripoli, arrived on the Artza two weeks ago. Occupation—storekeeper. His mother is already in the *maabarah*, she came two weeks ahead of him; now he is joining her. Medical report: one child affected with inactive trachoma. Value of baggage—eight pounds. Hadad Za'irah, forty-one, has a husband waiting for her in a *maabarah*. She came with two children. Medical report: one little girl sick with phabus (a head disease), one little boy, inactive trachoma. Value of baggage— 35 pounds.

Those who cannot read put away the documents in their pockets. Those who can read continue to examine them. But they are in the minority. Only Mr. Linshe Joseph makes an impression; he is dark-complexioned with long earlocks, he knows all the letters in the Holy Tongue, and he reads the pink-colored paper word by word. But the truck has now moved and most of the passengers who hid their passports celebrate the parting with long-drawn-out wails.

This, then, is The Other Israel—behind the grey curtains of tents and behind the silver-colored walls of tin. A new homeland— for those who have just alighted from the large truck. A setting for family life, for childhood, for love, for bringing up children who will be happier than their parents.

The Oriental communities are in one camp, on the left side of

the highway. They are variously referred to as "wild animals,"
"blacks," or "schreckliche menschen" (terrible people) or "good
Jews"—all depending on the observer's mood. The Ashkenazi Jews
are in the other camp, on the right side of the highway. They are
known as "the more civilized people," because they know how to
use a knife and fork.

Between the tents of the camps are ropes hung with underwear
and blankets, for drying or airing. Blouses from Egypt and Iraq
flutter in the winter breeze, socks from Tunis and Morocco, un-
mentionables from Poland and Rumania, Hungarian towels, Persian
pajamas. Sewage water comes up from a badly covered pit and
flows like a small stream among the tents, into a natural stream
passing through the northern edge of the *maabarah*. Half-naked
children float their paper boats in it; they feel at home in this place—
it is three months now that they have been living in the Homeland.
A little girl raises her expressionless eyes, half-shut with trachoma.

Behind the barbed wire fence of the camp on the right, stands
a Rumanian woman about forty years old, three months in the
country. Her remarks are characteristic of the moods prevalent
among the European immigrants.

"So they brought here some more blacks. We've got enough
blacks in this *maabarah* already."

Her husbands adds: "When I sold my house in Ploesti, I wasn't
told I'd have to live with Africans. The Jewish Agency should
take us away from here, say, to Tel Aviv."

This request is addressed to a man who came to receive the
immigrants, a stoutish man, perspiring profusely, dressed in a
leather jacket, with an extinguished cigar between his thick lips, an
immigrant from the Argentine. This is the liaison officer between
the officials of the Absorption Department and the immigrants, the
man in charge of the beds and mattresses and blankets, when they
are there, and the lavatories and showers (when there is water.)
Like all office holders in the *maabarah,* including the man who
lights the lanterns at night, he is a member of Mapai. His official
title is the *hatzran* or court manager.

The *hatzran* has instructions to settle me in a tent. I show him
my document, according to which I am a new immigrant by the

name of Akiva Olon from Rumania, twenty-four years old who arrived on the SS. *Transylvania* on December 23. I can tell by the man's experienced look that I stand out here as an "intellectual," at any rate, as one who can read and write. "All right," he says, "we'll put you up in a good tent, so you won't have to be with black barbarians."

I tell him I want to be with barbarians. He shrugs his shoulders. A Polish immigrant, who has been here for some time, is more outspoken: "Don't do it. You can get a venereal disease." Somebody else remarks: "Meshuga."

The dozen Iraqi families meantime are waiting on the sides of the road. Their relatives in the *maabarah* come running. At first there is kissing all around. While the men, who are generally dressed in European—or rather semi-European—clothes, are busy kissing their relatives in the *maabarah,* who are clad in underwear, the women stand apart, all dressed in Oriental fashion, in long colored housedresses which cover their bodies. Some carry their children in their arms, others are nursing them. Some of the women climb down from the truck with pots and burners in their hands as if ready to make straight for the kitchen. The kitchen, ladies, is now in the living room, which is also the berdoom and the nursery and the clubroom for playing cards and *shash-bash* and for drinking *arak,* and, begging your pardon, occasionally used as a lavatory. It is situated in an American tent, five by five meters, with a pole in the center for hanging the clothes.

There are four of us in the tent. The tent is grey, its floor is of the same color—of the fine thick dust of the Beisan Valley. There are four beds, two wooden boxes covered with Arabic inscriptions, two burners, one pitcher, a number of pots, some suits of clothes hanging on nails driven into the tent pole and serving also for hanging up the kerosene lamp which is lit up on nights when a bon-fire is not kindled.

The odor is the peculiar Iraqi odor. I learned with time that the more primitive the people the more pronounced the peculiar odor in their dwellings. There is a different smell in a Yemenite tent than in an Iraqi tent and the same applies to the Moroccan shack or the Turkish hut. This time it was not just an odor but a vapor composed of gaseous substances emanating from the pots and the remnants of food, from the clothes scattered in the tent, on the floor, on the beds and on the hooks, from the unaired mattresses in which the air settles more and more firmly until it becomes of the essence of the thing, from the full garbage pail standing in the middle of the tent. The garbage could hardly be seen, so covered was it with flies of all sizes peculiar to this spot. The curtains of the tent were lowered and, as I later found out, they are hardly ever raised. For that reason, the tent is practically never given an airing, and for the same reason it is partially dark nearly all the time. In the right hand inside corner stood my bed, opposite it was the double bed of the married couple, made up of two single beds placed together. In the third corner was the fourth bed which also served as a table; in the morning it was covered by an old nightgown or housedress and milady prepared the meals on it.

My arrival gave rise to general surprise, and, to some extent, even resentment. An Ashkenazi in an Iraqi tent? For three months the dwellers of these tents lived in the State of Israel without making the personal acquaintance of any European Jew, with the exception of some officials of the Jewish Agency or the foreman of the Afforestation Department of the Jewish National Fund. They concluded I must have committed some misdemeanor. The cousin of the man to whom the tent belonged even asked me later if I had some disease. While casting wondering glances and asking questions, the Iraqis were holding a consultation in an Arab dialect I found difficult to follow: the dialect of the Baghdad Jewish ghetto. Two young men from a neighboring tent came in to take part in the conference. In the meantime I discovered that the bed on which I sat served as pasture ground for lice and other vermin.

After a brief period of embarrassment we made acquaintance. This tent belongs to young people who, as I found out, are easier to make friends with than their elders. Besides myself the tent is inhabited by Rahman, a tailor from Baghdad, twenty-three years old, due to join the Israel army in another couple of weeks, who in the meantime is not working but eating off the table—or rather the floor—of his cousin Selim, who earns about six pounds a week. Selim himself is twenty-seven, his wife Nagiba twenty-four, a quiet woman dressed in the same old housedress by day and by night, who looks like thirty-five. Selim too, is a tailor. This evening there is a fifth inhabitant, a third cousin who came from the *maabarah* in Jerusalem to visit his relatives. The first question they ask is where is my family? I fabricate a story to satisfy them and tell them all my folks perished at the hands of the Germans during the War. Then comes the second question: How many Jews did the Germans kill? More than the hoodlums killed in Iraq during the Rashid Ali riots in Baghdad? Did the Jews defend themselves?

*　*　*

In a small cafe near the *maabarah,* five out of the nine tables are taken. Around those five tables five languages are spoken. At the first table, Arabic; at the second, Rumanian; at the third, Polish; at the fourth, Yiddish; at the fifth, Hebrew: that is where a Rumanian immigrant and an Iraqi immigrant found a common medium.

A brown-skinned man with an acquiline nose, dressed in work clothes, comes up to the marble counter.

"Give me some candy," he says in Arabic, taking a coin out of his pocket.

"Voo-ess?" (What) asks the woman behind the counter leaning on it with both arms.

The man thinks for a while, then utters: *"Ten ugah."* (Hebrew: give cookie.)

"Ah, ugah? Bevakashah!" (Please) Why didn't you say so?

One way or the other, Hebrew today is the Esperanto of the Ingathering of the Exiles, the only common language of people from the East and from the West, from the North and from the South. Few study it systematically, but even in the poor ungrammatical way it is being used it serves as a common medium of contact among the many immigrants in their everyday life. Iraqis acquire the use of Hebrew to be able to tell a Polish neighbor in the *maabarah* to take away his trunks from other people's tents; a Persian learns Hebrew to tell a Tunisian to stop pushing in the line or he'll knock his teeth out. Real religious fervor for the Holy Tongue is to be found among the Yemenites who, more than the others, study the language because, as they put it in their own quaint Hebrew, "this is our speech, the speech of our country and our Homeland."

Immigrants from Arab countries learn more, those from European countries learn less. Rumanians and Poles know that with Yiddish one can get along in Israel, sometimes even better than with Hebrew. But this easy road is not open to the immigrants from the Orient. They learn Hebrew to be able to express themselves on the simplest matters. Still, only fifty people in a *maabarah* of 200 families attend courses in Hebrew.

The greatest hope lies in the young generation. The way the children adapt themselves is amazing. Were a group of immigrant children to be brought to Tel-Aviv, into a Sabra milieu, it would not be surprising if after two or three months they chattered in Hebrew and sang the Hebrew songs of Israel. But the fact that this result was accomplished here, in the *maabarah,* is especially noteworthy. For, as far as I know, there is not a single child of school age in this place who was born in the country. They are all immigrants. And yet, to hear them speak on the street, to follow them to the playground, to listen to them is actually to hear the Hebrew language pushing out from their little mouths the Arabic, the Rumanian, the Yiddish, the Serb, the Czech, the Polish languages.

Zecharia Nissim

◆

A YEMENITE BOY IN ISRAEL

WHEN I WAS A small child in Yemen I went to study in a school called a *madras*. Not one *mari* (teacher) taught me, but a sort of partnership. All of them taught me a little of the same thing—Bible, Ein Yaakov, Gemara. Many things were lacking in my studies and one of them was grammar. But as against this, the stripe and the stick were not wanting.

When father had taught me to work he sent me to the Arab villages. My trade was a good one and I could earn enough to secure a respectable livelihood. We were six souls at home and my earnings were not of one kind but of all sorts together—one kilogram of barley, a quarter of a kilogram of wheat, four hundred grams of beans, eight hundred grams of millet, thirteen eggs, some coffee and two bundles of kindling wood. This was the income of a full week. On Friday I would load all this onto my back in a sack, and make my way home.

Before we heard the good news of going up to Eretz Israel I once passed by an Ishmaelite on his right hand. Suddenly I saw that he was calling me, "Come hither you dog of a Jew! You must pass me on the left hand and not on the right. Remember that next time!" And he lifted up his stick and gave me what I deserved and sent me on my way. But God saw this and much time did not pass before we were instructed by the Rabbi of our village to transfer all we had to the Arabs and whatever they agreed to pay we should accept, for the Miracle of the Redemption was at hand. We did as we were instructed and made ready for the journey. The Rabbi called the whole village to a meeting to give information and to assign duties. And these were the men upon whom special duties were laid. Mr. Shillen Nagar and Mr. Shalom Cohen and Mr. Yihyeh Casfan, all of whom today live in Mesilot Zion. The orders were that no one in the village travel alone, but the whole village together. The money must be divided equally among rich and poor so that all might reach the Land together. Afterwards they would return the money given to them as a loan. This we did before we made our way to the city of Sanaa. The flour and the bread we transported on the camels and the asses together with the oil and the coffee. I remember that we had neither spoon nor fork and ate with our hands like the Bedouin.

Our journey from Sanaa to Hasiani took a fortnight, and there we rested for a week, until the Director from Aden, who had gone forth from the Land to aid the emigrants, came. And I remember when the Director of the Jewish Agency who had gone forth to aid the emigrants called to all of them, and from whoever had money he took, and to those who had none he gave generously. Here in truth I saw care, as one cares for little children that have just been born. The Director took the money and went to the King to pay him for the journey of all the families together. I remember that he told us to make ready for the journey and we made ready happily and with a good heart. We packed our goods, removed them to the trucks, gayly and with a glad heart. Then they said to us, "Not today but tomorrow." And on the second day we went forth, our Director going before us in a jeep and twenty-five trucks after him and every one singing and reciting Psalms. For God had given his aid and our Government was strengthened and to all of our brethren, the Children of Israel, the State of Israel called out saying: "Arise ye that wander in the desert, go up out of the wilderness, go up to your new land. Enough your 2,000 years of exile under the hand of strangers who have not known you and who have not dealt kindly with you."

We continued upon our journey, the Arabs closing the way before us every five kilometers and demanding money. We paid them a little and they asked for more and we gave them more, for whatever they asked they were given. In one of the places there came Englishmen, who sought to search all our goods as well as our persons, for they thought that we had gold. And they even opened the Sefer Torah and searched, and they pried into every little thing. They took our clothes from off our backs, even our shoes, but found nothing. So again we packed and again we traveled until we came to the Immigrant Hostel near Aden. And there appeared *madrichim* and *madrichot* (instructors) who spoke Hebrew and said to us, "Come in here, please! We will bring your goods." And then other people came with bread and tea and all sorts of vegetables saying, "Eat with good appetite."

That evening we saw a radio in our camp and people were saying that a box had been found which spoke. On the second day they called us to move into the tents which they had set up for us. So we moved into them. They called us to get our provisions from the store and my father went to the store and received rations for six people and he appeared in our tent and he could not carry all the rations he had received. And I can even remember what they were. Meat, five kilograms; bread, ten loaves; two kilos of dates, a little coffee, sugar and tomatoes. I remember when they called to the young people to come and eat in the common kitchen. I was the first to go and get food which I had never eaten before in my life. The women instructors cooked it, nice and clean, and we sat on chairs and ate from a table. We took a shower every day and put on clean clothes for we had been given clothes, clothes from Eretz Israel. All the instructors and directors visited us in our tents and showed us how to keep everything clean, and there was plenty of everything that we required. Even wine was not wanting, for the directors distributed wine besides giving us all the good of God.

Then I saw people were going to the Land, each in his turn. They were all registered and whoever it was whose turn came was told to make ready for the trip in the airplane. Everyone was glad and waited for his turn. And I, despite all the good things I had to eat, had no patience, for I only waited for the day when I would travel in the plane.

Some of the *madrichim* gathered and taught us to sing and to speak a little Hebrew. Then they called our family to go up to the Land and I rejoiced. We rose early in the morning together with the families traveling with us, all of us meeting at one place. The car came to take us to the aerodrome in Aden, naming each family according to the list. And then three girls from Israel appeared and they weighed us on a scale. We packed all our goods and loaded them on the plane and took our seats. Some of us sang and some just sat and talked.

We heard them starting the engine and we began to be a little afraid. Then one of the directors who was traveling with us told us to sing "May the living God be magnified." So we began to sing. The plane moved slowly and we began to rejoice. Two hours passed and chocolate and tea and cake and sweets were handed to us. Between every two seats there was a jug full of water and we all drank and spoke of the going forth from Yemen.

We did not know where we were nor the names of the places over which we were passing for we still did not know the world. And in the course of those eight hours that we flew, we saw dry land and sea, villages and towns, but we did not know what it all was. Then we came to Lydda. They took us down carefully, gave the children nice blankets and took us into one of the rooms where they gave us bread and jam and hot tea and we ate and drank. Two girls and some young men called our names according to our immigration certificates. We did not know what we had signed. They finished registering us and the buses came to take us away. We loaded our luggage on the bus and they took us to the Beth Olim Immigrant House in Ein Shemer.

The instructors welcomed us very warmly, took us into the dining room, gave us food and then took us into one of the big rooms where we would sleep. In the morning we washed and prayed and went to eat in the dining room. We finished eating and they called us to come and get our equipment. My father went and received for each of us, three blankets, a cup, various utensils, a bed, mattress and clothing. We moved into the tents, two small families in a tent and one big family in a tent. They showed us the water taps and the shower bath so that we could wash.

Conditions improved from day to day. The food became better and a little order and cleanliness were introduced. I remember how in Yemen I used to help my mother carry a tin of water for a distance of at least one kilometer and sometimes three or four. In addition I used to help her grind three or four kilograms of wheat or barley or millet or a mixture of all three. But here the tap was next to the house, the meal was already ground, the bread was baked and no burden rested upon us. One day every week the instructors took us from Beth Olim to clean our camp. The teachers taught us some Hebrew and a little arithmetic and songs and fine melodies.

I was the first to leave the lessons and went to look for work. I went to Karkur on the first day and also on the second but found no work. On the third day I went to a place called Kfar Pines. I met a woman who asked me if I wished to help her. I was very glad and said "Yes." She said, "Follow me!" I accompanied her to the poultry feed store and I took the feed and loaded it on my back. She gave me half a pound and told me that if I wished to work and earn half a pound every day then I should come early in the morning and be at her house at seven o'clock. I returned to the camp happy that already I had half a pound. Next day I rose early, washed my face and went. As I left the camp I began to pray. Before I reached the village I had finished my prayers more or less. I came, changed the water in the poultry run, took the cows out of the barn, took some manure to the fields, cut green-stuff for the cattle, came home, ate. Then the woman left and I took the milk to the creamery and went back again and took manure again to the fields, returned home again, fed the chickens, collected the eggs, put them in the cellar, cleaned them, took them to the store and then I went home to the camp. Thus I continued for three months, ploughing and manuring in season. They grew very fond of me and I of them and I used to eat with them. Whenever I stayed too late, I used to sleep over at their house. There I learned to speak Hebrew and to plough and to sow and to do all manner of work. I loved farming and no longer wanted any other work.

It so happened that the farmer for whom I worked was an instructor in a Beth Olim. I told him that I was a new immigrant and that I wished to be a member of a moshav. One day I was sent to Luzim in the Jerusalem Corridor. I passed through the Sharon and the Shefela (cloastal plain) until I came to the Judean Mountains. I came to Luzim and asked "Where is Jerusalem?" The instructor answered, "There she lies before you. Can you see those big houses?" I answered, "Yes," He said to me, "That is Jerusalem!"

I worked for three days and then made a trip to Jerusalem. I walked three kilometers to Castel and from there I traveled to Mahaneh Yehuda, walked about a little and noted the signs so that I should not forget from where I had come. I bought three bottles of wine, some cinnamon, and a little strong pepper.

One day soldiers who are called engineers appeared. They planned and constructed the place where we lived and departed in peace. Some days later we were told that we must move from this place. Altogether, with our relatives, we were nineteen families. They brought another forty families and we pitched tents for them and ourselves. The cooperative store also moved over to the new site, supplies were regular and work was plentiful. We, together with the newcomers who had been brought, knew each other well, and and they, indeed, were good people who clung to us and we were as one flesh.

We lived in tents for four months; then the *pahonim* (tin huts) arrived. We worked and erected the *pahonim* and moved in. The smaller families for whom there were no tin huts remained in the tents. But before that time people had come from the Ministry of Social Welfare and had brought us plenty of clothes, some of which were good and some of which were bad and worn. They also built two shower baths for us, one for men and one for women. Now there began to be order and cleanliness. Our instructor worked and helped us a lot, sincerely and with a good heart. We chose a Local Committee and a Religious Committee, five members in each.

Conditions began to improve and slowly we began to be happier. Then the Committee informed us that teachers would come from Jerusalem to teach us Hebrew. And indeed on Tuesday, Mr. Yaacob Maimon came with ten of his students. They began to teach us Hebrew and a little arithmetic. Then this mari came to us every week together with his students. They came at four o'clock and taught us until eight, and continued thus for a year.

We, the young people, were called to go to the Gadna, (military youth organization), but we did not know what it was. My father did not wish to permit me. I began to cry and said to him that if

he did not let me go they would take me for two years in the
Army. At last he agreed and said, "If it is only for a month, go; but
remember, you must say your prayers every day." I was glad and
said, "Yes." They said they would take us in another week. We
said, "Very well." I remember that at that time the army used to
send us soldiers from the Reserve to help us. And indeed they
helped us and taught us to sing and to dance. For the children
and the old people the conditions were very good. The women
learned to cook a little better than before. Women who had volunteered to work in the *ma'abarot* taught our womenfolk to sew and
to wash and to cook and to bake cakes and all sorts of other
good things. The lessons in Hebrew and in arithmetic progressed.
All that we studied we understood. Mr. Maimon's students from
the Seligsberg School in Jerusalem continued to volunteer for work
in the *Ma'abarot*.

For us, the young people of Luzim, the time came to go out to
the Gadna course. They came to take us, and we traveled far to a
place called Damun on Mount Carmel. We arrived in the evening,
were given our equipment and went to the wooden huts. They took
us to the dining hall, we formed ranks and entered to receive
food. We ate and returned to our huts to rest. Then our commander
came and began to talk to us about the matters of the Gadna and
why they had brought us. They made us a little familiar with the
situation, then we rested and talked for two whole hours. Then he
said: "You must go to sleep now before they put out the lights."

I was glad and went to make my bed and to sleep. Early in
the morning at ten minutes to six they woke us and told us to go
out immediately, and that within five minutes we should be outside in vests and short trousers. We obeyed the order and went out.
The commander told us to form threes, gave us a little drill, then
we ran for two kilometers and returned at half past six. Before
seven we had to wash, fold our blankets and make our beds. Then
we were told that the time for breakfast had come. Then again the
commander came, formed us into threes and took us in to eat.
We finished the meal before half past seven, washed our plates and
spoons and made ready for the inspection of our huts. Our officers
came to carry out the inspection and they found that we knew

nothing. They called us outside, took out one of the beds and showed us how it should be done so that all of us arrange them the same way. Then we went out to get our uniforms. We were very glad but did not know how to put them on properly. The officers came and showed us. Then this, too, was arranged more or less. But it was a little difficult for us to understand how to use puttees. But I found that it is written, "All beginnings are hard." Until we learn, then everything is all right.

Half the day we had lessons and half the day we drilled, until they showed us the style and correct way of doing things.

When the month ended my commander came to me and told me that I had excelled and that I must register for a course of Mem-Kafim (section commander). He gave me a note and sent me to the commander of our course, Asher Parhi, who I will remember all the days of my life. He registered me and said, "I hope you will succeed as you have up to now." I said "Shalom" to him and gave him the names of some of the boys who I thought were good. He noted them down, fifteen of them.

We learned all sorts of new things, dances and games, and we sang fine songs. When they came to pin our badges on us they began with those who had excelled in the platoons. We were four platoons and four boys and one girl had done very well. Then high officers came and wished us good luck. When we had finished with the parade they prepared for the farewell party that was held that night. The party was very nice. They gave us chocolate, each of us two packets, a bottle of gazoz (soda), cakes, biscuits and all sorts of good things. On the next day in the morning we handed in our equipment and went home on leave. We were very glad and our parents were even gladder. We told them we had only five days leave and that we were returning to the course. My father refused to consent, so I told him that we had already finished and that we were returning for a week of examinations. He did not believe me. I pacified him until he said, "Very well!" On the day they took us we were a little homesick but that was not terrible for I knew that we must learn something more and develop. Then we returned for a fortnight's preparation for the Mem-Kafim course. In that fortnight we learned a lot. They took us for a three-day hike through Upper and Lower Galilee, so that we got to know Tiberias and Safed. From Tiberias we went to Ein Gev in a boat and from Ein Gev to Dagania and Afikim. When I remember that day my heart is fit to burst for on that day seven policemen were killed on the Syrian border.

We returned to Damun where we remained for a number of days after which we were taken for Rosh Hanikra, where the course was to be held. No tents had been pitched, neither for us nor for those who were to come after us. We ate lunch and then put up the tents so that we would have somewhere to sleep. There were fifteen of us, including four girls.

That night everything was put in order and the next day we began to put up tents for those who were to come two days later —making 125 new immigrants and Israelis altogether. We worked hard those two days until we had done everything necessary, so that when the others came the camp was ready. Then they started putting us through our paces. In the first week it was a little difficult but we soon got over our fears and our sufferings and did all that we had to do willingly. Whoever wishes to build a house must first lay the foundations. Understanding this I carried on gladly with the rest of the group. A number of my friends from Luzim left and returned home because they could not carry on. I was the only one of our village who remained.

We began with a morning run, making our beds and tidying up our tents, going out to parade and hoisting the flag. When evening came we said, "And it came to pass at midnight." The night had many advantages, but also many disadvantages. In order to become familiar with its difficulties, we went out on night-training. The idea of the first exercise which our instructors gave us was to enable us to learn the nature of the night. On the second night we learned seeing and hearing and on the third orientation in the dark. Thus our training continued by day and by night, and we made some progress. They began to teach us judo, then a little drill, camp-craft, lectures, and games of bringing verbal messages. When we had learned all this we went out once again for night-training. Then they decided to organize an ambush by the road to take messages from us and we had to be very careful if we wished to come back safely. When our commander sent me with such a message, a light sweat covered my body. I began to advance in the dark of the night. I examined what was before me and what was behind. I saw a tree and mistook it for a man. If I heard a lizard on the ground or a frog jumping, I was certain it was a hidden enemy. Suddenly there was a roll of thunder and the sound of firing was close by. I dropped to the ground according to the rules of field-craft which I had learned. My breath stopped and only resumed when everything was quiet. Not all of us had the courage to walk up-right after this. Our only desire was to reach camp without mishap as soon as possible. Every rustle in the trees sounded terrifyingly loud. I did not know what to do. Suddenly I resolved that I could not continue like this and so I began to run if only to get out of the dark. By the time I reached the camp, I was bathed in sweat.

We began to work on club organization. Then we were required to work at handicrafts and not with rifles and bullets, but just with paper and a handkerchief and all sorts of other games.

"Is this not an affront to the honor of the future Mem Kaf* of the Gadna" I asked my commanding officer.

"No, my dear fellow. When you go out to work among the young people of the *ma'abarot,* it is not enough to instruct them only in military matters. You must work among them as a teacher so that they will understand. We will meet and live with the youngsters twenty-four hours a day. We shall even spend our leisure with them. And it must be useful leisure within the frame-work of games in the club. We shall make them accustomed to this more useful form. Haverim, show a proper spirit towards club work. You can be sure that your standing as Mem-Kafim will increase as you yourselves advance in this field."

On the next morning, when we rose, our eyes were but half-open but we were glad. They called upon us to put on our packs and to fill our water bottles and we set forth.

My company was proud that it had succeeded in overcoming its weariness. Let us admit—a march over the mountains of Galilee is very tiring. We were hungry and thirsty; the fatigue was nigh

---

* Section commander.

unbearable. And when we approached Nebi Yusha Police Post
some of us just sank to the ground. Our officers explained to us
where we were and showed where we still had to go. When we
moved from that place and entered Ramot Naphtali we were tired
but happy. We rested for ten minutes and started again, and behold
before us we saw a great slope leading down to the Valley of
Huleh. Our officers explained a little about the draining of the
Huleh. We rested again and continued our march around the Valley
and so we came to Yesod Ham'alah. Our spirits were good and we
were very cheerful and we sang and marched in step until we
reached our destination. As we rested, some of us rose to prepare
lunch. The rest was a welcome one after the march with full packs
on our backs. We were ordered to clean our arms before we set
out again. We did so, inspecting all our equipment to make sure
that nothing was missing. Everything was in order. We buckled
on our packs, mounted the lorries and began to move towards our
camp. In the lorries we began asking each other if we had been
very tired. And everyone answered and said, "No," he had not
been very tired. We knew that the eyes of hundreds of people were
fixed on us, and the mistake of any individual would be counted
against the Gadna. We knew that the honor of the Gadna was at
stake and that we dared not fail. Indeed in those moments we cast
aside our weariness, we forgot all aches and pains and marched in
gladly and proudly. We had stood the test.

All these things we learned in a course that lasted three months
and which included a varied program, the main subject of which
was field craft. The other subject that was very important was
practical sport to which sixty hours were devoted. The same number
of hours were set aside for camp-craft, drill, judo, rifle drill, route
marching, physical exercise and games, education and culture, discipline and routine. All these a section commander must know by
heart. Moreover, the commander must be patient and kind—though
not to excess—towards his men.

I will now tell you what happened in the meantime in my
parent's home at Luzim. But first of all I must tell about Esther,
the wife of Mr. Maimon who, too, began to go out to the
ma'abarot together with the women who had volunteered to teach

the wives of immigrants how to cook and sew, and keep things clean and neat. She organized the women in the *ma'abarot* and found them work in the city on a monthly or an hourly basis. When I go to the city I always visit Mr. Maimon. And when I come to their house, it is full of women and children and old men and they are all eating, sometimes cakes and sometimes bread and margarine and jam. The kettle is always full of boiling water, and everyone drinks what he wishes, tea or coffee. They all sit on chairs—Yemenites, Iraqis, Kurds. Everyone who has made Esther's acquaintance is invited to visit her house and to drink something. Her many friends always remember her cheerful smile. She is a woman who can serve as an example for she has opened her house to immigrants and is anxious that they should have work and clean clothes, and always be cleanly dressed and go to work on time and keep everything in order, so that we all become a little better educated than we were previously.

We were told that we must go from Luxim to Katra, our permanent moshav. At Katra we had already worked for a year on the construction of terraces, on ploughing and pruning trees. The people agreed to move. We put up tents, dismantled the aluminum huts and transferred them to Katra. But some of the families did not want to move. They said there was not enough land and that they had old people with them. The families who had agreed to the transfer left for Katra. After a while they brought a number of Yemenite families from another place and there were still not the full number planned for. Conditions began to improve and people began to live upon their deserted and desolate land. I betook myself to Kfar Vitkin. I decided to learn something from the best settlers in Eretz Israel.

While I was in Kfar Vitkin, two brothers were killed in Katra. One of them was the village guard and the other went out to help him bring back the mules. I well remember how on that day I went out to work, sad and not knowing what was amiss with me. At evening I returned from my work and went to wash. When I came out, my employer told me that the men had been killed in the Jerusalem Corridor. When I had finished eating, I took Hador and in it I read the names of the two men whom I had

known so well from our moshav. My head began to go round
and round, my heart was unsettled and I could not sleep all night.
In the morning I got up sadly, and my hands could do no work.
I went to my employer in the barn and began to speak to him. Then
he said to me, "If you wish to go, then go." He asked me if
I had money and so everything was arranged. I stood by the road
of Kfar Vitkin and the truck of the District Council came past
on its way to Jerusalem. So I was able to attend the funeral of
the two dead men. I consoled their relatives and on the same
day returned to Kfar Vitkin. Mr. Yaakov Maimon and his wife
participated in the funeral and accompanied the bereaved families
to Katra. And every day they came to comfort them and to tell
them not to lose heart. Their position was very bad but there was
no cause for anxiety because their friends and relatives helped
them and brought trucks to transfer their goods to Rosh Ha'ayin.
They went back into the Immigrant Camp and began to work.
I returned to Kfar Vitkin and continued working without having
to worry about my own family.

One day I went to work in the fields with a hay-rake. It was
the first time we were working with a rake and I was taking
it home. The mare was a new one and when she heard the noise
of the wheels of the rake, she bolted. A wagon was in front
of us but I could not stop her and she mounted the wagon and
I fell and was hurt.

My neighbor, into whose wagon I had crashed, took me to
the clinic. The doctor came, examined me and immediately tele-
phoned to the Beilinson hospital. They sent to take me and there
I lay for three weeks. It was the first time I had been in a
hospital. When I saw the doctor come to me with injections, I
remembered the remedies of Yemen. There instead of an injection
they used an iron skewer.

I wish to say a few words about the Bottinsky family for whom
I used to work. There I received the education I still needed and I
thank them, as I do the Kaplansky family and the family of
Zahara Hurwitz: indeed from nearly all the people of Kfar Vitkin
I learned something. I also remember a Yemenite family from whom

I learned to make clothes and to cook Yemenite soup and to bake bread in the oven and to make *skhuk* and *khilbeh*.

Not long after this I left Kfar Vitkin in order to help my family. I came home to Katra and I began to work and registered for guard duty.

All along I had wanted to have a cupboard or a table or something else. For almost a year I kept on longing until finally I bought a cupboard and an ice-chest and a table. In time we shall also buy chairs. Meanwhile we used two benches which I myself had made. Then I decided to buy a goat. But here I failed. I was also thinking of a boiler to heat water so that we could bathe. But how could I buy a boiler when my wage was IL.700 a day and there were six mouths to feed at home? And clothes were still lacking and also shoes. The most important thing was to educate the children and to take care of them, including washing, clothing and food. In Yemen we used to wash in the Mikveh and not far off Ishmaelites lived and the Mikveh had no roof. So the Arabs used to throw stones at us and curse, for they did not want us to wash in front of them. And whoever did not obey them they took him to prison where he would lie for days until a bribe was paid. Then they would go and ask for the King's* permission to release him. If the King consented, the man was let out and if he did not, he remained. Thus, we were persecuted at the hands of strangers. But now that we had a shower-bath in the house, we could wash in peace, your own friend did not see you, nor did an Ishmaelite curse you. And so we wish to continue until God will help us and we can settle down like all the old-timers in this country.

I have some idea of what they experienced, those who are now veterans until they achieved their present position. I know that it was only by great suffering that they acquired Eretz Israel. And they have suffered enough. They have gone through enough as in the days of Haman the Wicked. And even today I can see these veterans do not just sit at home and rest, but go forth to help their immigrant brothers, to teach them, to see that they have every

---

* In the feudal state of Yemen, each village head bears the title of "King."

good thing and that they lack nothing and that they should know what was done in the Land before they came. The young people serve in the Gadna and the working youth goes to schools. The women and the old folk are taught to perform various tasks at home. The children are taken care of in schools and kindergartens. The condition of the immigrants is improving steadily and they are forming their ties with the homeland. Those of us who came a year or two ago must instruct those who come today, and he who comes today, within six months or a year will have to help those who come after him. Thus we shall be a single people, "all Israel comrades," with no distinction between those who come from Yemen and those who come from Morocco, and those who come from Poland and those who come from Iraq, and those who come from America. All of us together will build up a country that will be an example to the whole world. How? Through unity, love and friendship, through physical and mental effort, and none of our enemies will ever overcome us. Our family is the only one of Yemenites living among immigrants from Kurdistan who have settled in Katra. The people are good and they have found favor in my eyes. They work well and honestly and they love and respect each other. The hearts of some of them are still sore from what they suffered in the Exile as we ourselves suffered. Every Jew coming from the Exile, even if he were rich, suffered persecution, and only God delivered us from the hands of the Gentiles until we came to the shores of our homeland, the land of our fathers.

*   *   *

Now I will conclude with a blessing to all Israel that we succeed in striking root in our young homeland, we and all the children of Israel. Amen. So may it be His Will.

M. Z. Frank

◆

CAFE KADIMAH

THEY TELL ME the place was once a swanky Arab cafe-chantant.
It is situated on Hamrah Square in the heart of what used to be
the Arab world of Lower Town Haifa, near the port. That whole
throbbing esoteric world of which this cafe was once the center
suddenly disappeared after the battle of April 20, 1948; and all
that remains of it, save memories, are the old mosque on the road
to Nazareth, the huge mass of rubble of the former Arab slums
and underworld, and the houses now inhabited by new immigrants.
Occasionally, on week days, an Arab or a Druze wanders in.

I knew it as Café Restaurant Kadimah, with the name inscribed
in large Hebrew letters, and the walls inside hung with the pictures
of Weizmann, Ben Gurion, and even Herzl and Bialik. Only an
old-fashioned Zionist would call his business "Kadimah." It is a
word, meaning "onward" or "forward," which used to be the
favorite of Zionist clubs and Zionist publications in the days of
Herzl.

To say that the owner of Café Restaurant Kadimah was a
Zionist is an understatement. He is a vatik—an old-timer, a veteran
pioneer. His name is Yitzhak Nadav. He is a tall, broad-shouldered,
powerfully built man in his early sixties, with a handsome fair-
complexioned face that immediately catches your attention. It is
a jovial likeable face, with character and personality. I was introduced to him by Abba Hushi, Mayor of Haifa, when we came in
one night during the heavy rains in the winter of 1951-52, to check
on rescue work. The Mayor remarked to me that Yitzhak was worth
knowing.

When I found myself alone with the Mayor's driver, Benjamin, he told me more about Yitzhak Nadav: that he was a friend of the great, the man with an interesting history, and a Yemenite. The latter was hard to believe.

"I never saw a Yemenite who is so fair-skinned," I said, looking at Benjamin, whose eyes and hair are as black as coal. Benjamin is a Yemenite, born in Haifa. His father, with other Yemenite stone-masons, was brought to Haifa to build the Technion, sometime in 1911 or 1912. "I was born when they finished the threshold," Benjamin liked to jest, "my younger brother came with the window-sills."

"But he is so tall, and talks Yiddish like a Litvak, and anyway he looks like a Litvak."

Benjamin threw back his head, made a clacking sound with his tongue, Arab fashion, and I proceeded to make further inquiries elsewhere. Yitzhak, it turns out, was born in the Old City of Jerusalem, of a father who came from Yemen and a mother from Morocco. As a youngster, he mingled with the Ashkenazim, from whom he learned to speak a racy idiomatic Yiddish, and fell under the influence of the idealistic ragamuffins who came from Russia and tried to turn not only Palestine but the whole world topsy-turvy. When Ben-Zvi organized Hashomer, the secret order of "guards" or "sentinels," Yitzhak Nadav joined it and became known as Yitzhak the Yemenite.

I came across his name and even his picture in a large anthology devoted to that period. The occasion for the picture was a daredevil exploit performed by five boys and one girl, when they uprooted all the saplings planted in 1908 by the Jewish National Fund in what was to be the Herzl Forest, and then replanted them without pay. This was their way of forcing upon the management of the National Fund the policy of using Jewish hands to plant Jewish trees. The little putsch in 1908 set a policy for Zionist institutions from which they have never deviated.

The girl in the picture, seated on the floor, is Miriam Baratz, now the famous milkmaid grandmother of the oldest collective settlement in Dagania. Of the boys, Yitzhak is by far the best-looking, with a shock of wavy hair. He is the only one in the group holding a gun, which he seems to be training on the cameraman. Despite the frown on his face—fashionable among people brought up in the Russian tradition—he looks like a boy playing a prank and showing off with his gun. When I first met him, he seemed to be showing off with his Yiddish.

I began frequenting Café Restaurant Kadimah, where I could obtain good Oriental food—*pitta* and *humus*—and the best fish I ate in Israel, out of Lake Kinneret, and black coffee, at reasonable prices, and where on Saturday nights I could see the color of Israel or rather of what is known as "the other Israel"—the Israel of the immigrants. I often brought my friends there, Israelis and American tourists, to observe the color. One Saturday night I brought as my guest Dvorah Simhoni, the niece of Miriam Baratz. She knew Yitzhak and told me that in recent years he had been a well-to-do merchant who had enjoyed contacts with the British, which put him in a position to help the Haganah. When the British left, he lost his fortune. Through his connections, he secured from the Custodian of Abandoned Property a lease on the former Arab cafe-chantant.

Yitzhak greeted us cordially and entered into a conversation with Dvorah about old times and about her aunt. He went over the details of that famous sapling episode, praised Miriam Baratz as a great woman, and ended up by sighing: "Oh, what a fine *hevrah* (crowd) we had in those days! That was really a *hevrah!*" Then he excused himself and went about his work. He evidenced little enthusiasm for the customers who now occupied his attention. These were not the dedicated pioneers who knew the supreme happiness of suffering for an ideal, who laid the foundations of Jewish labor, a Jewish defense, and of the Hebrew language in the country, and many of whom laid down their lives or gave their children's lives on the altar of Israel's freedom. These, the frequenters of Café Restaurant Kadimah, only came because they had to come; they grumble at every difficulty and expect Israel and the Jews of the world to pamper them. At least, such was the attitude one could read into Yitzhak's face and manner when he dealt with his customers. Hawk-like, he watched his establishment from his vantage point, near the bar, giving instructions to the waiters, rushing over to a spot of potential trouble, and returning, when he had a chance, to talk with us. He found time to tell us about Ben-Gurion in the days when they worked and dreamed and suffered together at Sejera, in the Galilee: "He'd keep quiet most of the time, never even say 'Shalom'. But, then, at a meeting, he'd get up to speak and did he speak!"

Aside from the three of us, nobody in the place spoke Hebrew. The waiters mostly spoke Arabic, the customers Rumanian and Ladino; occasionally, Yiddish was heard on the lips of an older couple. Ladino and Rumanian sound strikingly alike and have similar Romance vocabularies, so that an outsider could hardly tell one from the other even if he caught a word here and there. But it was not difficult to tell the difference between the stolidly dull Salonikans who spoke Ladino and the chattering laughing volatile Rumanians. Nearly all Salonikans came into the place in family groups, sitting around a table, the husband wearing an air of self-importance as he drank his beer; the wife, squat, plump, dark-complexioned and obeisant, bustling about the children. The Rumanians were for the most part young couples, absorbed in dancing. Their faces looked vacant.

A few persons stood out. There was a rather attractive woman past her prime who came in to sell nuts and almonds, wrapped in tiny pieces of newsprint, humming some operatic air as she flitted from table to table, and now and then making a witty remark in good German or in cultured Rumanian which sounded so different from the Rumanian spoken around her. She had an intelligent face lined with wrinkles which bespoke suffering, a cynical air and a good singing voice. The tall stout Transylvanian band-leader, who addressed the other musicians in Magyar, had a shrewd indulgent smile on his genial broad face as he played Hungarian and gypsy music and American jazz, a flicker of tolerant disdain in his perspicacious eyes.

There was also the magician. He did not look Jewish at all. Perhaps he was not. The new immigration brought a number of non-Jewish husbands and wives and even political refugees who joined the large exodus, as in the days when the Israelites left Egypt under Moses. But the magician looked as if I had seen him somewhere. It was in a book. I once read a couple of books by Panait Istrati, the Rumanian novelist, who depicted the polyglot underworld of the port cities of his native land. That magician seemed to have stepped out of those pages.

The magician swallowed fire, put swords down his throat, and performed other such tricks. It was always at about nine o'clock on Saturday nights, when the crowd was largest and its money still unspent. Whether Yitzhak paid the magician or the magician paid Yitzhak for the concession—he was always rewarded with coins by an appreciative audience—I do not know. But it was a form of entertainment that was unthinkable among the *vatikim*. It was an innovation brought in with the surge of the large immigration. Yitzhak himself could entertain only contempt for such things. Not that he was a man of books or an intellectual. But he was a *vatik* and had the notions of a *vatik*, of what constituted culture and what was worthwhile in human life.

There was only one evening, early in the year of 1952, when Café Restaurant Kadimah was filled with men and women whom Yitzhak Nadav delighted to honor. That evening the sounds of the Hebrew language, spoken in the accents of the *vatikim*, reverberated through its spacious high-ceilinged dining hall.

The occasion was the marriage of Malka, Yitzhak's comely, vivacious daughter, to an officer in the parachutist corps. The wedding ceremony took place on a Friday afternoon in the Carmelia Court, a hotel operated by the Histradrut. Like all wedding ceremonies of the non-religious in Israel, it was a pretty drab affair; a traditional, orthodox ritual, without the spirit of orthodoxy in the participants, without the spirit of the hora dance, and without the parade practices which American Jews have incorporated into their wedding ceremonial. But a wedding it was, a wedding of two young soldiers in the Defense Army of Israel—Malka was then on reserve duty—and attended by young veterans of the War of Liberation and by army officers and soldiers.

Many venerable old-timers were there, sitting at the tables which set forth the frugal refreshments of the austerity regime, gossiping about politics, former days, and their contemporaries who had now risen to high office. The Transylvanian band-leader was there, with his two assistants, to play the traditional wedding tunes and the melodies that recalled the recent episodes of Israel's war. He must have practiced upon those airs for the occasion. He now wore a different expression—none of that habitual indulgent disdain, but a serious respect for his audience. And as he played it, respect, too, for the March of the Palmach.

The father of the bride appeared to be more interested in gossiping with his old cronies than in performing his ceremonial duties.

Yitzhak's real self awoke only in the evening, at the Café Kadimah. A unique gathering was assembled from distant parts, as well at a few chosen notables of Haifa—all come to celebrate with Yitzhak the Yemenite and to recall the days of Hashomer. They hailed from Jerusalem, from Tel Aviv, and from Kfar Gileadi on the Syrian border, the old survivors of Hashomer who had defended the first Jewish settlements and founded new ones, who had ploughed and sowed and built. This was a reunion of the *vatikim,* of Yitzhak's comrades-in-arms.

The windows of the cafe were coated with calcimine to keep out the curious stares of the immigrant riff-raff on Hamrah Square. Among the honored guests were Manya Shochet and Itzhak Ben-Zvi; and the widow and sons of Alexander Zaid, the hero of Sheikh Abrekh; and Pinya Shneurson, nicknamed "Kalipta" (Eucalyptus) because of his height, who fought at Trumpeldor's side at Tel Hai and took over the command when the famous one-armed hero fell; and men and women from Kfar Gileadi, who forty years before formed the first strategic settlement in the country— to safeguard the northern boundary of the future Jewish State. Keila Gileadi was there, the widow of the hero after whom the kibbutz is named. There was not a man or a woman among the guests whose name or picture is not familiar to every student of Zionist history.

Itzhak Ben-Zvi and Manya Shochet were the most notable participants at the gathering. The two, who had traveled different roads in political philosophy, greeted each other cordially—Manya, a wizened, whilte-haired little woman with unusually mobile features, and Ben-Zvi, looking less the warrior than anyone present,

slouched in his chair, the focus of attention. He seldom addressed
anyone, but answered questions in an amiable tone, his face always
unsmiling. With his pallor of a scholarly recluse, he could more
readily be taken for the chaplain of these weather-beaten pioneers
and fighters, than for the founder of their organization. They treated
him with the deference given to a spiritual leader.

But they did not give the impression of a mere flock who follows
a sheperd. Strength of personality was written on the features of
everyone of them—features which told the saga of the revolutionary
period in Jewish history, of the culture which was a strange fusion
of the Talmud and Dostoyevsky; of the daring lonely dreams and
yet more daring and lonely pilgrimage to the desert land; of the
struggle with one's self and with Nature and with Arabs; of the
triumph of the will; of the apparent serenity after a life of storms.
The men and women from Kfar Gileadi, those who remained at
their post in the wilderness and made it, painfully, into a garden,
who did not go as emissaries to far-off lands, or to office desks in
the city—these stalwarts dominated the scene.

Yitzhak Nadav's face radiated happiness and admiration as he
hovered among his old comrades, pouring out drinks, seeing to it
that everyone had a double portion of fish from Lake Kinneret,
exchanging pleasantries and good wishes, recalling old times.

What a pity the people from Daganiah could not make it! If
only Miriam Baratz was here—the reunion of the old *hevrah* would
be complete. Yes, why didn't Daganiah come? Are they coming
later? Thus the exclamations and questions flew. Yitzhak was too
busy being happy to dwell on the absence of his old comrades from
Daganiah. "Ai, Abba, Abba!" he said to the Mayor of Haifa, as
he served him drinks, "Why weren't you with us in those days!
What a *hevrah* that was! Ai, was that a *hevrah!*"

This was the greatest compliment he could have paid. It meant
that if Abba Hushi were old enough, he would have qualified to be
among the handful of men and women who blazed the trail that
he and his contemporaries were later to follow. The Mayor ac-
knowledged the compliment by admonishing me: "Frank, don't
miss a thing of what you see! This is history!" There was, in fact,
more history in the evening than anyone knew: several months

later, the most silent and unobtrusive of the guests was to become
the second President of Israel.

The Mayor and his friends, including myself, were invited as
a special privilege to this "gathering of the *vatikim*," a privilege
which all of us appreciated. Among these privileged—or, rather,
underprivileged—guests there were those who once drained marshes,
contracted malaria, jaundice, dysentery and other diseases, who endured hunger and danger to play their part in pioneering. But they
came after the close of the First World War on a wave of popular
enthusiasm, supported by the World Zionist Organization, with
international sanction, under the spotlight of the world's regard.
The *vatikim*, however, the men and women of Ben-Zvi's generation, who came when the Turks ruled Palestine, when official
Zionist leadership frowned on their utopian dreams, when they were
a small lonely band, ridiculed by the older settlers—these were
the real pioneers. The members of the generation which succeeded
them, present at the gathering, looked at their seniors with eyes
of beatific adoration.

There were no speeches at the celebration. But as the meal drew
to a close, the *vatikim* began to sing. They sang the songs of the
Second Aliyah, of the pioneers of the first decade of this century.
Their favorites were not the Zionist songs and hymns of their day,
but rather passages from the Bible and the Prayer Book which
their hassidic forefathers had endowed with new meaning and
which they in turn endowed with a still newer meaning.

> "Bring ye righteous offerings, say unto the Lord. . . ."
> "Purge thou our heart to serve thee truthfully. . . ."
> "Behold, how good and how pleasant it is for brethren
>   to dwell together."

When the singers were young, ragged and hungry, they used
to sing those verses with delirium, with abandon, stomping their
feet in a wild weird hora, as if forcibly driving away all doubt,
all bitterness, all thought of flight or retreat. But now in 1952, at
Malka's wedding party, these were songs of triumph and achievement, and the singers were sedate successful farmers, who had
the finest cows in the country, the finest dining hall in Israel, the

most attractive rest-house, the most comfortably appointed kindergarten for their grandchildren. Their songs had become the paeans
of men and women whose daring dreams of an Israel reborn had
come true.

I watched a couple facing me across the table. The man seemed
to sing as if he were merely performing a routine. And yet, in the
intense concentrated expression on his face, one could read powerful
feelings and moving memories. He did not look at his wife and
she did not look at him. But it was as though they were singing to
each other, that every throb in her voice, every shade of emotion
immediately communicated itself to him. An inner light shone in
her liquid dark eyes, her cheeks were aglow, her face was trans-
figured with bliss, her raven-and silver crowned head swayed to
the rhythm of the lines, to the meaning of the words, to the
memories of a dedicated youth and to the serene realization of
accomplishment.

> "Blessed be our God,
> Who created us for His glory,
> Who separated us from the erring,
> Who has given us the Law of Truth,
> Who has implanted within us eternal life."

I first heard that song in my childhood, when it was sung by
bearded earlocked hassidim, the adherents of the Saint of Retchitza,
Reb Sholem-Ber, Kalipta's grandfather, in my home town on the
Dnieper. It was from such places that Kalipta and his contemporaries
brought these and similar verses to the fields and hills and marshes
of the desert land to sustain them in their trials as the words once
sustained their ancestors in the ordeals of old.

* * *

The *vatikim* fell silent. From the table of the Sabras, headed
by the bride and groom, came a solo:

> "A breeze in the evening is blowing."

Clap-clap, answered a dozen pair of hands.

> "The bonfire in camp is aglowing."

Clap-clap. And all the Sabras at the table swaying from side to side, took up the lilting refrain:

"Tai-ra-ra-rai, ra-ra-rai, ra-ra-rai!"

The bright open bold faces of the Sabras had no rich complexity of clashing civilizations written on them; they appeared sure of themselves. The songs they sang were songs of recent battles, of desert camping in the war they had won or in preparation for it. Their memories of fallen comrades were fresh memories and the result of their struggles more obvious.

The *vatikim* looked toward the Sabras, who kept on singing.

"All around us storms are raging,
But our heads are kept erect;
Ever ever in the forefront,
We, the soldiers of Palmach;
From Metullah to the Negev,
From the desert to the sea. . . ."

The words had a direct and immediate bearing on fighting for one's country, quite unlike the songs of the *vatikim*, who first took up the guns in behalf of the homeland. Here, perhaps, lies the chief difference between the generation of immigrant pioneers and the Sabras.

Towards midnight, as previously arranged by Yitzhak, a photographer arrived, and all the *vatikim*—that is, only the former members of Hashomer—were asked to pose. Ben-Zvi was seated in the center of the front row, with the father of the bride seated on the floor in front of him. Everybody, including the unsmiling Ben-Zvi, tried to smile: American influences have finally penetrated even to the *vatikim*. It is no doubt the only known picture in which Ben-Zvi is shown with a smile.

A young man, Sharon Weitz, turned to me with moist eyes. It was one of the rare occasions when I have seen a Sabra shed his protective cynicism and give way to his feelings:

"Look at them," he said to me, "they are old now. I remember them when I was a child, when they used to come to my father's house. They were young then. They wore Russian rubashkas, Arab abayas and kefiyas, carried guns, rode Arab mares. They boasted long mustaches. They were shomrim. Now look at them! They are old."

The next night I returned to Café Restaurant Kadimah on Hamrah Square. The place was again filled with dancing, chattering Rumanians and dull stolid Salonikans. The Transylvanian band-leader once more wore his smile of indulgent disdain. His band now added the march and the songs of the Palmach to its repertoire of Hungarian gypsy tunes and American jazz. But Yitzhak Nadav was not there.

I revisited the place many times, but I never saw Yitzhak there again. He evidently conceived a distaste for it, and soon sublet the place to an Iraqi immigrant, who introduced a startling innovation: the menus were now written in Hebrew and Rumanian, instead of Hebrew and English, as is the general custom in Israel.

BIOGRAPHICAL NOTES

◆

AUTHORS WHOSE WORKS have been used and some individuals whose names occur in the book are included in the following notes. These notes do not purport to be exhaustive. The number of lines devoted to an individual does not necessarily bear any relation to his position or general importance.

AGNON, SAMUEL JOSEPH (original surname Czaczkes). Born in Galicia in 1888. Migrated to Palestine in 1907. Spent the years 1914 to 1924 in Germany. Has lived in Jerusalem since 1924.

Foremost living master of Hebrew style, which is a blending of several traditional styles employed even when dealing with modern subject matter. Stories, such as "The Minyan" given in this book, often deal with the supernatural, conveying the authentic spirit of the believer.

Best known book in English: *The Bridal Canopy*, translated by I. M. Lask.

All Hebrew works by Agnon are published by Schocken Books.

AUERBACH, EPHRAIM. Born in Belzi, Bessarabia, 1892. Migrated to Palestine in 1912, during the latter part of the Second Aliyah. Deported in 1915. Joined the Zion Mule Corps under Trumpeldor. When the British withdrew from Galipoli and the Zion Mule Corps was disbanded, Auerbach migrated to the United States.

One of the leading Yiddish poets and journalists in the United States. Member of editorial staff of *Day-Morning Journal*, New York.

AVINOAM-GROSSMAN, REUBEN (or Reuven). Born in Chicago. 1905. Settled in Palestine in 1929. Educator and writer. Only major figure among Israeli poets who is of American birth. Published many translations, including some of Shakespeare's plays in Hebrew and an anthology of American poetry. Adopted surname of Avinoam (Father of Noam) in memory of his son, Noam, who fell in the battle for Jerusalem early in 1948. Appointed by Ben-Gurion to set up and head a special department at the Ministry of Defense to perpetuate the memory of the heroes fallen in the War of Liberation of 1948. *Gvile Esh* (Scrolls of Fire) published in the summer of 1952, is the first and so far the largest (over 800 pages) of a series of projects by the department.

BAR-JOSEPH, JOSHUA. Born in Safed, 1912. One of the leading native writers in Israel. Most of his stories deal with the life of the "Old Yishuv," that is, the religious community which ante-dated modern Zionist colonization. His recent trilogy, *Ir Kesuma* (Enchanted City) tells the saga of the hassidim of Safed from the early part of the nineteenth century until the ravages of the First World War. It is one of the most ambitious works of fiction produced in Israel.

BARASH, ASHER. Born in East Galicia, 1889. Died in Tel-Aviv in 1953. Settled in Palestine in 1914. Leading writer of fiction.

BARATZ, JOSEPH. Born in Kuznitza, Ukraine in 1890. Came to Palestine in 1906. Worked as itinerant farm laborer and stonemason. Organized Jewish laborers in Jerusalem who, with the co-operation of Professor Schatz, of the Bezalel Art School, sought to acquire the higher skills in stonemasoning. That was part of the "Conquest of Labor" as practiced in the city.

"I was about seventeen years old and had never before done any manual work. I would return after a day's labor with bleeding swollen hands . . . go out into the yard, lean on one of the trees and cry like a child. . . . I was afraid I'd never make a good laborer, and I was lonesome for my mother . . ."

In 1911 he helped found the first collective settlement in Palestine, Daganiah, where he still lives. Over the years he has been to Egypt, Europe, South America, the United States and Canada on various missions. During the Second World War he donned a soldier's uniform in the Jewish Brigade. Published several books and articles. Latest in English *A Village by the Jordan* published in England. Member of the Knesset (Israel Parliament) since 1949.

BARATZ, MIRIAM (wife of Joseph). Born in Bohuslav, Ukraine, 1900. One of a family of eight. Father operated a ferry. Ardent Zionists. Nearly all settled in Palestine. Miriam was one of the first girls in the Second Aliyah to do manual work like the men. Met Joseph in the Galilee, helped in the founding of Daganiah, where she still lives. Writes occasionally.

"The energy and the exuberance we enjoyed in those days helped us to endure the greatest hardships."

BAR-DAVID, MOLLY LYONS. Born in Rosthern, a small town in Western Canada in 1910. Came to Palestine in 1936. Lives in Jerusalem. Married to Dutch-born Jaap Bar-David. Frequent contributor to *Jerusalem Post, Hadassah Newsletter* and other publications. Author of *My Promised Land* (G. P. Putnam's Sons, New York, 1953).

BEN-GURION, DAVID (original surname Green). Born in Plonsk, Poland, 1886. Chief founder of the State of Israel and its first Prime Minister. Father was a small town solicitor and an ardent Zionist. David studied Hebrew and spoke it fluently before entering the Russian high school in Warsaw. In 1903 he was co-founder of Poale-Zion (Labor Zionists) in Poland. In 1905 he joined the Jewish self-defense. Settled in Palestine in 1906. Jointed the editorial staff of labor weekly in 1910. Studied at Constantinople. Deported from Palestine in 1915 and went to America, where he collaborated with Ben-Zvi, as he had since 1910 in Palestine. Returned in Jewish Legion under Allenby in 1917. Steadily rose as leader, first of the labor movement (for a long time general secretary of the Histadrut) and later as leader of the Zionist movement. Became Chairman of the Zionist Executive in 1935, which moved its seat from London to Jerusalem. Continued in this post until he became Prime Minister.

Writings and speeches embrace many subjects, but deal mostly with national and social problems and with the philosophy of history.

In 1907, when the Socialist International still looked askance at the Zionist idea, Ben-Gurion, in the name of Poale-Zion, authored a memorandum pleading for admission.

BEN-YEHUDA, ELIEZER (original surname Perlman). Born in White Russia in 1858. Died in Jerusalem in 1923.

First man in modern history to employ the Hebrew language in conversation for every occasion.

Received an intensive rabbinical education in his early youth, but soon fell under the influence of modern ideas and became a Russian revolutionary. Went to Paris to study, where he supported himself by translations. The Garibaldi war for the unification of Italy and the revolt of the Balkan peoples against Turkish rule turned him to the Zionist idea. In 1882 suffering from tuberculosis, against the warnings of physicians, he came to settle in Jerusalem, bringing his young bride. From the moment he landed on the soil of Palestine, he refused to speak any other language but Hebrew. Immediately adopted a Hebrew surname. Was the first to adopt the Sephardi pronunciation as the standard. The ultra-religious leaders of Jerusalem excommunicated Ben-Yehuda and persecuted him, but the younger Zionists soon rallied to his banner and helped him in the spread of Hebrew speech in the Sephardi pronunciation.

In 1915, despite his Ottomanization and despite his preachment for loyalty to the Turkish Empire, Ben-Yehuda was deported. He spent the years of the First World War in the New York City Library, working on his Lexicon.

BEN-ZVI, ITZHAK (original surname Shimshelevitch). Born in Poltava, Ukraine in 1884. Second President of Israel, outstanding authority on Oriental Jewish communities, founder of Hashomer. Oldest son of a business man and an active Zionist. Both Ben-Zvi's parents were descended from families of rabbinical scholars in Lithuania and White Russia.

Itzhak was given a modernized Hebrew schooling and was later sent to a Russian secondary school in Poltava, and to the University in Kiev. He came under the influence of the Russian socialist movement, but retained the Zionist sentiments. Soon became one of the earliest theoreticians of a movement which sought to combine Socialism with Zionism. In 1905 he visited Palestine for his summer vacation. Two years later he settled there.

Before settling in Palestine, he was active in the Jewish self-defense. Arms were cached at his father's house. A search made by the police during Itzhak's absence resulted in the arrest of the whole family and their subsequent exile to Siberia. Itzhak who was away managed to evade police.

On coming to Palestine, he registered at the inn as Itzhak Ben-Zvi, to avoid attracting attention. In time he adopted Ben-Zvi as his Hebrew surname. He edited first a Yiddish, then a Hebrew weekly, taught secondary school in Jerusalem, studied the life and mores of the Samaritans, Karaites, Kurdish Jews, Persian Jews, etc., as well as the Druze and the Arabs.

Together with Ben-Gurion and others he went to Constantinople to study Turkish law, returned to Jerusalem when the war broke out in 1914. Was deported, landed in New York, collaborated with Ben-Gurion in writing a book on Palestine, in working for a Jewish Congress, for organizing a Jewish Legion and a pioneer organization (Hechalutz). Finally returned to Palestine under General Allenby's command, as a member of the Jewish Legion. For many years he was

Chairman of the Executive Council of the Palestine Jewish Assembly. In 1952, when Ben-Zvi was inducted as the second President of Israel, his father, Zvi Shimshi was present at the ceremony.

BIALIK, HAYIM NAHMAN (or Chaim Nachman). Born near Zhitomir, Ukraine, 1873. Died in Vienna (on the operating table) in 1934. Foremost Hebrew poet in modern times. Received traditional Jewish education at his grandfather's home and at the famous Yeshiva of Volozhin (in White Russia). Steeped in Jewish lore. Self taught in modern culture. Although Bialik wrote few poems which may be termed Zionist, he exerted a tremendous influence on the shaping of Zionist sentiment among the Jews of Eastern Europe. His influence was especially powerful among the generation that produced the Second Aliyah. For many years Bialik lived in Odessa, where he thrived as a publisher of Hebrew books. As the result of an intercession by Maxim Gorki, Bialik was allowed by the Bolsheviks to leave Russia. Finally settled in Tel-Aviv in 1924. During the decade that he lived in Palestine he was the central figure of the Yishuv.

BOURLA, YEHUDA. Born in Jerusalem, 1886. Scion of a Sephardi rabbinical family that settled in Palestine two hundred years ago. Bourla is the foremost Hebrew writer on Sephardi and Oriental Jewish life. He studied in Jerusalem at a Sephardi yeshiva, and the Hebrew Teachers' Institute (modern Zionist). Lived in Damascus, Syria for several years. Served in the Turkish Army in 1915-1918. Former director of the Israel Ministry of Minorities. Bourla's first book was published in 1918. Published several additional works including one of three volumes and of two volumes.

BRENNER, JOSEPH HAYIM. Born in Northern Ukraine in 1881. Killed by Arab rioters in Jaffa in 1921. Brenner knew poverty all his life. First a brilliant yeshiva student, he became a private tutor, who refused to receive a remuneration more than he needed for his bare subsistence. For a brief period he was librarian of a cultural Jewish club in Homel, White Russia. His sojourn in Homel resulted in a series of gloomy sketches and short stories in Hebrew, describing the life of that city's poor Jews, living in "The Pit." The Collection bears the title *Emek Achor* (Valley of Desolation). After a term in the standing army of the Czar, from which he escaped, he found his way to London, where he taught himself the printing trade. He edited, published and printed with his own hands a Hebrew magazine *Hame-*

orer (The Awakaner), which he himself addressed and mailed. In his magazine Brenner called upon self-respecting Jewish youth to migrate to Palestine. In 1909 he migrated himself and vainly sought to remain incognito, also trying to adjust himself to manual labor. His fellow-workers insisted that he do literary work. Brenner was by far the gloomiest Hebrew writer of his day and perhaps of the whole modern era.

BUSSEL, JOSEPH. Born in a small town in White Russia in 1891. Drowned in Lake Tiberias in 1919. At the age of eight he lost his father. Until the age of fifteen, he studied the Talmud, then became affected by modern ideas and, at the age of sixteen, was a Zionist propagandist. Went to the Kherson province in the South of Russia to train among Jewish farmers for life in Palestine and finally went to Palestine late in 1907. In Petah Tikvah, where it was customary for the young pioneer's "labor market" to offer their day's work for a pittance, the Jewish farmers would feel Bussel's muscles, look at his pale face and slender body and disqualify him. Bussel went to Rehovot, where he "conquered the hoe." From Rehovot he went to the Galilee and joined the group that sought to create a communal settlement. Eventually he became the leader of the group at Daganiah. It was Bussel who prevailed upon his hotly debating comrades to choose the name "Daganiah" (cornflower) for their settlement. In 1917 he married Hayuta Gavze from his home town. Two years later he was stricken with yellow fever, but refused to take care of himself. When the boat in which he crossed Lake Kinneret capsized, he was too weak to swim and was drowned.

CARMEL, MOSHE. Born in Poland in 1911. Came to Palestine in 1924. Member of Kibbutz Na'an since 1937. Haganah office since 1941. Brigadier general in command of northern district for Israel Defense Army in 1948-50.

EILON, AMOS. Born in Vienna. Came to Palestine as a child. Gifted young journalist. On staff of Haaretz, Tel-Aviv. Author of book, *Jerusalem Never Fell* (in Hebrew).

GILEADI, ISRAEL. Born in Russia in 1866. Died of malaria in the Galilee in 1918.

One of the founders of Hashomer and leader of the Galilean sho-merim. During the First World War, Gileadi, with a group of other shomerim, founded the strategic outpost on a high hill overlooking Syria, one of the earliest collective settlements in Palestine. After the founder died the settlement was named Kfar Gileadi.

HANKIN, or HENKIN, YEHEZEKIEL (not to be confused with Joshua Hankin). Organizer and leader of first Jewish self defense unit in Russia in 1903; one of the organizers and leaders of Hashomer; one of the first hunters and explorers among Jews in Palestine in modern times. Died of yellow fever during the First World War.

HERZL, THEODOR (Hebrew name Benjamin Ze'ev). Born in Buda-pest in 1860. Died in a resort in Austria in 1904. Founder of the World Zionist Organization (1897). Termed by Max Nordau "the greatest Jew in a thousand years." Came from a cultured assimilated middle class family. Moved to Vienna for an education. On graduating as Doctor of Laws, young Herzl took to writing and soon joined the staff of the *Neue Freie Presse* which sent him to Paris. Among other assignments, Herzl had to report the Dreyfus case and became con-vinced that anti-Semitism was incurable, except through the reconcen-tration of the Jewish people in their own land. Led the Zionist move-ment from 1897 until his death from a heart attack in 1904. The most revered name in the Zionist movement and in Israel.

HUSHI (also KHOUSHY), ABBA (original surname Schneller). Born in Turka, Galicia in 1898. Mayor of Haifa since 1950. Israel's most distinguished mayor. Studied in Vienna. Settled in Palestine in 1920. Worked on the roads at the settlement of Beth-Alpha and as stevedore in the port of Haifa. Rose as leader of Haifa's organized labor and helped organize Arab labor. Resigned his seat in the Knesset and his position as Secretary of Haifa Labor Council when he was elected Mayor of Haifa.

IBN-ZAHAV, ARI. Born in Poland in 1899. Spent some years in Ger-many. Settled in Palestine in 1922. Academic secretary of Hebrew University 1924-1946. First book published in 1925. Prolific writer on historic and contemporary subjects. Recent English translation of his *David and Bathsheba* published by Crown Publishers, New York.

IMBER, NAPHTHALI HERZ. Born in Galicia in 1856. Died in New York in 1910. Poet and scholar. Author of *Hatikvah*.

JABOTINSKY, VLADIMIR (Hebrew name Ze'ev). Born in Odessa in 1879. Died in New York in 1940. Brilliant writer, orator and poet in Russian and several other languages, including Hebrew which he learned late in life. Among famous translations: Poe's *Raven* into Russian; Bialik's poems into Russian; Dante's *Inferno* from Italian into Hebrew. Best-known original novel, *Samson*.

Stormy petrel of the Zionist movement. First to advocate Jewish Legion during World War I. First to advocate large military organization for the Jewish community of Palestine. Sentenced to fifteen years in the prison of Acre after taking part in organizing defense of the Jews during Jerusalem riots in 1920. Freed by Sir Herbert Samuel. Barred by the British from entering Palestine. Criticized Weizmann's gradualist policy and his confidence in the British. Quarreled with organized labor in Palestine and the Zionist movement, originally because they supported Weizmann, later for their economic policies. Organized the Revisionist wing within the WZO, which, in 1935, broke away and became the New Zionist organization. Was involved in bitter feud with Labor, which accused him of fascistic tendencies.

Jabotinsky's strongest influence was on his disciples who, after his death, broke away from the New Zionist Organization and founded the Irgun Zvai Leumi (National Military Organization), headed by Menachem Beigin, and the Lohame Herut Israel (Fighters for the Freedom of Israel)—respectively known as IZL and Lehi. These organizations, with representatives in the United States and other countries, refused to accept the authority of the WZO and the Haganah and carried out acts of terror and assassination in Palestine and independent political activity abroad.

KATZENELSON, BERL. Born in Bobruisk, White Russia in 1887. Died in Jerusalem in 1944. Next to A. D. Gordon and J. H. Brenner, whom he survived, was foremost spiritual leader of Jewish Labor in Palestine. Prominent in world Zionist councils. Came to Palestine in 1909. Worked in Petah Tikvah and other colonies in Ben-Shemen, in Kinneret, which he helped found as one of the first collectives in the country. Later member of Hulda, another collective. Joined the Jewish Legion Palestine unit in 1917.

"He was the great architect of the structure of our life," said a veteran pioneer of the Second Aliyah (Mordecai Segalor). Katzenelson said about himself that when he left for Palestine, it was not with any faith in the future of the Zionist idea, but out of sheer desperation and national pride. If it was destined for the Jewish people to leave the arena of history, he wanted to be among the few who would go down fighting.

KLEBANOFF, YERUHAM. Came to Palestine in 1908 as member of the Romny group, which formed the first "commune" of the Second Aliyah (see Baratz: "Daganiah," p. 84). At first the group followed the principle of building the land without regard to personal satisfaction, and worked one year in a place to prepare it for others. The group lived in Ben Shemen, Hadera, Kinneret, Daganiah and finally broke up. Klebanoff then joined the Hashomer Organization of the Galilee and later became one of the organizers and leaders of Hashomer in Judea. After World War I he smuggled himself into Soviet Russia to salvage the Zionist Archives and to free members of his family. Was caught by the Secret Police and sentenced to die as a "Zionist spy," but escaped. Joined Rutenberg's staff to pioneer in the electrification of the country. Has held a position in the Rutenberg Company since then.

KRINITZI, ABRAHAM. Born in Grodno, Eastern Poland in 1886. Mayor and main founder of Ramat Gan. Came to Palestine in 1905. Now furniture manufacturer. Chairman of the Executive of Israel Manufacturers Association.

LAVI, SHLOMO (original surname Lefkowitz). Born Plonsk, Poland, 1883, boyhood friend of Ben-Gurion. Writer, member of the Knesset since 1949. Came to Palestine in 1905. He was a co-founder of Kibbutz Ein-Harod, where he still lives, and of Hakibbutz Hameuhad. He was a member of Hashomer and served in the Jewish Legion in World War I and in the Jewish Brigade in World War II. Published several novels and a volume of short stories.

MOSENSON, MOSHE. Born in Ein Ganim in 1915, a small settlement in the Judean Plains. Never wrote professionally until publication of *Letters from the Desert*. Editor of *Bama'aleh*.

MOSENSON, YIGAL. Brother of Moshe. Born in Ein Ganim in 1917. One of the best-known native writers. Best known works *Sands of the Negev* (a play) and *The Way of a Man* (a novel). In private life, a farmer.

NETTER, CHARLES. Born in Alsace in 1826. Died in Mikveh Israel in 1882. Founder and first director of the first agricultural school for Jews. School is still controlled by the Alliance Israelite Universelle whose employe Netter was in 1868, when he founded it.

NISSIM, ZACHARIAH. Born in Yemen in 1935. Came to Israel in Operation Magic Carpet in 1949.

NITZAN, SHLOMO. Young Israeli poet and journalist. Came to Palestine as a child.

REUBENI (also REUVENI), AARON (original surname Shimshelevitch; half-brother of President Ben-Zvi). Born in Poltava, Ukraine in 1887. Settled in Palestine in 1910, after escaping from Siberia where the Shimshelevitch family had been exiled by the Czarist government. In his youth, Reubeni refused to follow the school routine, but spent his time in reading and writing. Began writing in Russian, later used Yiddish and finally mastered the Hebrew language enough to become one of the leading writers of the Second and Third Aliyah periods. His works include descriptions of Jewish tramps in America, where he lived between 1904 and 1906; life in the Siberian tundras; novels and short stories of life in Palestine, especially of Jerusalem. Writes also in other languages, including English, on social and scientific topics.

REICHENSTEIN, SHLOMO. Born in Poland in 1900. Died in Palestine in 1944. Middle class home. Studied Hebrew in his youth. Spent some time in Russia during and after the War of 1914-1919. Came to Palestine in 1919, worked as a farm laborer for about one year and joined the first group which founded Tel-Joseph and Ein-Harod in the Emek. Lived in Ein-Harod until his death. When incapacitated by a wound inflicted by Arabs, Reichenstein served as a waiter in the communal dining hall. Wrote in his spare time. During the last days of his life he wrote in the mornings and attended to his work as waiter from one to eleven p.m. Published short stories and began writing a trilogy of the life in the Emek, of which *Genesis* is the first volume. Died shortly after the publication of *Genesis*.

RUPPIN, ARTHUR (Hebrew name Shimeon). Born in Prussia in 1876. Died in Jerusalem in 1942. Economist and social scientist who became converted to the Zionist idea in his youth. Sent by the WZO to Palestine in 1907. A year later he was sent to open the Palestine Office of the World Zionist Organization—its first venture in colonization work —on a budget of eight hundred pounds a year. Ruppin's open-minded approach and his ability to value the human element in economic ventures, according to Berl Katzenelson, saved the early Zionist endeavor from disintegration and ensured the constructive contributions of the young pioneers of the Second and Third Aliyah. Among his many achievements Katzenelson lists: organizing the building of Tel-Aviv; founding the Palestine Land Development Company; Yavnieli's mission to Yemen, and others. Arthur Ruppin was perhaps the first prominent German Zionist to settle in Palestine.

SHAMIR, MOSHE. Born in Israel in 1921. Leading member of the younger school of Hebrew writers. Spent many years in a kibbutz and in Palmach (striking force of Haganah). His novel *He Walked in the Fields,* especially the dramatized version, brought him fame. His latest work, *A King of Flesh and Blood,* published in 1954, is the most ambitious historical novel written by any young Israeli writer.

SHERTOK (SHARETT), MOSHE. Born in Kherson, the South of Russia, in 1895. Second Prime Minister of Israel. Distinguished linguist. Shertok was brought to Palestine by his parents and spent some time in an Arab village, where his father kept a farm. Studied at the Herzliah Secondary School, in Constantinople, served in the Turkish army, studied at the London School of Economics, became a journalist and later an official of the Histadrut and the Zionist Organization, where he rose to become Political Secretary of the Jewish Agency, a post held until May 1948, when he became Israel's first Foreign Minister.

SHIDLOVSKY, ALIZA. Born in Ukraine in 1897. Settled in Palestine in 1913. Member of the collective settlement of Kinneret, which she joined soon upon her arrival. One of the leaders of the Histadrut and the Moetzet Hapoalot (Women Workers' Council), where she has held several important positions. Visited America on missions for the movement.

SHIMONOVITZ (also SHIMONI), DAVID. Born in Bobruisk, White Russia in 1886. In 1909, already one of the leading young Hebrew poets, he settled in Palestine. After several years as manual laborer and watchman, he accepted, in 1914, a position as teacher in the Herzliah Secondary School in Tel-Aviv which he still holds. Distinguished poet. Subjects: lyrical; the landscape and pioneer sagas of the Homeland; biblical. Translated into Hebrew works by Lermontov, Pushkin, Tolstoy and Heine.

SHOHAT (also SHOCHAT), MANYA. Born in Russia in 1879. Came to Palestine after stormy revolutionary career in 1904. One of the founders of Hashomer, of Haganah and of Kfar Gileadi, where she has lived since its establishment. Writer and speaker.

SILVER, ABBA HILLEL. Born in Lithuania in 1893. Brought to the United States as a child. Prominent Reform rabbi. One of the most distinguished orators in America. Leader of the American Zionists during the 1940's when the political fate of the Homeland was being decided. Chairman of the American Zionist Emergency Council and of the American Section of the Jewish Agency for Palestine. Resigned both positions after a sharp dispute with the Israeli leadership.

SPRINZAK, JOSEPH. Born in Ukraine in 1885. One of the most distinguished leaders of the Second Aliyah. Speaker of the Knesset since 1949. Settled in Palestine in 1908. Engaged in manual labor. Studied at the American University at Beirut, Lebanon. Leader of Zeire-Zion and editor of party weekly. Prominent leader of Histadrut and ruling bodies of the Zionist movement.

SMILANSKY, MOSHE. Born in Talpino, Ukraine, in 1874. Died in Rehovot in 1953. Foremost literary spokesman of the First Aliyah, whose long life-span took him across the Second and the Third Aliyah up to the first five years of the State. Leading farmer and communal leader. Soldier of Jewish Legion in 1917.

Came to Palestine in the fall of 1890, as the first member of a Zionist family planning to settle. When Moshe's father was forced to change his plans, he insisted on remaining. Worked first in Rishon-le-Zion, later in Hadera, which had just been established, but was forced to leave it on account of the heavy malaria epidemic, which took many lives. He planned to return after rebuilding his strength, but his mother exacted a promise from him that if he stayed in Palestine, it would not be in Hadera. He then bought a plot of land in Rehovot, where he lived until his death. Smilansky's many writings include short stories and novels, dealing with the life of the pioneers and with Arab life, and lively articles on current topics, as well as technical articles on farming.

During the first few years of his life in Palestine, Moshe Smilansky often went to Han Manauli situated outside Jaffa to receive mail from home or to get news of "Stepmother Russia, for whom I still yearned," or on business. There he met colonists from all over the country and listened to the tales of story-telling teamsters, thus gathering the first materials for the chronicles of the early pioneers.

SHENHAR, YITZHAK (original surname Shenberg). Born in Proskorov, Ukraine, 1904. A leading writer of fiction. Came to Palestine in 1924. Worked for seven years as a laborer and as a railroad clerk. Editor for Schocken Publishing Company since 1942. Published seven original works and Hebrew translations of more than a dozen French, German, Russian and English classics.

SZOLD, HENRIETTA. Born in Baltimore in 1860. Died in Jerusalem in 1945. Most distinguished American Jewess of her age. Founder of Hadassah Women's Zionist Organization. Social work leader in Jewish Palestine. Founder of Youth Aliyah. (See introduction to Chapter 10.)

TABIB, MORDECAI. Born in Rehovot in 1910. Young writer, dealing mostly with the life of the Yemenite community. Parents came from Yemen with Yavnieli.

TCHERNICHOVSKY (also TCHERNIKHOVSKY, also CHERNIKHOVSKY), SAUL. Born in Crimea in 1875. Died in Tel-Aviv in 1943. Contemporary of Bialik, whose rival he was for the first place in modern Hebrew poetry. Perhaps a greater artist than Bialik, he was far less steeped in Jewish tradition and was less akin in the spirit to the yeshiva-bred pioneer, but perhaps more akin to the native born sabra. "Outwardly," says Simon Halkin, his poetry appears Hebraic only in idiom; in subject matter it is largely universal . . . Yet . . . he also proved the poet of the historic Jewish tragedy as well as the singer of the most fervent faith in Jewish survival." (*Modern Hebrew Literature*, Schocken Books, New York.)

Tchernichovsky came to Palestine in 1924, in the same group as Bialik.

TRUMPELDOR, JOSEPH. Born in Piatogorsk, Caucasus in 1880. Died at Tel-Hai, while defending the settlement in 1920.

Most famous hero of pre-State Jewish Palestine. Day of his death still solemnly observed. See Jabotinsky's account in Chapter 6.

TALMI, MENAHEM. Born in Ramat Gan in 1926. Spent his early youth in Ben-Shemen Youth Village and in training for life in a kibbutz. Worked as farmer, shepherd, guard, youth instructor. Joined the ranks of the Haganah in December 1947 and took part in some of the main battles. Edited several collections of stories about Israel's military struggles.

WEIZMANN, CHAIM. Born in Motel, White Russia in 1874. Died in Rehovot in 1952. First President of Israel. During the generation before the State, the leader of the world Zionist movement. Famous chemist. He taught chemistry at the University of Geneva in 1901-04, at the University of Manchester in 1904-16; directed the British Admiralty Laboratories in 1916-19; was chairman of the Daniel Sieff Research Institute at Rehovot in 1934-50, of the Weizmann Institute of Science, also at Rehovot, in 1944-50, and all through World War II was honorary adviser to the British Ministry of Supply.

YAARI, YEHUDA. Born in Galicia in 1900. Came to Palestine in 1920. A leading writer of fiction. Member of Kibbutz Beth-Alpha for five years. Librarian of University for two years. Studied in U. S. A. and Canada. Officer of the Keren Hayesod. Author of short stories and novels (about ten volumes). Story printed in this collection, first published in Davar in 1934, has been translated into English numerous times.

YAVNIELI, SHMUEL. Born in Russia 1884. Came to Palestine in 1903. Emissary to the Jews of Yemen in 1909, sent by the Palestine Office (under management of Arthur Ruppin) and Hapoel Hatzair. Scholar and historian. Now official in Ministry of Education. Yavnieli's swarthy complexion was one of his major qualifications for his mission to Yemen.

ZAID, ALEXANDER. Born in Siberia 1886. Killed by Arabs in Sheikh Abrekh, 1938. Came to Palestine in 1904, with a group from Vilno. Worked in the orchards of Petah-Tikvah, in the stonemasons' commune in Jerusalem, organized by Baratz. Was among the founders of Hashomer, of Kfar Gileadi, pioneered in shepherding and almost every other activity for Jewish colonization.

ZEMACH, SHLOMO. Born in Plonsk, Poland, in 1886. Versatile writer and scholar. Came to Palestine in 1903. Worked as a manual laborer. Helped found Hashomer Hatzair. Studied agriculture at Sorbonne and became principal of Mikveh Israel. Writings include short stories, memoirs, discussions on agriculture, on philosophic and cultural problems.